Proceedings
IBM Scientific Computing Symposium
Combinatorial Problems

Proceedings OF THE
IBM Scientific Computing Symposium ON
Combinatorial Problems

March 16-18, 1964

IBM®

DATA PROCESSING DIVISION
WHITE PLAINS, NEW YORK

This volume is one of a series of proceedings of scientific computing symposiums which have been held by IBM to advance and summarize the art of computer applications to the solution of scientific problems.

PREFACE

This book is based on the third in a series of meetings organized by IBM to provide an opportunity for information exchange among leaders in various fields of mathematical and scientific computer usage. As in the earlier meetings, our aim has been to bring together those people who have broad experience and who have made significant contributions on the use of digital computing equipment in their fields of specialty. Similar volumes are planned for meetings covering other topics of interest to the scientist, mathematician, and engineer.

The IBM Scientific Computing Symposium on Combinatorial Problems was held at the Thomas J. Watson Research Center in Yorktown Heights, New York, on March 16, 17, and 18, 1964. The symposium was organized into five sessions, two sessions being devoted to operations research with special emphasis on linear programming and the other three sessions covering combinatorial problems in finite geometry and number theory, chemistry and biology, and statistical mechanics. Papers were presented by leading members of the scientific community from universities, government, and industry. After each presentation, the floor was open for periods of informal discussions, some of which have been included in modified form in these proceedings.

There are numerous applications of the solution of combinatorial problems by data processing systems. Mathematicians and scientists who utilize computers in problem-solving and in research cannot work very long without encountering problems which center on the question of which patterns and properties of objects satisfy specified rules or constraints. At certain times, as in operations research, we are asked to find optimal patterns, and, at other times, to count patterns or to enumerate those which satisfy the specified rules. The techniques and methods of combinatorial mathematics have been applied to these problems, and from the earliest days of digital computing such problems have represented a most fruitful and important utilization of the capability of data processing systems.

This book could not have been published without the cooperation of the speakers who presented papers and made them available for publication. Special thanks are due Dr. Alan Hoffman, the technical planning coordinator, whose intimate knowledge of the people and the subjects in the field of combinatorics was invaluable in planning and organizing the sessions.

We wish to thank the participants in this symposium for spending their time with us and for helping us get a closer view of the contemporary picture of the state of the art in the solution of combinatorial problems.

ROSTER

General Chairman

ROBINSON, L., Director of Scientific Computing,
IBM Corporation, White Plains, N. Y.

Program Chairman

TUCKER, A. W., Professor, Department of Mathematics,
Princeton University, Princeton, N. J.

Session Chairmen

SESSION I

LEIBLER, R. A., Director,
Institute for Defense Analyses, Princeton, N. J.

SESSION II

TOMPKINS, C. B., Professor of Mathematics and Director of Computing Facility,
University of California, Los Angeles, Calif.

SESSION III

KUHN, H. W., Professor of Mathematical Economics, Department of Mathematics,
Princeton University, Princeton, N. J.

SESSION IV

YANG, C. N., Professor, School of Mathematics,
The Institute for Advanced Study, Princeton, N. J.

SESSION V

GALE, D., Professor, Department of Mathematics,
Brown University, Providence, R. I.

Research Technical Adviser

GOLDSTINE, H. H., Director of Mathematical Sciences,
Thomas J. Watson Research Center, IBM Corporation, Yorktown Heights, N. Y.

Symposium Technical Planning Coordinator

HOFFMAN, A. J., Research Staff Member, Thomas J. Watson Research Center,
IBM Corporation, Yorktown Heights, N. Y.

Symposium Program Manager

TARNOFF, N. H., Scientific Programs Administrator,
    IBM Corporation, White Plains, N. Y.

Session Coordinators

SESSION I

BERGQUIST, J. W., Advisory Systems Engineer, Willis H. Booth Computing Center,
    California Institute of Technology, Pasadena, Calif.

SESSION II

NEDVIN, A., Systems Engineer,
    IBM Corporation, Forest Hills, N. Y.

SESSION III

PALL, G. A., Systems Engineer,
    IBM Corporation, Philadelphia, Pa.

SESSION IV

McKEEHAN, J. B., Advisory Systems Engineer,
    IBM Corporation, Washington, D. C.

SESSION V

MARQUARDT, G. R., Senior Systems Engineer,
    IBM Corporation, St. Paul, Minn.

Regional Symposium Program Coordinators (IBM)

FEDERAL REGION

FULTZ, C. G., Systems Engineering Manager,
    IBM Corporation, Washington, D. C.

EASTERN REGION

GUEBERT, W. R., Scientific Marketing Manager,
    IBM Corporation, New York, N. Y.

WESTERN REGION

LUKE, J. W., Director, Systems Research and Development Center,
    IBM Corporation, Palo Alto, Calif.

MIDWESTERN REGION

PORTER, J. C., Manager of Scientific Computing,
    IBM Corporation, Chicago, Ill.

General Participants

ALEXANDER, J. H., Research and Development Staff Member,
General Atomic Division, General Dynamics Corporation, San Diego, Calif.

ANDERSEN, E., Operations Research Analyst,
Merrill Lynch, Pierce, Fenner & Smith, Incorporated, New York, N. Y.

ANDERSON, A., Assistant Director of Research,
Thomas J. Watson Research Center, IBM Corporation, Yorktown Heights, N. Y.

ANDERSON, A. E., Staff Mathematician, Computation Laboratory,
George C. Marshall Space Flight Center, Huntsville, Ala.

ANDREWS, W. G., Mathematician,
Thiokol Chemical Corporation, Elkton Division, Elkton, Md.

BAKER, J. A., Lawrence Radiation Laboratory,
University of California, Berkeley, Calif.

BALINSKI, M. L., Associate Professor, Department of Economics,
Wharton School of Finance and Commerce, University of Pennsylvania,
Philadelphia, Pa. *and* Mathematica, Princeton, N. J.

BECKWITH, J. H., Assistant Director, Applied Mathematics Division,
Esso Research and Engineering Company, Florham Park, N. J.

BERGONZI, E., Research Staff Member, Thomas J. Watson Research Center,
IBM Corporation, Yorktown Heights, N. Y.

BERNSTEIN, L. A., Commodity Economist,
Merrill Lynch, Pierce, Fenner & Smith, Incorporated, New York, N. Y.

BURG, C. J., Manager, Operations Research,
A. O. Smith Corporation, Milwaukee, Wis.

BUSACKER, R. G., Mathematician, Graph Theory,
Research Analysis Corporation, McLean, Va.

CALKIN, J. W., Associated Universities, Incorporated,
Brookhaven National Laboratory, Upton, N. Y.

CAMPAIGNE, H. H., Chief, Office of Research,
National Security Agency, Fort George G. Meade, Md.

CAPP, W. B., Senior Project Engineer,
Gulf Research & Development Company, Pittsburgh, Pa.

CHASEN, S. H., Scientist, Advanced Research Organization,
Lockheed-Georgia Company, Marietta, Ga.

CHENEY, R., Richfield Oil Corporation,
Los Angeles, Calif.

COURANT, R., Courant Institute of Mathematical Sciences,
New York University, New York, N. Y.

DANTZIG, G. B., Professor, Operations Research Center,
College of Engineering, University of California, Berkeley, Calif.

DAVIS, W., Applied Mathematics Department,
Hercules Powder Company, Incorporated, Wilmington, Del.

DeCARLO, C. R., IBM Director, Systems Research and Development,
IBM Corporation, White Plains, N. Y.

DiDONATO, A. R., U. S. Naval Weapons Laboratory,
Dahlgren, Va.

DORN, W. S., Manager, Computing Center, Department of Mathematical Sciences,
Thomas J. Watson Research Center, IBM Corporation, Yorktown Heights, N. Y.

DORWEILER, V. P., American Oil Company,
Whiting, Ind.

DUREK, T. A., Mathematician, Management Science Branch,
U. S. Air Force Headquarters, Washington, D. C.

EBERLEIN, P. J., Assistant Director for Analysis, Computing Center,
University of Rochester, Rochester, N. Y.

EDMONDS, J., Mathematician,
National Bureau of Standards, Washington, D. C.

FASSBERG, H. E., Advanced Mathematician, Optimal Processes,
Research Analysis Corporation, McLean, Va.

FIACCO, A. V., Chairman, Nonlinear Programs Project,
Research Analysis Corporation, McLean, Va.

FISHER, J. L., Manager, Management Science Division,
The Atlantic Refining Company, Philadelphia, Pa.

FISHER, M. E., Wheatstone Physics Laboratory,
King's College, University of London, London, Eng.
visiting at The Rockefeller Institute, New York, N. Y. (1963–64)

FLANAGAN, C. A., Research Mathematician,
U. S. Naval Ordnance Test Station, China Lake, Calif.

FREITAG, H., Manager, Design Automation, Thomas J. Watson Research Center,
IBM Corporation, Yorktown Heights, N. Y.

FULKERSON, D. R., Mathematician,
The RAND Corporation, Santa Monica, Calif.

FUNDERLIC, R. E., Section Head, Central Data Processing, Nuclear Division,
Union Carbide Corporation, Oak Ridge, Tenn.

GALENTINE, P. G., JR., Director, Research and Technology, Headquarters,
U. S. Air Force Systems Command, Andrews Air Force Base, Md.

GIBBS, J. H., Professor, Department of Chemistry,
Brown University, Providence, R. I.

GILFORD, D. M., Director, Mathematical Sciences Division,
Office of Naval Research, Washington, D. C.

GILLESPIE, R., Senior Research Economist,
General Motors Research Center, Detroit, Mich.

GILMORE, P. C., Thomas J. Watson Research Center,
IBM Corporation, Yorktown Heights, N. Y.

GOLDBERGER, M. L., Professor, Department of Physics,
Princeton University, Princeton, N. J.

GOLDMAN, A. J., Chief, Operations Research Section,
Applied Mathematics Division, National Bureau of Standards, Washington, D. C.

GOLDSTEIN, A. J., Technical Staff Member, Computing Research Department,
Bell Telephone Laboratories, Incorporated, Murray Hill, N. J.

GOLDSTEIN, M., Courant Institute of Mathematical Sciences,
New York University, New York, N. Y.

GOLOMB, S. W., Associate Professor of Electrical Engineering and Mathematics,
University of Southern California, Los Angeles, Calif.

GOMORY, R. E., Thomas J. Watson Research Center,
IBM Corporation, Yorktown Heights, N. Y.

GRANT, R. B., Manager, Engineering and Operations Analysis Division,
Phillips Petroleum Company, Bartlesville, Okla.

GRAU, A. A., Professor of Mathematics and Engineering Sciences,
The Technological Institute, Northwestern University, Evanston, Ill.

GREENBERG, H., Associate Professor,
Department of Industrial Engineering and Operations Research,
School of Engineering and Science, New York University, New York, N. Y.

GREENBERG, H. J., Assistant Director of Mathematical Sciences,
Thomas J. Watson Research Center, IBM Corporation, Yorktown Heights, N. Y.

GREGORY, R. T., Professor of Mathematics and Assistant Director,
Computation Center, University of Texas, Austin, Tex.

GRIESMER, J. H., Thomas J. Watson Research Center,
IBM Corporation, Yorktown Heights, N. Y.

GRUENBERG, H. S., Manager, Operations Research,
National Biscuit Company, New York, N. Y.

HALE, M. E., Manager, Computer Applications and Analysis,
Allison Division, General Motors Corporation, Indianapolis, Ind.

HALL, M., JR., Professor, Department of Mathematics,
California Institute of Technology, Pasadena, Calif.

HANAN, M., Thomas J. Watson Research Center,
IBM Corporation, Yorktown Heights, N. Y.

HERZOG, B., Manager, Engineering Methods Department,
Ford Motor Company, Dearborn, Mich.

HOFFMAN, A. A. J., Director, Computer Center,
Texas Christian University, Fort Worth, Tex.

HOFFMAN, E. R., Staff Specialist, Technical Service Department,
Technical Center, St. Regis Paper Company, West Nyack, N. Y.

Hu, T. C., Thomas J. Watson Research Center,
IBM Corporation, Yorktown Heights, N. Y.

Hughes, R. R., Head, Applied Mathematics Department,
Shell Development Company, Emeryville, Calif.

Humbaugh, P. R., Statistician,
Texaco Research Center, Glenham, N. Y.

Hurwitz, A., Computing Facility,
University of California, Los Angeles, Calif.

Jacks, E. L., Assistant Department Head, Computer Technology Department,
General Motors Research Laboratories, Warren, Mich.

Jacobs, W., Visiting Staff Member,
Institute for Defense Analyses, Princeton, N. J.

Johns, E. C., Assistant Group Leader, Computer Process Control,
International Paper Company, Georgetown, S. C.

Johnson, R. M., Head, Analytical Systems Development Section,
Industrial Engineering Division, The Procter & Gamble Company,
Cincinnati, Ohio

Joksch, H. C., Technical Staff Member,
The MITRE Corporation, Bedford, Mass.

Jones, E. L., Central Research and Engineering,
Texas Instruments, Incorporated, Dallas, Tex.

Kac, M., Professor,
The Rockefeller Institute, New York, N. Y.

Karp, R. M., Research Staff Member, Thomas J. Watson Research Center,
IBM Corporation, Yorktown Heights, N. Y.

Karreman, H. F., Mathematics Research Center, U. S. Army,
University of Wisconsin, Madison, Wis.

Kaufman, G. M., Assistant Professor,
Alfred P. Sloan School of Industrial Management,
Massachusetts Institute of Technology, Cambridge, Mass.

Keenan, T. A., Director, Computing Center,
University of Rochester, Rochester, N. Y.

Kingston, P. L., District Scientific Marketing Representative,
IBM Corporation, Syracuse, N. Y.

Klee, V. L., Professor, Department of Mathematics, University of Washington,
Seattle, Wash. *and* Boeing Scientific Research Laboratories,
The Boeing Company, Seattle, Wash.

Knight, D., Technical Center,
St. Regis Paper Company, West Nyack, N. Y.

Korth, J. J., Manager, Scientific Marketing,
IBM Corporation, White Plains, N. Y.

Kral, O. A., Manager, Applied Mathematics and Technical Computing,
Minnesota Mining & Manufacturing Company, St. Paul, Minn.

KRONE, L. H., Manager, Applied Mathematics,
Monsanto Company, St. Louis, Mo.

LASERSON, G. L., Director of Research, Research and Development Division,
American Machine & Foundry Company, Springdale, Conn.

LEHMER, D. H., Professor, Department of Mathematics,
University of California, Berkeley, Calif.

LETTS, R., Divisional Project Manager, Lederle Laboratories,
American Cyanamid Company, Pearl River, N. Y.

LEWIS, C., Senior Analyst, Operations Research,
General Mills, Incorporated, Minneapolis, Minn.

LEWIS, D. A., Manager, Computing Division Research Department,
Caterpillar Tractor Company, Mossville, Ill.

LUCAS, T. R., Engineer, Digital Analysis Group,
Martin Company, Orlando, Fla.

MAKKY, S., Research Specialist, Mathematical Analysis Unit,
Division Systems Administration and Technical Support,
Commercial Airplane Division, The Boeing Company, Renton, Wash.

MARTCH, H. B., Manager, Operations Research Group,
El Paso Natural Gas Company, El Paso, Tex.

MARTINO, R. L., Manager, Advanced Systems,
Olin Mathieson Chemical Corporation, New York, N. Y.

MASON, D. D., Professor and Head of the Department of Experimental Statistics,
North Carolina State of the University of North Carolina at Raleigh,
Raleigh, N. C.

McCORMICK, G. P., Advanced Mathematician, Nonlinear Programs,
Research Analysis Corporation, McLean, Va.

McCREADY, R. R., Technical Assistant to Manager of Data Processing and
Computing, Ling-Temco-Vought, Incorporated, Arlington, Tex.

McCUNE, D., Supervisor, Applied Mathematics,
Jones & Laughlin Steel Corporation, Pittsburgh, Pa.

McSHANE, E. J., Department of Mathematics,
University of Virginia, Charlottesville, Va.
visiting at The Rockefeller Institute, New York, N. Y.

MEGGITT, J. E., Thomas J. Watson Research Center,
IBM Corporation, Yorktown Heights, N. Y.

METZGER, R. W., Senior Systems Development Engineer, Midland Division,
The Dow Chemical Company, Midland, Mich.

MEYER, H. I., Manager, Computer Department,
United Gas Corporation, Shreveport, La.

MILHORN, H. T., Research Assistant,
University of Mississippi Medical Center, Jackson, Miss.

MILLAR, G. H., Director of Research,
Deere & Company, Moline, Ill.

MILLS, H. D., Manager, Systems Analysis,
IBM Corporation, Rockville, Md.

MITCHELL, G. J., Chief of Computing Laboratory,
Institute for Defense Analyses, Princeton, N. J.

MOORE, R. L., Manager, Operations Research,
The Mead Corporation, Dayton, Ohio

MORGAN, B. S., Directorate of Mathematical Sciences,
Applied Mathematics Division, U. S. Air Force Office of Scientific Research,
Washington, D. C.

MORRIS, R. H., Associate Director of Business Operations Analysis Staff,
Eastman Kodak Company, Rochester, N. Y.

MOTCHANE, L., Director,
Institut des Hautes Études Scientifiques, Bures-sur-Yvette, France

NEWMAN, T., Director, Research and Engineering,
American Bosch Arma Corporation, Garden City, N. Y.

NOVOSAD, R. S., Chief, Applied Mathematics Section,
Martin Company, Denver, Colo.

ODEN, P. H., Thomas J. Watson Research Center,
IBM Corporation, Yorktown Heights, N. Y.

OWENS, R. H., Acting Head, Mathematical Sciences Section,
National Science Foundation, Washington, D. C.

PALERMO, F. P., Advanced Systems Development Division,
Mohansic Laboratory, IBM Corporation, Yorktown Heights, N. Y.

PATTERSON, A. L., Senior Member, Head of Department of Molecular Structure,
The Institute for Cancer Research, Philadelphia, Pa.

PICKERING, H. L., Computing-Operations Research Supervisor,
Pan American Petroleum Corporation, Tulsa, Okla.

POLYA, G., Professor, Department of Mathematics,
Stanford University, Stanford, Calif.

RAY, T. L., Senior Engineer,
Esso Research and Engineering Company, Florham Park, N. J.

RAY-CHAUDHURI, D. K., Research Staff Member,
Thomas J. Watson Research Center, IBM Corporation, Yorktown Heights, N. Y.

RIORDAN, J., Technical Staff Member, Mathematics Research Department,
Bell Telephone Laboratories, Incorporated, Murray Hill, N. J.

ROBERTS, R. C., Head, Mathematics Department,
U. S. Naval Ordnance Laboratory, Silver Spring, Md.

ROLNICK, L. S., Systems Analyst,
Gulf Oil Corporation, Houston, Tex.

ROTA, G.-C., Professor of Mathematics,
The Rockefeller Institute, New York, N. Y.

RYSER, H. J., Professor, Department of Mathematics,
Syracuse University, Syracuse, N. Y.

SAALBACH, C. P., Supervisor, Mathematics and Programming,
Westinghouse Astronuclear Laboratory, Pittsburgh, Pa.

SANDERS, P. G., Manager, Applied Mathematics,
Abbott Laboratories, North Chicago, Ill.

SANDIFORD, P. J., Professor at Graduate School of Business and
Director of Air Transportation Research, McGill University, Montreal, Can.

SCHMITT, S. A., Technical Staff Member,
Institute for Defense Analyses, Princeton, N. J.

SHANKS, D., Consultant, Applied Mathematics Laboratory,
David Taylor Model Basin, Washington, D. C.

SHELSON, W., Chairman, Operations Research Group,
The Hydro-Electric Power Commission of Ontario, Toronto, Can.

SHERMAN, S., Professor, Department of Mathematics,
Wayne State University, Detroit, Mich.

SINKOFF, M. D., District Scientific Marketing Representative,
IBM Corporation, White Plains, N. Y.

SPEYER, J. F., Associate Professor of Biochemistry,
New York University School of Medicine, New York, N. Y.

SPRATT, T. L., Production Research Laboratory,
Sun Oil Company, Richardson, Tex.

SWEENEY, D. W., Senior Programmer,
IBM Corporation, Poughkeepsie, N. Y.

TAUB, A. H., Professor of Mathematics and Director of Computer Center,
University of California, Berkeley, Calif.

TEAGUE, W. B., Systems Research and Development,
IBM Corporation, White Plains, N. Y.

TU, Y.-O., Thomas J. Watson Research Center,
IBM Corporation, Yorktown Heights, N. Y.

TUCKER, G. L., IBM Director of Research, Thomas J. Watson Research Center,
IBM Corporation, Yorktown Heights, N. Y.

TUTTE, W. T., Professor, Department of Mathematics,
University of Waterloo, Waterloo, Can.

VERNIER, C. M., Assistant Director for Data Sciences,
Department of Data Management, U. S. Veterans Administration,
Washington, D. C.

VOTAW, D. F., JR., Associate Department Head, Systems Analysis Department,
The MITRE Corporation, Bedford, Mass.

WALKER, W. F., JR., Scientific Marketing Representative,
Eastern Regional Office, IBM Corporation, New York, N. Y.

WALKUP, D. W., Staff Member, Mathematics Research Laboratory,
Boeing Scientific Research Laboratories, The Boeing Company, Seattle, Wash.

CONTENTS

Pure Mathematics

1
Squared Rectangles

W. T. TUTTE

University of Waterloo, Ontario

A rectangle is said to be "squared" when it is dissected into two or more squares. If no two of these squares have the same size, the squared rectangle is "perfect."

Consider the union of the horizontal sides of the squares of a squared rectangle. It consists of disjoint horizontal segments. We call these the "horizontal dissectors" of the squared rectangle. There is also, of course, a family of vertical dissectors.

We can represent a squared rectangle R by an electrical analog, a graph P. The vertices of P correspond to the horizontal dissectors of R. Those which correspond to the upper and lower horizontal sides of R are the positive and negative "poles" of P, respectively. The edges of P correspond to the squares, or "elements," of R. Each edge joins the vertices representing the upper and lower sides of the corresponding square (see Figure 1).

With each edge of P we associate a "current." The magnitude of this current is measured by the side of the corresponding square, and the current is directed from the vertex representing the upper side of the square to the vertex representing the lower side. It is an easy matter to verify that the resulting distribution of currents satisfies Kirchhoff's laws for a network of unit conductances. The total current is supposed to enter the network at the positive pole and to leave at the negative pole. Currents are specified by numbers and arrows in Figure 1.

The graph P, with its poles distinguished, is the "horizontal p-net" of R. On joining its poles by a new edge A, we obtain the horizontal "completed net" or "c-net" of R. In a c-net G, we do not usually distinguish the poles. There may be several choices for them, corresponding to p-nets of different squared rectangles.

It can be shown that c-nets are planar and, correspondingly, that p-nets can be drawn in the plane so as not to separate their poles. Normally,

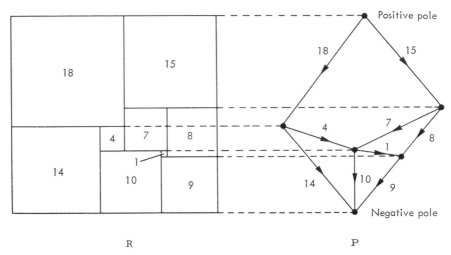

R   P

FIGURE 1. Graphical representation of squared rectangle

the horizontal and vertical c-nets are dual graphs. The exceptional case
is that in which R has a "cross," a point which is a corner of four squares.

A squared rectangle is called "simple" if it contains no smaller squared
rectangles. It can be shown that the c-net of a simple squared rectangle
is 3-connected; that is, it cannot be decomposed into two subgraphs,
each having two or more edges, such that their common part has at most
two vertices and no edges.

Several workers have been moved to make a catalog of simple squared
rectangles. The first such catalog was made in Germany shortly before
the Second World War. R. Sprague of Berlin was able to fit some of the
rectangles of this catalog together so as to make a perfect squared square
of 55 elements, that is, a square dissected into 55 smaller squares, all of
different sizes (see Sprague, 1939).

The German catalog was made without the use of graph theory. Brooks
et al. (1940) at Cambridge used the method of first listing the 3-connected
planar graphs of n edges. Each such graph can be interpreted as a c-net
in several ways, one way for each symmetry class of edges. For each
choice of poles, we can solve Kirchhoff's equations and so derive a squared
rectangle (I omit the rigorous proof of this). Not all the squared rectangles
derived in this way are simple or perfect. Some of them even have fewer
than n edges, because of the appearance of zero currents. But all the
simple squared rectangles of n edges must appear among them.

The Cambridge catalog was completed up to $n = 13$, and several
perfect squares were built from its rectangles. The smallest of these had

26 elements and a side length of 608. The elements and sides of a squared rectangle are always commensurable, and it is customary to represent them as integers without a common factor.

T. H. Willcocks, an amateur mathematician of Bristol, later found a perfect square of 24 elements and side length 175 (see Willcocks, 1948 and 1951). He obtained this square by a clever use of an imperfect rectangle; this was his reward for including imperfect rectangles in his catalog.

Another catalog was made during the Second World War by C. J. Bouwkamp of Eindhoven (see Bouwkamp, 1946 and 1947). Some years later, he determined to extend this catalog by using the electronic computers at the Philips Computing Centre. He seems to have had two main reasons for his course of action. First, he wanted to show that computers could be applied advantageously to the problems of graph theory. Second, he was anxious to find the smallest possible perfect squared square.

There are two steps in such a program: (1) you must list the 3-connected planar graphs of the appropriate numbers of edges and (2) you must solve Kirchhoff's equations for the p-nets associated with each one. The second step is said to be routine, but the first step presents difficulties.

Fortunately, I was able to tell Bouwkamp of a theorem which makes it possible to catalog the graphs (see Tutte, 1961). First, let us note that the 3-connected planar graphs ("c-nets" for short)[1] go in dual pairs. As an example of a c-net, we have the "wheel" of order n, where $n > 3$. This consists of a polygon with n vertices and one extra vertex joined to each member of the polygon. Wheels give rise to no perfect rectangles but are nevertheless important. Those of orders 3, 4, and 5 are shown in Figure 2. Each wheel is its own dual.

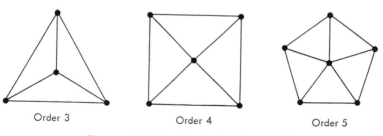

Order 3   Order 4   Order 5

FIGURE 2. "Wheels" of orders 3, 4, and 5

---

[1] Actually, these graphs represent a special kind of c-net.

A second rule about c-nets is that when one face, necessarily not a triangle, is subdivided by a diagonal, a new c-net results. The basic theorem is that if a given c-net is not a wheel, then either it or its dual can be derived from a simpler c-net by subdividing a face.

For a detailed account of the programming of a machine to apply this theorem, reference may be made to a thesis written by one of Bouwkamp's colleagues, Duijvestijn (1962). The work resulted in the construction of a table of all simple squared rectangles, perfect and imperfect, of up to 15 elements. There are 4,094 of them, and there are no perfect squared squares among them (see Bouwkamp, Duijvestijn, and Medema, 1960).

Part of the work consists of calculating the "complexity" C of each c-net. This is the number of spanning trees. Theoretical work, recorded in Brooks *et al.* (1940), shows that for the p-net of a perfect squared square, C must be of the form nk^2, where every element of the dissection (with C as the horizontal side of R) has a side divisible by nk. This seems to explain why there is no "perfect square" of 15 elements or less. But it also suggested to the Eindhoven group a method of extending their search for perfect squares. Having listed the c-nets of 16 edges, for example, they would calculate the complexities. But they would work out only the corresponding squared rectangles for complexities of the form nk^2 with a reasonably large value of k.

They acquired a vast amount of numerical information about c-nets and their complexities and satisfied themselves that there could be no perfect square with fewer than 20 elements. They thought the time required to search for perfect squares of 20 elements would be prohibitive.

P. J. Federico of Washington has made an ingenious use of the Eindhoven catalog (see Federico, 1963). He selects a squared rectangle from the list. Then he reinterprets the pattern, making the rectangle a square and one of its elements a rectangle. Solving the corresponding equations, he dissects a square into $n - 1$ squares and one rectangle. When he is lucky, he can fill the rectangular element with a rectangle from the catalog and so obtain a perfect square. He has found a great many new perfect squares, one of the 25th order. But Willcocks' 24th-order square remains unrivaled as the perfect square of smallest known order.

Besides the problem of the smallest perfect square, there is the problem of the smallest simple perfect square, containing no smaller squared rectangle. Empirical methods have not been able to touch this problem, but some progress has been made with a theoretical method which we developed at Cambridge. This starts with the observation that it is very simple to construct diagonally symmetric squared squares (naturally imperfect). The method then develops into the fascinating art of destroying the symmetry of a graph without losing all its consequences. We were eventually able to construct a simple perfect square of 38 elements. Until a few days before the presentation of this paper, the record was held by Willcocks with 37 (see Federico, 1963). Then the 25th-order simple perfect square shown in Figure 3 was discovered by John Wilson of the University of Waterloo.

Elements

4	23	50	93	149
15	25	62	100	157
16	27	67	113	167
19	33	87	135	179
22	34	88	143	211

FIGURE 3. John Wilson's simple perfect square of order 25 (503 × 503)

Very recently, it has become possible to get some clue as to the asymptotic behavior of the number of simple perfect rectangles of n elements as n approaches infinity (see Tutte, 1963). First, we agree to call a c-net "rooted" when one edge is specified as the "root," the root is given a direction, and its two incident faces are distinguished as "right" and "left." If C_n is the number of (3-connected) rooted c-nets of n edges, it has been found that

$$C_{n+1} = 2(-1)^{n+1} + R_n,$$

where the function R_n is given recursively as follows:

$$S_n = 27n^2 + 9n - 2,$$

$$R_0 = 0,$$

$$S_n R_{n-1} + 2S_{n-1}R_n = \frac{2 \cdot (2n)!}{(n!)^2}.$$

This leads to the asymptotic formula

$$C_n \sim R_{n-1} \sim \frac{2n^{-5/2}4^n}{243\sqrt{\pi}}.$$

(By $f(n) \sim g(n)$ we mean that $f(n)/g(n) \to 1$ as $n \to \infty$.)

It is a plausible conjecture that almost all c-nets are asymmetrical. If so, the number of unrooted c-nets is given asymptotically by

$$\frac{C_n}{4n} \sim \frac{n^{-7/2}4^n}{486\sqrt{\pi}}.$$

It is another plausible conjecture that an asymmetrical c-net gives rise to n simple perfect rectangles in general, one for each edge. If this result is general enough, then, since c-nets go in dual pairs, we can write the asymptotic formula for the number of simple squared rectangles of n edges as

$$\frac{n+1}{2} \times \frac{C_{n+1}}{4(n+1)} \sim \frac{n^{-5/2}4^n}{243\sqrt{\pi}}.$$

Here we have also assumed that hardly any c-nets are self-dual. It seems that a lot of theoretical work will have to be done if these conjectures are to be rigorously justified.

REFERENCES

BOUWKAMP, C. J. 1946. On the dissection of rectangles into squares (paper I). Proc. Acad. Sci. Amsterdam, 49:1176–88.
———. 1947. On the dissection of rectangles into squares (papers II and III). Proc. Acad. Sci. Amsterdam, 50:58–78.

BOUWKAMP, C. J., A. J. W. DUIJVESTIJN, and P. MEDEMA. 1960. Tables relating to simple squared rectangles of orders 9 through 15. Eindhoven, Neth.: Technische Hogeschool, Department of Mathematics and Mechanics.

BROOKS, R. L., C. A. B. SMITH, A. H. STONE, and W. T. TUTTE. 1940. The dissection of rectangles into squares. Duke Math. J., 7:312–40.

DUIJVESTIJN, A. J. W. 1962. Electronic computation of squared rectangles. Printed thesis, Technische Wetenschap aan de Technische Hogeschool te Eindhoven. (Address of author: Philips Computing Centre, Eindhoven, Neth.)

FEDERICO, P. J. 1963. Note on some low-order perfect squared squares. Canad. J. Math., 15:350–62.

SPRAGUE, R. 1939. Beispiel einer Zerlegung des Quadrats in lauter verschiedene Quadrate. Math. Z., 45:607–8.

TUTTE, W. T. 1961. A theory of 3-connected graphs. Proc. Acad. Sci. Amsterdam, 64:441–55.

———. 1963. A census of planar maps. Canad. J. Math., 15:249–71.

WILLCOCKS, T. H. 1948. Fairy Chess Rev., vol. 7 (Aug./Oct.).

———. 1951. A note on some perfect squared squares. Canad. J. Math., 3:304–8.

2

Numerical Analysis of Finite Geometries

Marshall Hall, Jr.
California Institute of Technology

INTRODUCTION

A projective geometry of three dimensions or higher is necessarily Desarguesian and so may be coordinatized by a division ring. If the geometry is finite, the division ring is finite and so, by Wedderburn's famous theorem, is necessarily a finite field $GF(p^r)$. Thus, we may regard these geometries as known, recognizing that there remain many interesting problems about them which are still unresolved.

The most compelling problem in the study of finite geometries is the determination of the finite planes. There are known three different non-Desarguesian planes of order 9 (that is, containing $9 + 1 = 10$ points on every line). At present, every known plane is of prime power order, and the known planes of prime order are Desarguesian.

The next section gives a brief account of the general theoretical background. The third section describes the searches which have been made for cyclic planes, since in this case the theory permits an extensive search. The fourth section describes the machine search for semifields (not necessarily associative division rings). The final section deals with the numerical analysis of planes of small order, being chiefly concerned with a complete search for planes of order 8 and partial searches for planes of orders 9 and 10.

GENERAL BACKGROUND

A projective plane π is a set of points $\{P\}$ and lines $\{L\}$ together with an incidence relation $P \in L$, which we read "P is on L" or "L contains P," satisfying the following axioms:

P1. *There is one and only one line containing two distinct points.*
P2. *There is one and only one point on both of two distinct lines.*
P3. *There are four points no three of which are on a line.*

Of these axioms, P3 merely excludes certain "degenerate" planes, which might consist of a number of points on a line, a single point not on the line, and lines joining this point to the points of the other line. An axiom equivalent to P3 says that every line contains at least three points.

From these axioms, it is easy to show that if one line contains a finite number of points, then every other line contains the same number of points. If this number is $n + 1$, we say that π is of order n. It follows easily that every point is on $n + 1$ lines, that the total number of points is $n^2 + n + 1$, and that the total number of lines is $n^2 + n + 1$.

In a projective plane, we may call any particular line the "line at infinity." If we delete this line L and the points on it, the remaining points and lines form an "affine plane" in which lines which formerly intersected in a point of L no longer intersect and are called "parallel." For an affine plane, the axiom P1 still holds, but P2 must be replaced by the Euclidean postulate

P2*. *Through a point P not on a line L_0 there is one and only one line L parallel to L_0.*

For an affine plane, P3 may be weakened to

P3*. *There are three points not on a line.*

A finite affine plane of order n contains n^2 points, n on each line, and $n^2 + n$ lines in $n + 1$ parallel pencils.

It is not difficult to show that given an affine plane we may, in a unique way, adjoin a "point at infinity" to each line of a family of parallel lines and put a "line at infinity" through the points at infinity to form a projective plane. Thus, for purposes of construction, we may construct either an affine or a projective plane, since the transition from one to the other is so elementary.

A "Latin square" is an n-by-n square in which the numbers 1 to n are placed so that each number appears exactly once in each row and column. Two Latin squares are said to be "orthogonal" if, when superposed, the n^2 cells contain each pair ij (i from the first square, j from the second exactly once) of the n^2 pairs ij ($i, j = 1, \cdots, n$). Three or more squares are "mutually orthogonal" if any two of them are orthogonal. We have three mutually orthogonal 4-by-4 squares:

$$
\begin{array}{cccc}
1 & 2 & 3 & 4 \\
2 & 1 & 4 & 3 \\
3 & 4 & 1 & 2 \\
4 & 3 & 2 & 1
\end{array}
\qquad
\begin{array}{cccc}
1 & 2 & 3 & 4 \\
3 & 4 & 1 & 2 \\
4 & 3 & 2 & 1 \\
2 & 1 & 4 & 3
\end{array}
\qquad
\begin{array}{cccc}
1 & 2 & 3 & 4 \\
4 & 3 & 2 & 1 \\
2 & 1 & 4 & 3 \\
3 & 4 & 1 & 2
\end{array}
\tag{2.1}
$$

If we consider the n^2 cells of an n-by-n square as points, then we may consider each row as a line of n points, these forming a set of parallel lines; similarly, the columns give a second family of parallel lines. If we have a Latin square, the n cells containing the same number i will be considered to form a line; as i runs from 1 to n, this gives a family (or pencil) of parallel lines. Thus, a Latin square is a representation of three pencils of parallels. A Latin square orthogonal to the first square gives a fourth pencil of parallel lines. And k mutually orthogonal Latin squares yield $k + 2$ pencils of parallel lines. Thus, a set of $n - 1$ mutually orthogonal Latin squares gives the $n + 1$ pencils of parallel lines in an affine plane of order n. The converse is almost immediate. Thus, the three mutually orthogonal squares of order 4 in (2.1) represent the five pencils of parallels in the affine plane of order 4.

The chief result on the existence of finite planes is the Bruck-Ryser theorem (see Bruck and Ryser, 1949):

If there is a finite plane of order n and if $n \equiv 0, 1 \pmod 4$, then integers x, y exist such that $n = x^2 + y^2$.

This shows that there is no plane for orders 6, 14, 21, $\cdots$ and for infinitely many further orders. Since $10 = 3^2 + 1^2$, this theorem permits (but does not guarantee) the existence of a plane of order 10.

CYCLIC PLANES AND DIFFERENCE SETS

Suppose that a finite projective plane π of order n has a cyclic collineation of order $v = n^2 + n + 1$ which is transitive and regular on the v points of π. We call the plane π a "cyclic plane," and the points may be represented by the residues modulo v. If we know which points $a_0, a_1, \cdots, a_n \pmod v$ lie on one line L_0, then on line L_i ($i = 0, \cdots, v - 1$) we have the points $a_0 + i, a_1 + i, \cdots, a_n + i \pmod v$. Thus, any line of π determines the entire plane. Let us take

$$L_0: a_0, a_1, \cdots, a_n \pmod v. \qquad (2.2)$$

We readily find that (2.2) determines a plane of order n with the ith line containing points $L_i: a_0 + i, \cdots, a_n + i \pmod v$ if and only if,

$$\text{for } d \not\equiv 0 \pmod v, \quad \text{there exist} \quad a_i, a_j, a_i - a_j \equiv d \pmod v. \qquad (2.3)$$

For this reason, the residues in (2.2) are called a "perfect difference set modulo v," and the determination of these perfect difference sets is equivalent to finding cyclic projective planes.

If from a finite projective plane we delete a particular line at infinity and its $n + 1$ points, we have n^2 points and $n^2 + n$ lines forming a finite affine plane. In such a plane, we may have a collineation α fixing one point, the origin $\mathcal{O}$, which is transitive and regular on the remaining $n^2 - 1$ points. Here α necessarily moves the $n + 1$ lines through $\mathcal{O}$ in a cycle, and α is cyclic on the remaining $n^2 - 1$ lines. Write $N = n^2 - 1$. Then the points may be represented by residues modulo N, and the ith line M_i through $\circ$ contains the points

$$M_i:\ \circ,\, i,\, i + (n+1),\, \cdots,\, i + n^2 - n - 2, \qquad i = 0,\, \cdots,\, n. \qquad (2.4)$$

The lines L_i not through $\circ$ are of the form

$$L_i:\ b_1 + i,\quad b_2 + i,\ \cdots,\ b_n + i \pmod{N},\quad i = 0,\, \cdots,\, N-1. \qquad (2.5)$$

Here

$$b_1,\ \cdots,\ b_n \pmod{N} \qquad (2.6)$$

are an affine difference set and define a cyclic affine plane if and only if,

$$\text{for } d \not\equiv 0 \pmod{n+1}, \quad \text{there exist } b_i, b_j, b_i - b_j \equiv d \pmod{N}. \qquad (2.7)$$

It has been shown by Singer (1938) that every Desarguesian finite projective plane has a cyclic representation and by Bose (1942) that every Desarguesian affine plane has a cyclic representation as above. Table I is a list of the difference sets for small values of n.

TABLE I

Projective difference sets modulo $v = n^2 + n + 1$

$n = 2$	1, 2, 4 (mod 7)
$n = 3$	0, 1, 3, 9 (mod 13)
$n = 4$	3, 6, 7, 12, 14 (mod 21)
$n = 5$	1, 5, 11, 24, 25, 27 (mod 31)
$n = 7$	1, 6, 7, 9, 19, 38, 42, 49 (mod 57)
$n = 8$	1, 2, 4, 8, 16, 32, 37, 55, 64 (mod 73)
$n = 9$	0, 1, 3, 9, 27, 49, 56, 61, 77, 81 (mod 91)
$n = 11$	1, 8, 9, 11, 25, 37, 69, 88, 94, 99, 103, 121 (mod 133)

Affine difference sets modulo $N = n^2 - 1$

$n = 2$	1, 2 (mod 3)
$n = 3$	0, 1, 3 (mod 8)
$n = 4$	1, 2, 4, 8 (mod 15)
$n = 5$	0, 1, 5, 14, 22 (mod 24)
$n = 7$	0, 1, 5, 7, 26, 35, 38 (mod 48)
$n = 8$	1, 2, 4, 8, 16, 21, 32, 42 (mod 63)
$n = 9$	0, 1, 3, 9, 22, 27, 34, 38, 66 (mod 80)

A *multiplier* of a difference set D is a residue t such that the mapping $x \to tx$ of residues is a collineation of the plane. For cyclic planes, it has been shown by the author (Hall, 1947) in the projective case and by Hoffman (1952) in the affine case that every prime p dividing n is a multiplier and that there is a line fixed by all multipliers. The examples in Table I have this property.

The existence of the multiplier is a powerful tool in the search for difference sets by machine. Mann and Evans (1951) have carried out a search showing that for $n \leq 1,600$ a projective difference set exists only if n is a prime power.

THE SEARCH FOR SEMIFIELDS—PLANES OF KNUTH

A system $R(+, \cdot)$ with a unit in which (1) addition is an Abelian group, (2) the distributive law $(a + b)m = am + bm$ holds, and (3) $ab = 0$ implies $a = 0$ or $b = 0$ is called a Veblen-Wedderburn system after the original discoverers of such systems (see Veblen and Wedderburn, 1907). A finite Veblen-Wedderburn system may be used to coordinatize a finite projective plane, and the plane will be non-Desarguesian if the system is not a field. If, instead of (2), we have the other distributive law (2'), $a(b + c) = ab + ac$, we also obtain a plane. The planes satisfying (1), (2'), and (3) are geometrically the duals of those satisfying (1), (2), and (3). If both (2) and (2') hold, we call R a "semifield" or "nonassociative division ring," where "nonassociative" means "not necessarily associative." If R is associative, it is a finite field $GF(p^r)$. In any event, the addition in R will be an elementary Abelian group; since the addition is of prime power order p^r, the plane π will be of order p^r.

The interesting question is: For which orders p^r do there exist non-Desarguesian planes as well as Desarguesian ones? For even exponents $r = 2s$, the author (Hall, 1943) constructed a Veblen-Wedderburn system in the following way: If $F = GF(p^s)$, take the elements of R to be $a + bu$, where $a, b \in F$ and where u is an indeterminate. Addition in R is defined by

$$(a + bu) + (c + du) = (a + c) + (b + d)u. \tag{2.8}$$

For $C \in F$, we have the multiplication rule

$$c(a + bu) = (a + bu)c = ac + bcu. \tag{2.9}$$

If $b \neq 0$, and if $x^2 - ex - f$ is irreducible over F, where $e, f \in F$, we put

$$(a + bu)^2 = e(a + bu) + f. \tag{2.10}$$

The rules (2.9) and (2.10) together with the distributive law (2), or alternatively (2') but not both, define a system R which is not a field except in the special case $p^{2s} = 2^2 = 4$.

A ring satisfying both distributive laws of order p or p^2 is necessarily a field. For $n = p^{st}$, where t is odd, $p \neq 2$, and $t > 1$, Albert (1952 and 1960) constructed semifields by defining R, taking the elements of R as those of $GF(n) = F$, making addition in R the same as that in F, but defining a new product $a \circ b$ for R from that in F by the rule

$$a \circ b = (ab^u + a^u b), \qquad u = p^s. \qquad (2.11)$$

This product must be further modified so that R has a unit, but then R yields a semifield of order $n = p^{st}$ and thus a non-Desarguesian plane of order n. For even powers $n = p^{2s}$, $s > 1$, and g a nonsquare in $GF(p^2) = F_1$, Albert gives the rule

$$(a + bu)(c + du) = (ac + b^p c^p g) + (ad + bc)u, \qquad (2.12)$$

where $a, b, c, d \in GF(p^s)$ and where u is an indeterminate. The rules (2.11) and (2.12) provide means for constructing semifields of all orders $n = p^m$, p odd, $m \geq 3$, and so with corresponding planes. Albert later gave a modification of rule (2.11) applicable to orders 2^{4m} of 2^{qs}, q an odd prime, $s > 1$.

Albert's methods left open the questions of the existence of semifields of order 2^q, q a prime, and the existence of non-Desarguesian planes of these orders. It was known (see the final section) that for orders 2, 4, 8 only the Desarguesian plane exists. Kleinfeld (1960) made a machine survey of the Veblen-Wedderburn systems of order 16 with a left nucleus of order 4 and found, besides the finite field, the system of (2.10) and two semifields.

Knuth (1965) and, independently, Walker (1963) made machine searches for semifields of order 32. A total of 15,950 such systems were found, yielding the Desarguesian plane and five other planes. The most gratifying result of this search was that Knuth was able to generalize one of these systems to find non-Desarguesian planes of all orders 2^m, m odd, $m \geq 5$, thus resolving the questions left open by Albert's constructions.

Let $F = GF(2^m)$ be the field of order $n = 2^m$, m odd, and let F have a basis $1, x, x^2, \cdots, x^{m-1}$ over $GF(2)$. Define $R(+, \circ)$ as having the same elements as F and the same addition. Define the multiplication $\circ$ in R by distributive laws and by the rules

$$x^i \circ x^j = x^{i+j} \quad \text{if} \quad i, j = 0, \cdots, m-2,$$

$$x^{m-1} \circ x^i = x^i \circ x^{m-1} = x^{m-1} x^i + x^{2i} + x^i, \quad i = 0, \cdots, m-2, \quad (2.13)$$

$$x^{m-1} \circ x^{m-1} = x^{2m-2} + 1.$$

Here, if y, z are elements in the additive group A_{m-2} of F generated by $1, x, \cdots, x^{m-2}$, the rules (2.13) take the form

$$y \circ z = yz,$$

$$x^{m-1} \circ y = x^{m-1} + y^2 + y, \qquad (2.14)$$

$$x^{m-1} \circ x^{m-1} = x^{2m-2} + 1.$$

Every element of R is of the form y or $x^{m-1} + y$. We have the following consequences of (2.14):

$$y \circ z = yz,$$

$$(x^{m-1} + y) \circ z = (x^{m-1} + z + 1 + y)z,$$

$$(x^{m-1} + y) \circ (x^{m-1} + z) = (x^{m-1} + y + 1)^2$$

$$+ (x^{m-1} + y + 1)(x^{m-1} + z + 1) + (x^{m-1} + z + 1)^2 .$$

$$(2.15)$$

Here, the fact that $A \circ B = 0$ implies $A = 0$ or $B = 0$ is clear in the first two cases, while we note that $x^{m-1} \notin A_{m-2}$. In the third case, we note that $U^2 + UV + V^2 = 0$ in $GF(2^m)$ implies $U = V = 0$, unless there is an element w satisfying $w^2 + w + 1 = 0$; but then w generates $GF(2^2)$, and this is not a subfield of $GF(2^m)$ if m is odd. Hence, in all cases, $A \circ B = 0$ implies $A = 0$ or $B = 0$, and so the rules (2.13) define a semifield for m odd. It is not a field for $m \geq 5$, since we find

$$(u^{\frac{m-1}{2}} \circ u^{\frac{m-1}{2}}) \circ u \neq u^{\frac{m-1}{2}} \circ (u^{\frac{m-1}{2}} \circ u).$$

For $m = 3$, the field F is defined by one of the relations $f_1(x) = x^3 + x + 1$ or $f_2(x) = x^3 + x^2 + 1$. Here, the circle product found from $f_1(x)$ is the ordinary product found from $f_2(x)$, and vice versa, and so for $m = 3$ the rules define the field $GF(2^3)$.

NUMERICAL ANALYSIS OF PLANES OF ORDER AT MOST 10

Construction of the planes of orders 2, 3, 4, and 5 is quite easy to do by hand. They are unique and are the Desarguesian planes which may be represented by either the projective or the affine difference sets listed in Table I.

There is no plane of order 6. Historically, this fact is a consequence of Tarry's proof (see Tarry, 1900 and 1901) that there is no pair of orthogonal 6-by-6 Latin squares. But, today, it follows more easily from the Bruck-Ryser theorem.

The 7-by-7 Latin squares were listed by Norton (1939), whose interests were chiefly statistical. He also listed the orthogonal sets of 7-by-7 squares and so succeeded in showing that there is only one plane of order 7, the Desarguesian plane. An omission in Norton's list was found by Sade (1951), but this did not invalidate the conclusion as to the uniqueness of the plane. A more direct proof of the uniqueness of the plane of order 7 was given in companion papers by the author (Hall, 1953 and 1954) and by Pierce (1953).

The Norton list, together with Sade's correction, formed the basis for a machine search for all planes of order 8. This was described by the author jointly with others (see Hall, Swift, and Walker, 1956). This search was based on the fact that the multiplicative loop of a plane of order 8 is given by a Latin square of order 7. Geometrically, if we take three points A, B, O not on a line, then the pencils of lines through A, B, O are determined by a Latin square of order 7. This configuration consists trivially of the three sides of the triangle A, B, O and nontrivially of seven more lines through each of A, B, O, whose intersection pattern is determined by one of the 147 distinct 7-by-7 Latin squares. Choosing the triangle A, B, O judiciously in the plane, we need to consider only 100 of the 147 squares. If we number the 64 finite points of the plane (x, y), where $x, y = 0, \cdots , 7$, we may take for the finite lines eight lines $x = a$ and eight lines $y = b$; a further line will contain eight finite points (i, a_i), where $i = 0, \cdots , 7$, and this may be represented simply by the permutation

$$a_0 \ a_1 \ a_2 \ a_3 \ a_4 \ a_5 \ a_6 \ a_7 \ . \tag{2.16}$$

In this notation the omission found by Sade takes the form:

$$
\begin{array}{cccccccc}
0 & 1 & 2 & 3 & 4 & 5 & 6 & 7 \\
0 & 2 & 1 & 4 & 5 & 6 & 7 & 3 \\
0 & 3 & 4 & 5 & 7 & 1 & 2 & 6 \\
0 & 4 & 5 & 7 & 6 & 3 & 1 & 2 \\
0 & 5 & 6 & 2 & 3 & 7 & 4 & 1 \\
0 & 6 & 7 & 1 & 2 & 4 & 3 & 5 \\
0 & 7 & 3 & 6 & 1 & 2 & 5 & 4 \\
\end{array}
\tag{2.17}
$$

This is the full pencil of lines through $(0, 0)$ except for $x = 0$ and $y = 0$. The machine was asked to adjoin six further consistent lines through $(1, 1)$ and also six through $(2, 2)$.

Adding twelve lines in this way was possible for only one square: the square of lines beginning with 0 followed by 1 2 3 4 5 6 7 and the cyclic rearrangements of the seven nonzero numbers. For this square, the twelve lines could be added in exactly four different ways. From here, completion by hand was easy. Two of these starts could not be completed, while the other two both led to the Desarguesian plane.

This particular problem illustrates in a practical way the efficiency which may be obtained by an appropriate interplay between machine programs and hand methods. A program requiring the machine to find all consistent lines and so find the entire plane would have been hopelessly complicated, and most of it would have been used only twice. An initial program which added only the six lines of the $(1, 1)$ pencil gave far too much output to be processed by hand. The choice of adding twelve lines did not greatly complicate the program and gave so few answers that the rest was easy by hand.

Numerical analysis of planes of orders 9 and 10 is only partial. For order 9, besides the Desarguesian plane, there are three others. A search was made for all planes of order 9 that have the elementary group of order 9 as addition in some presentation (see Hall, Swift, and Killgrove, 1959). The known four planes all have this property, but no other planes exist with this property. A similar search was carried out by Killgrove (1960) for planes of order 9 with a cyclic additive group, and it was found that there are no such planes.

At present, no plane of order 10 has been found. Formerly, it had been thought that the Euler conjecture might be true and that no pair of orthogonal 10-by-10 Latin squares could exist. A machine search failed to find such a pair. Later, Bose, Shrikhande, and Parker disproved the Euler conjecture, and Parker actually exhibited the first pair of orthogonal 10-by-10 Latin squares (see Bose and Shrikhande, 1959; Bose, Shrikhande, and Parker, 1960; and Parker, 1959). Parker later found a large number of such pairs by machine methods superior to those used earlier. The first method was an attempt to construct both squares of the orthogonal pair simultaneously, adding a cell at a time and back-tracking when a conflict was reached. Parker took one 10-by-10 Latin square (and this choice could be random). He then found all possible transversals and, in a second program, tried to form a Latin square from the transversals which would necessarily be orthogonal. In application, Parker has found that about half of the squares he chose at random had one or more orthogonal mates. From the standpoint of machine procedure, the virtue of this method, as compared to the first, seems to be that the construction of the transversals involves a certain amount of work which is done only once, whereas the equivalent of this part of the search (and here "equivalent" is used very loosely) was done many times over in the first method. In any event, Parker's method has had many successes, and the first has had none. From this experience, I look with favor on a program which can accomplish a search in two (or more) stages, including a first significant part which does not have to be repeated in a subsequent search. In this way, we make the sum of separate steps, rather than their product, a measure of the time consumed.

The discovery of the orthogonal pairs of Latin squares gave new impetus to the search for a plane of order 10. As things stand at present, a complete search seems to be out of the question. No pair of orthogonal squares found so far can be extended to a triple of orthogonal squares, whereas the plane amounts to a set of nine mutually orthogonal squares. If we assume that there is a nontrivial collineation in a plane of order 10, this reduces the amount of labor sufficiently to bring the completion of the search within reason. Elementary considerations show that the possible primes dividing the order of a collineation group are 2, 3, 5, 7, 11, 37. Two theorems of Hughes (1957b) exclude two possibilities: that p should equal 2 and that the number of fixed points should be even. Two easy arguments exclude 7 and 37. I have been considering the other possibilities and have eliminated by hand methods the cases $p = 11$ and $p = 5$ when the fixed points are the eleven points on one line. The case $p = 5$ with exactly one fixed point is being searched for on the computer at the Jet Propulsion Laboratory with the help of Leonard Baumert. There remain two cases with $p = 3$: one case in which there are eight fixed points on a line and a further point not on the line, and the other case with three fixed points forming a triangle.

The $p = 5$ search falls into two stages. In the first stage, a 20-by-20 matrix with entries 0, 1, 2 must be found satisfying certain properties. Each row contains two 2's, six 1's, and fourteen 0's. Two rows in the top half or bottom half have inner product 4, whereas a row in the top has inner product 5 with a row in the bottom. So far, no such matrix has been found. If one is found, it will describe the distribution of 20 sets of five points on the lines, the points in a set being those of an orbit of the collineation of order 5. The second stage, if such a matrix is found, will consist of assigning indices 0, 1, 2, 3, 4 (modulo 5) to the five points of each of the 20 sets; when this is finished, the plane will be found. But if there is success in the first stage, the second stage will be vacuous.

L. J. Paige carried out some machine searches in the known non-Desarguesian planes of order 9 and found a large number of ovals. This work has not yet been published.

REFERENCES

ALBERT, A. A. 1952. On nonassociative division algebras. Trans. Amer. Math. Soc., 72:296–309.

———. 1960. Finite division algebras and finite planes *in* Combinatorial analysis (Proceedings of symposia in applied mathematics, vol. X), ed. R. BELLMAN and M. HALL, JR. Providence, R. I.: Amer. Math. Soc., 53–70.

BOSE, R. C. 1942. An affine analogue of Singer's theorem. J. Indian Math. Soc., 6:1–15.

BOSE, R. C., and S. S. SHRIKHANDE. 1959. On the falsity of Euler's conjecture about the non-existence of two orthogonal Latin squares of order $4t + 2$. Proc. Nat. Acad. Sci. U. S., 45:734–37.

BOSE, R. C., S. S. SHRIKHANDE, and E. T. PARKER. 1960. Further results on the construction of mutually orthogonal Latin squares and the falsity of Euler's conjecture. Canad. J. Math., 12:189–203.

BRUCK, R. H., and H. J. RYSER. 1949. The nonexistence of certain finite projective planes. Canad. J. Math., 1:88–93.

HALL, M., JR. 1943. Projective planes. Trans. Amer. Math. Soc., 54:229–77.

———. 1947. Cyclic projective planes. Duke Math. J., 14:1079–90.

———. 1953. Uniqueness of the projective plane with 57 points. Proc. Amer. Math. Soc., 4:912–16.

———. 1954. Correction. Proc. Amer. Math. Soc., 5:994–97.

HALL, M., JR., J. D. SWIFT, and R. KILLGROVE. 1959. On projective planes of order nine. MTAC, 13:233–46.

HALL, M., JR., J. D. SWIFT, and R. J. WALKER. 1956. Uniqueness of the projective plane of order eight. MTAC, 10:186–94.

HOFFMAN, A. J. 1952. Cyclic affine planes. Canad. J. Math., 4:295–301.

HUGHES, D. R. 1957a. A class of non-Desarguesian projective planes. Canad. J. Math., 9:378–88.

———. 1957b. Collineations and generalized incidence matrices. Trans. Amer. Math. Soc., 86:284–96.

KILLGROVE, R. 1960. A note on the nonexistence of certain projective planes of order nine. Math Comput., 14:70–71.

KLEINFELD, E. 1960. Techniques for enumerating Veblen-Wedderburn systems. J. Assoc. Comput. Mach., 7:330–37.

KNUTH, D. E. 1965. A class of projective planes. Trans. Amer. Math. Soc., 115:541–49.

MANN, H. B., and T. A. EVANS. 1951. On simple difference sets. Sankhyā, 11:357–64.

NORTON, H. W. 1939. The 7 × 7 squares. Ann. Eugen., 9:269–307.

PARKER, E. T. 1959. Construction of some sets of mutually orthogonal Latin squares. Proc. Amer. Math. Soc., 10:946–49.

PIERCE, W. A. 1953. The impossibility of Fano's configuration in a projective plane with eight points per line. Proc. Amer. Math. Soc., 4:908–12.

SADE, A. 1951. An omission in Norton's list of 7 × 7 squares. Ann. Math. Statist., 22:306–7.

SINGER, J. 1938. A theorem in finite projective geometry and some applications to number theory. Trans. Amer. Math. Soc., 43:377–85.

TARRY, G. 1900. Le problème des 36 officiers. C. R. Assoc. Franç. Av. Sci., 1:122–23.

———. 1901. Le problème des 36 officiers. C. R. Assoc. Franç. Av. Sci., 2:170–203.

VEBLEN, O., and J. H. M. WEDDERBURN. 1907. Non-Desarguesian and non-Pascalian geometries. Trans. Amer. Math. Soc., 8:379–88.

WALKER, R. J. 1963. Determination of division algebras with 32 elements *in* Experimental arithmetic, high-speed computing and mathematics (Proceedings of symposia in applied mathematics, vol. XV), ed. N. C. METROPOLIS *et al.* Providence, R. I.: Amer. Math Soc., 83–85.

DISCUSSION

S. SHERMAN: There is a problem concerning the 12-tone scale that V equals N plus 1. V is 12, and N is 11. Take your project of difference sets. I have done this for the 12-tone scale. I wonder whether any of the theory developed here would be relevant to such a notion of difference sets or whether this tabulation does not apply.

M. HALL, JR.: What are the properties of your 12-tone scale?

S. SHERMAN: The requirement is that if a represents a permutation of $(0, 1, 2, \cdots, 11)$ so that $\{a_0, a_1, \cdots, a_{11}\} = \{0, 1, 2, \cdots, 11\}$, then, for each $d(1 \leq d \leq 11)$, there is a j $(0 \leq j \leq 10)$ such that $a_{j+1} - a_j \equiv d \pmod{12}$. In an alternative representation, one considers permutations σ of $(1, 2, \cdots, 11)$ so that $\{\sigma_1, \sigma_2, \cdots, \sigma_{11}\} = \{1, 2, \cdots, 11\}$ such that (for all i, j satisfying $1 \leq i \leq j \leq 11$) $\sigma_i + \sigma_{i+1} + \cdots + \sigma_j \not\equiv 0 \pmod{12}$.

M. HALL, JR.: There may be such. It is related, although I think you will not get the answer. The uniqueness is the chief clue here.

S. SHERMAN: If we look merely at the differences, there are a little over 3,800 such sequences, these sequences being 11 long.

M. HALL, JR.: But you will get everything quite a number of times.

S. SHERMAN: No, each difference occurs but once.

M. HALL, JR.: I see.

D. H. LEHMER: This is very interesting. This is also Arnold Schoenberg's problem, and we ran this on the SWAC in 1956.

S. SHERMAN: I checked with you at Boulder in 1963.

D. H. LEHMER: I did not understand what you were talking about. We went up to 30-tone scales with these things.

S. SHERMAN: You exhausted all the sequences?

D. H. LEHMER: There were so many 12-tone sequences that we had to choose. I remember that there were 3,500 or 3,800 [3,856, to be exact].

S. SHERMAN: I understand some work has been done on this at the IBM Systems Research Institute, although the paper has not yet been published.

3
Combinatorial Types in Number-Theory Calculations

D. H. LEHMER

University of California, Berkeley

It has been requested that my contribution to the program of this symposium on combinatorial analysis should deal with number theory. According to the late P. A. M. MacMahon, combinatorial analysis and number theory are different subjects. Of course, this opinion was voiced in 1915, and both terms have had their meanings enlarged in the past half century, especially combinatorial analysis. Nevertheless, I feel that there still are good reasons to distinguish between these subjects. A glance at the titles of the other papers presented at this symposium will confirm this belief. The question is more nearly whether number theory is part of combinatorial analysis. Still, I would think not. What appears to be true is that computer technology is bringing about a closer connection between these subjects, and I take as my text the affirmation that a wider knowledge of combinatorial analysis is needed to make possible further research in the theory of numbers. In this brief contribution to the program, I hope to indicate what sorts of combinatorial problems are encountered in furthering this research.

Riordan (1958) opines that "anything enumerative is combinatorial." This definition would have been far too liberal for Leibniz, but I believe that today it is too restrictive. To be sure, before one goes about doing some well-defined operation, it would be helpful to know the number of different ways of doing it. There are many cases when this preliminary knowledge might deter even the stoutest heart from beginning a proposed operation. However useful this aspect may be, and in spite of the traditional intrinsic interest in the mere "number of ways" question, I think that this symposium will convince its attendees that we have already reached the point where we can begin to answer questions like: What *are* the different ways of doing it, and which is optimal? Surely such questions are also combinatorial. There are cases in which the number of ways of doing the operation comes out as a mere by-product of the investigation into the different ways.

Let me begin with a very simple example. In pursuit of an idea vaguely connected with the exact number of primes less than a given limit, I recently became interested in the infinite product

$$\prod_{n=1}^{\infty}\left(1 + \frac{x^n}{n}\right) = \sum_{m=0}^{\infty} a_m x^m$$
$$= 1 + x + \tfrac{1}{2}x^2 + \tfrac{5}{6}x^3 + \tfrac{7}{12}x^4 + \cdots .$$

I had some reason for believing that the coefficients a_m of this power series are never very large. I soon found a recursive formula for a_m in terms of previous a's and certain complicated divisor functions, but it was impossible from this to prove much about the size of a_m or even to prove the obvious fact that $a_m > 0$.

At this point, we bring in combinatorial analysis to get a good look at the a's. To each partition

$$m = k_1 + k_2 + \cdots + k_t$$

of m into positive integers, we assign the weight $1/(k_1 \, k_2 \, \cdots \, k_t)$. It is then clear, after a moment's glance at our generating product, that a_m is the sum of the weights of all possible partitions of m into distinct parts. The number $q(m)$ of such partitions was first discussed by Euler and is fairly well known and well tabulated. However, our concern goes much further: We have to produce these partitions and add their weights, not just count them.

It was a straightforward procedure to code up a routine to obtain the exact integer $m!a_m$ as well as a good approximation to a_m for $m = 1(1)100$. As a check, a tally produced $q(m)$. A look at the output convinced me that a_m is not only moderate in size but is also tending to a limit. I mentioned this conjecture in a letter to Professor Littlewood, and he replied with a proof. Soon afterward, I proved that

$$\lim_{m \to \infty} a_m = e^{-\gamma} = 0.5614594836,$$

where γ is Euler's constant. Here we see combinatorial analysis at work as a handmaiden to a number theorist.

I give next another, entirely different example, this one involving some concern with the economics of computing. About two years ago, I was doing some reconnaissance work connected with the Riemann hypothesis in which it was required to process all the 12×12 minors of a certain 12×20 matrix. By combinatorial analysis, in the sense of Leibniz, there are

$$\binom{20}{12} = 125{,}970$$

such minors, a number large enough to overburden the hand computer but not too large for a machine to process in due course of time. As my project was unsponsored, I had to impose on two of my friends. One friend had a machine five times faster than that of the other friend. I had resolved to beg for equal time from each friend. Thus, there remained only one small problem: Where should the job be split? That is, assuming that the slow machine begins at the beginning by processing the minor consisting of the first twelve columns, with what minor should the fast machine begin? The answer turns out to be the minor determined by columns

$$1, 2, 3, 6, 7, 12, 13, 14, 16, 17, 18, 19.$$

In solving the general problem implied here, I discovered a new, useful, unique representation of positive integers: namely, if k is a fixed integer (like 12) and m is any integer, then

$$m = \binom{a_1}{1} + \binom{a_2}{2} + \cdots + \binom{a_k}{k},$$

where the integers are strictly increasing, that is,

$$0 \le a_1 < a_2 < \cdots < a_{k-1} < a_k.$$

This representation can be used to find the rank of a given combination of n things taken k at a time in dictionary order and, conversely, to find the combination, given the rank.

At what must have been about the same time, this combinatorial representation was also discovered by Kruskal (1963) and by Dubins and Savage (1965). I am indebted to Professor Dubins for these references. He approaches the problem by asking how many positive integers $\le x$ have precisely k binary ones in their base-2 representation.

A third example arose in studying a problem of Hardy and Littlewood on integral inequalities. It also has economic overtones. We have a function $f(x_1, x_2, \cdots, x_n)$ of n small integer variables x_i. For each choice of the argument vector $(x_1, x_2, \cdots, x_n)$, the value of f is unpredictable and expensive to compute. Although f is not a symmetric function, if two adjacent x's are interchanged, f is only slightly perturbed, and its new value is obtained more cheaply from its preceding value than from a complete recalculation. Even so, the expense is not negligible. Given an argument vector $(x_1, x_2, \cdots, x_n)$, it is required to find the maximum value of f when the x's are permuted in all $n!$ ways. Now there is a good chance that some of the x's are equal. In this case, the number of distinct argument vectors needing examination may be very much less than $n!$. In fact, it will be only

$$P_n = \frac{n!}{a_1! \, a_2! \, \cdots}$$

in case there are, among the x's, a_1 of one value, a_2 of a second value, etc.

All the above considerations thus point to the need for a schedule, depending on a_1, a_2, $\cdots$, of $P_n - 1$ adjacent interchanges so that all P_n distinct permutations of $(x_1, x_2, \cdots , x_n)$ can be wrung from the given set of x's. It is not at all clear that such a schedule exists in all cases; in fact, it doesn't. However, for the simplest case of $a_1 = a_2 = \cdots = 1$, that is, all distinct x's, Johnson (1963) has given a very simple procedure from which such a schedule of interchanges can be at once written down. For example, in the simple case of $n = 3$, his scheme gives the successive permutations

$$(x_1, x_2, x_3)(x_1, x_3, x_2)(x_3, x_1, x_2)(x_3, x_2, x_1)(x_2, x_3, x_1)(x_2, x_1, x_3).$$

The interchange sequence could be described compactly by 2 1 2 1 2, using an obvious code. For the slightly more complicated case of $n = 4$, $a_1 = 2$, $a_2 = a_3 = 1$, $P_n = 12$, the interchange schedule is

$$3\ 2\ 1\ 3\ 1\ 2\ 3\ 1\ 3\ 2\ 1,$$

starting with (x_1, x_1, x_3, x_4). The first impossible case is $n = 4$, $a_1 = a_2 = 2$, $P_n = 6$, as we shall see later.

The question of how to automate the construction of such interchange sequences is answered by graph theory. Each of the P_n distinct permutations can be represented by a point in the plane. Those few permutations that are obtained from a given permutation by adjacent interchange correspond to a few points. These are joined to the point corresponding to the given permutation by simple paths. Doing this for each permutation point produces a graph. To construct an interchange sequence is to find a path through all P_n nodes of the graph. To construct an optimum interchange sequence is to find a path which visits each point once and only once, that is, a Hamiltonian path. For example, the graph corresponding to the last-mentioned case is shown in Figure 1. It is at once clear why a Hamiltonian path is impossible. The best that one can do is to introduce a side trip or "spur," as, for example, in the path $1 \to 2 \to 3 \to 5 \to 4 \to 5 \to 6$. In terms of the six permutations beginning with (x_1, x_1, x_2, x_2), the interchange sequence is 2 1 3 1 1 2, in which the two consecutive units indicate a spur. This slight blemish is of no practical importance

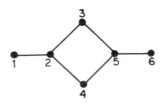

FIGURE 1. Graph of permutation problem for $n = 4$, $a_1 = a_2 = 2$

to our original problem. Simply by being on the lookout for equality between consecutive interchange indices, the computer can easily skip over the calculation of $f(x_1, \cdots, x_n)$ and pass on to the next interchange.

So far, we have merely shifted the difficulty from one medium to another. The Hamiltonian graph problem is a special case of the traveling salesman problem, in which certain distances are taken as infinite. For example, in Figure 1 the direct distances between 2 and 5, 3 and 4, 1 and 3, etc., are supposed to be infinite. Theoretically, we could use routines for the general traveling salesman problem, but I think this would be unwise. As a matter of fact, the graphs that arise from our permutation problem are far from typical. They have a very large number of nodes, but no node has more than $n - 1$ paths leading to or from it. This fact gives the graphs a long, ropelike structure. They can be colored in two colors. Another atypical local property is that any simple closed path in the graph contains an even number of nodes. The two pigtails (1 to 2 and 5 to 6) of Figure 1 are unusual. As a more typical case, we may cite that for which $n = 7$, $a_1 = 4$, $a_2 = 2$, $a_3 = 1$, $N = 105$, that is, $(x_1, x_1, x_1, x_1, x_2, x_2, x_3)$. Its graph has an average of four paths through each node.

In fact, this graph has 6 nodes of multiplicity 2,

25 nodes of multiplicity 3,

41 nodes of multiplicity 4,

29 nodes of multiplicity 5,

4 nodes of multiplicity 6,

and it has therefore 210 paths. I have obtained an interchange sequence for this graph with only two spurs, which can be shown to be the least possible. I have written a code for finding Hamiltonian paths that is particularly effective for graphs of our kind. Without going into details, that appear elsewhere (Lehmer, 1965), I may indicate the basic strategy on which the method is built. To start with, the nodes are given serial numbers arbitrarily from 1 to P_n. Starting at node 1, we inspect all the other nodes immediately joined to it and select the node of least multiplicity. If two or more are of least multiplicity, that one with least serial number is selected. Before departing for this node, we disconnect all other paths leaving node 1. This has the effect of reducing by one the multiplicity of all these other nodes. This strategy is repeated on arrival at the next node until, hopefully, all the nodes have been visited. If at any time a move is impossible, we retreat to the node just previously visited, creating in this way a "spur." If now no move is possible, we halt, regenerate the graph supplying new serial numbers, and try again. All graphs with $n \leq 7$ and all but 6 of the 22 graphs for $n = 8$ have been processed by this strategy and with the aid of certain simple theorems. Graphs with as many as 2,500 nodes are produced and processed in a few minutes. Coded output data are then available as inputs to many different permutation problems. The results thus have a sort of once-for-all quality that is satisfying. For $n = 4(1)7$, a list of results obtained is given in Lehmer (1965).

Problems involving trees (that is, cycle-free graphs, familiar objects in combinatorial analysis) arise rather naturally in theorem-proving by separation of many cases. Here again, the problem is not one of enumeration of trees. Rather, it concerns the automatic generation and processing of trees. In typical cases, each stem of the tree can produce only a small number of branches, say at most b. Each node N of the tree can then be associated with a vector whose dimension h is the height of the node above the root of the tree, that is, the number of nodes between N and the root. The components are taken from the nonnegative integers less than b. The first $h - 1$ components of the vector constitute the vector associated with the node N' of height $h - 1$ from which the given node N has branched, while the last component designates which of the several possible branches from N' has produced N. The components of any vector may in turn be thought of as the digits in the base-b expansion of a real number x that lies in the interval (0, 1). Of course, x is actually only a rational number whose denominator is a power of b, but x may be conveniently used to indicate progress in processing the tree in a methodical way and also as an input index for restarting an interrupted program. Many times, the method of proof varies with the height, and then x can be used to control the proof and hence the generation of the tree itself, a feature that is fairly essential in these days of "monitored operation."

For very elaborate proofs with well over a million cases, we cannot hope to store the corresponding tree in the memory. So the tree must "pass in review" timewise. Our concern is rather that the tree should not grow to such a height and breadth as to require a prohibitive amount of information and time to process it fully. These huge trees that we never really see are sometimes almost as large as the ones we dream about when we consider the possibility that the theorem we are trying to prove may not be true after all. Relegating the proof to the machine does not relieve the state of mind of the combinatorial analyst from its proverbial oscillation between "vain hope and groundless fear."

There are other varieties of combinatorial problems that I could mention. Some of these have not actually been dealt with for the reason that our present-day "one-bottleneck" computers cannot cope with them adequately.

REFERENCES

Dubins, L. E., and L. J. Savage. 1965. How to gamble if you must. New York: McGraw-Hill, chap. 6, sect. 4.
Johnson, S. M. 1963. Generation of permutations by adjacent transposition. Math. Comput., 17:282–85. (Also published as Memorandum RM-3177-PR. Santa Monica, Calif.: The RAND Corp.)

KRUSKAL, J. B. 1963. The number of simplices in a complex *in* Mathematical optimization techniques, ed. R. BELLMAN. Berkeley: Univ. of California Press, 251–78. (Also published as Report R-396-PR. Santa Monica, Calif.: The RAND Corp.)

LEHMER, D. H. 1965. Permutation by adjacent interchanges. Amer. Math. Monthly, 72:36–46.

RIORDAN, J. 1958. Introduction to combinatorial analysis. New York: Wiley.

DISCUSSION

J. EDMONDS: By spur, do you mean a side trip of length 1 only? You don't have spurs against spurs?

D. H. LEHMER: We use spurs of length 1. If you want longer spurs, you have to put into the code a memory of where you have been. You don't want to insist that the machine remember too many places where it has been. Our short spur is more convenient, and it is adequate.

J. EDMONDS: Is it your conjecture that there is always a spur path type of schedule?

D. H. LEHMER: You can deliberately and wastefully spur your way through any graph.

J. EDMONDS: The general existence of a spur path for the transposition problem does not seem obvious. However, it has been proved then?

D. H. LEHMER: Maybe I am not making myself clear. Given this graph, you can spur your way through it by providing enough spurs. The color difference will give you the fact that you must have at least so many spurs. If you do it in that many, then you should quit, because that is the best you can do. Thus far we have always succeeded. After all, these graphs are rather special.

R. M. KARP: Is it possible to compute the color difference of the graph by inspection of the kinds of marks being permuted without constructing a graph?

D. H. LEHMER: I'm not sure. There might be another way of doing it.

J. E. MEGGITT: What sort of features would you like to see in a machine that was designed to solve combinatorial problems?

D. H. LEHMER: I would like to see more special arithmetical units, not only addition and subtraction. We designed our first machine for ballistics research, and we are still trying to live this part of it down. We need attachments, if you like.

P. J. SANDIFORD: In industrial problems there are large numbers of combinations having values which practical people have decided should be rejected, by some mysterious method.

D. H. LEHMER: I don't know how they do it.

P. J. SANDIFORD: But you are given the existence of the present combination that they are using and which is presumably satisfactory. The next problem is to make permutations to neighboring states in directions which may result in improvement. Would this interchanging system of yours be helpful in exploring that part of the vast number of permutations which lie in the vicinity of one which is known to be relatively satisfactory?

D. H. LEHMER: Yes, if the function we are talking about is only slightly altered by a minor interchange like this, then you could start at this point and explore the neighborhood.

Chemistry and Biology

4

A Study of Macromolecular Configurations
Using Stochastic Methods

FREDERICK T. WALL
University of Illinois[1]

In this paper, by request, I am explaining more of the chemical significance of macromolecular configurations than was my original intention, which was to treat the problem as one of combinatorial mathematics alone.

I shall discuss the configurations of coiling-type macromolecules, that is, polymer molecules that constitute plastics, rubber, etc. Many polymers are of considerable importance; here, I shall confine myself primarily to rubber-like molecules. These characteristically consist of long chains that can assume a great variety of configurations.

The simplest model conceivable is a string of beads or a flexible chain (see Flory, 1953). Admittedly, this is an oversimplification, but it will serve our purpose. The basic idea is that the string or chain is completely flexible and that it can assume many different configurations. The left-hand side of Figure 1 gives an idea of what a long rubber molecule might look like in projection; it would exhibit quite a random size and shape.

Typical molecular weights can be several hundred thousand, perhaps a million. These correspond to many tens of thousands, perhaps a hundred thousand, atoms in the chain.

Such a random chain would encompass mostly free space. The "sphere of influence" is really quite dilute. A single polymer molecule by itself would, on the average, have a density within its sphere of influence like that of a thin gas. Nevertheless, there are important intramolecular interactions; these arise from the constraints imposed by the contour of the chain.

Why should the size and shape of a macromolecule matter? For one thing, it arouses our mathematical curiosity; that, I think, is a sufficient answer. However, a practical reason for working on this problem is that rubber is an important commercial commodity, principally because of

---

[1] Presently at University of California, Santa Barbara.

Without volume restriction   With volume restriction

FIGURE 1. Sizes of coiling-type molecules

its long-range elasticity. We want to know why anything is elastic and why rubber behaves as it does. Why, in particular, does rubber behave unlike metals?

A piece of rubber is a tangled mass of chains. There is not much free space in the rubber itself, even though any one molecule would be quite nebulous. These random chains are all enmeshed together, but the rubber can be given a more stable configuration by imposing crosslinks between different chains. These crosslinks are produced by the important process of "vulcanization."

Vulcanization consists simply of linking different molecular chains together so that they cannot be pulled completely apart. A piece of vulcanized rubber is really one single macromolecule formed by binding the originally separate molecules together by chemical bonds.

If we stretch a piece of rubber, the original molecules, or the segments between the crosslink points, will tend to line up in the direction of stretch. This means that they are constrained to assume configurations that are relatively improbable. The molecules do not naturally tend to be lined up but rather tend to assume the form of a random coil; this is so not because the random coil is energetically favorable but because it is most probable. A single molecule could conceivably be rolled up like a ball of yarn, or it could be straightened out to its maximum length, but, in general, molecules will exhibit random coil configurations with a wide distribution from an "average" appearance.

When we straighten out a molecule, the configuration becomes improbable; when we release the molecule, the configuration seeks to become probable again. Thus, the phenomenon of rubber elasticity is entropic, largely divorced from energy considerations. Accordingly, it would be helpful to know something about the dimensions of these molecules and what the distribution of these dimensions might be.

In order to describe a single coiling-type polymer molecule, let us return to the string-of-beads model. The first approximation that one might think of would be the unrestricted random walk. Let each vector connecting two adjacent beads assume any direction without reference to where other beads might be, subject only to the constraint that each vector is of fixed bond length.

The random walk application to the string-of-beads model, though it can serve as a crude approximation, has a serious inherent deficiency: It permits two beads to be in the same place at the same time. But does this really matter?

It definitely does matter, especially for short-range interactions and small loop closures. How important are long-range interactions? The fact that we must exclude all loops (that is, prohibit going to a point already occupied) could have considerable bearing on the average dimensions of these molecules. By stipulating that no two beads can occupy the same space, we are faced with what is called the "excluded volume" problem. The righthand side of Figure 1 shows what happens to a molecule when it is subject to the excluded volume effect.

To solve the excluded volume problem, we sought to generate, on a computer, statistical samples that might give us a better idea of the sizes and shapes of these molecules. Here is a description of our simple procedure (see Wall, Hiller, and Wheeler, 1954):

Calculations were carried out, for the most part, in the three-dimensional diamond-type lattice, but for illustration I show how it could be handled in two dimensions with 90-degree angles (see Figure 2).

After the first two steps (to the right and up), we select at random a vector in either of two directions. We can go to the right, as in (1) and (2), then down, as in (1), or up, as in (2). Or (after the first two steps) we can go to the left, as in (3) and (4), then up, as in (3), or down, as in (4). But (4) closes a loop, and so it is disallowed. Thus, in Figure 2, (1), (2), and (3) are listed as successes, (4) as a failure.

Our first calculations for the generation of random walks were carried out simply by selecting random vectors. After each vector addition, we checked to make sure that we had not closed a loop. We check by taking the last vector, adding to it the preceding vector, and so on, until we get back to the origin or find a zero vector sum. In the latter case, we throw out the configuration.

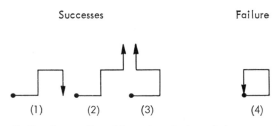

FIGURE 2. Random walks of four steps in two-choice square lattice

The foregoing discussion partly explains the background of why we are interested in this kind of problem and how it can be tackled. Since carrying out the most elementary work, we have also been concerned with such matters as the thermodynamics of these molecules in solution. With this end in mind, we can assume intramolecular interactions of such a character that, even though we exclude double occupancy, a favorable potential energy would cause portions of the molecule to get close together yet not overlap. If there are intramolecular attractions, they will tend to shrink the molecule. Moreover, there is a certain temperature at which attraction effects will just compensate for the excluded volume, at least with respect to some criteria.

Incidentally, if we were interested only in short chains, the problem would not be very difficult. If we were concerned with strings of only 20 or 30 beads, I think that we could carry out an exact enumeration on a computer, even though the total number of configurations is quite large. What really interests us are chains with hundreds and possibly thousands of links; hence, it would be virtually impossible to calculate and write down each distinguishable configuration with present equipment.

In three dimensions we use the diamond-crystal type of tetrahedral lattice (see Figure 3). We start at an arbitrarily chosen lattice point, indicated by (000) at the center of a cube, and first proceed to one of the four corners indicated, namely, (111), ($1\bar{1}\bar{1}$), ($\bar{1}1\bar{1}$), or ($\bar{1}\bar{1}1$). The second set of four vector choices is precisely the negative set of the first four; the third set of choices is again equivalent to the first; and so on.

In developing a chain in the tetrahedral lattice, we obviously rule out the return step, because that would immediately violate the excluded volume limitation, and we proceed by randomly selecting any of the three

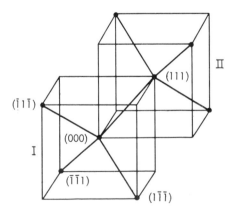

FIGURE 3. Diamond-crystal type of tetrahedral lattice
[After Wall, Windwer, and Gans, 1963, Figure 1]

vectors that might propagate the chain. The shortest loop we can form in such a lattice system is a loop of six. Of course, it is possible to have loops of eight, ten, twelve, and all other even numbers.

If one carries out chain generation as indicated, systematically testing to determine whether a random walk is a success and throwing out the failures, then the logarithm of the number of successful walks bears a linear relation to the number of steps. Figure 4 shows this for walks in a cubic lattice and a tetrahedral lattice.

The graphs indicate exponential attrition. The linear character of the graphs does not show up immediately for small values of n (the number of steps), but it is established very soon. After finding this relationship empirically, we were gratified to learn that it had already been predicted by Hammersley and Morton (1954), who proved that such an exponential behavior would be approached asymptotically. The limiting equation is

$$N_n = N_0 e^{-\lambda n},$$

where N_n is the number of walks left after n steps, N_0 is a constant (extrapolated value of N_n as $n \to 0$), and λ is an attrition constant.

For the four-choice simple cubic lattice, all bond angles are 90 degrees, so it is possible to close loops of four steps. For the tetrahedral lattice, we recall that the smallest loop has six links, and the attrition is less than it is for the four-choice cubic system. It is interesting that the number

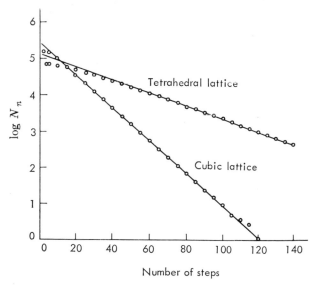

FIGURE 4. Logarithm of number of successful walks vs. number of steps for two lattices [After Wall, Hiller, and Wheeler, 1954, Figure 1]

of sample configurations falls off so rapidly. Starting with something like a quarter of a million walks, we found that our longest walk in the cubic system reached 120 steps. Actually, we lose about half of our sample walks every seven steps.

We cannot solve the problem of long walks by simply running a machine longer, because, for each additional 100 steps, we would have to increase the number of walks started by a factor of 2^{14}. (If a factor of 2 would take care of seven more steps, then 2^{14} should take care of 98 or roughly 100 steps.) Even with an exceedingly fast machine, this would be practically unattainable.

The attrition of sample configurations was our most serious problem. Although we did obtain much useful information, we also wanted to find some way of avoiding this difficulty. This requires paying particular attention to the proper weighting of machine-generated samples.

In generating chains, we want to obtain representative configurations for the specified number of links. In Figure 5, we see that after three steps there are two distinguishable configurations for the two-choice square lattice. After four steps, there appear to be four configurations, one of which must be thrown out. If we take cognizance of attrition by throwing out the disallowed configuration, the relative weights of the other three configurations should be equal. When a configuration like the fourth one fails, one must avoid trying to correct the last step by retrial, lest the third configuration be overweighted. The weights indicated in Figure 5 disclose the pitfall that attends trying to avoid attrition by retrials.

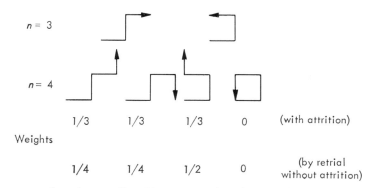

Weights				
1/3	1/3	1/3	0	(with attrition)
1/4	1/4	1/2	0	(by retrial without attrition)

FIGURE 5. Counting of allowable configurations for two-choice square lattice (with and without attrition)

To avoid bias in the generation of samples, one must be sure to maintain the proper sample frequency. Even though we cannot generate all possible configurations, we can employ a technique, which I call a "branching technique," to circumvent the difficulty (see Wall and Erpenbeck, 1959). This technique is illustrated in Figure 6.

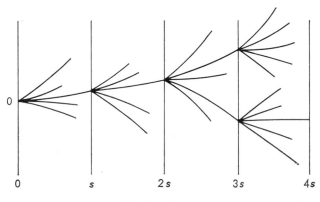

Number of steps

FIGURE 6. Branching technique
[After Wall and Erpenbeck, 1959, Figure 1]

We start by generating chains in a perfectly random way. If we fail to reach a certain length, we start again, and so on, until we reach a certain number of steps (say, s), which we shall identify as a branch point. We take note of that point and continue the process, except that, upon encountering a failure, we return to the sth point, instead of to the origin, and try again.

We must be prepared to try a predetermined number of times at each branch point. This number of times must not be contingent on the specific configurations; it is fixed at a convenient value prior to the actual starting of the computations.

In the example shown in Figure 6, our third trial succeeded to s steps, so we try to go another s steps to $2s$; this will be the next branch point. After we have exhausted the number of trials (say, five) that we agree to make from each branch point, we go back to the preceding branch point and start exhausting possibilities again.

We may expect to lose $e^{-\lambda s}$ of our samples between branch points. If we make p trials, we should choose p such that $pe^{-\lambda s}$ is of the order of unity; thus, we can propagate the chains indefinitely, without significant attrition and without serious proliferation.

For practical reasons, we want $pe^{-\lambda s}$ to be a little less than 1. We can stand a little attrition, though we do not want to lose a large fraction of our samples every 15 or 20 steps. If we lose a few in 100 steps, that is not so bad, for we can keep growing chains to great lengths before they ultimately die off. However, if $pe^{-\lambda s}$ is greater than 1, there is proliferation of samples. If this occurs, we can never fill out the branch points, because the propagation is faster than can be taken care of. As a result, too much emphasis would be placed on the stems of the chains and not enough on their far ends. Following this procedure, we found the only practical limitation to be the storage of the machine.

Figure 7 shows some of our empirical results obtained by machine calculations. The mean square of the end-to-end separation $\langle r_n^2 \rangle$ is plotted against the number of steps n on a log-log grid. The plots are practically linear. Without suggesting a theoretical basis for this fact, we can state that such an empirical representation may serve theoretical purposes for walks in both lattices. The slope of the lines appears to be characteristic of the number of dimensions, whereas the intercept depends on the lattice, coordination number, etc.

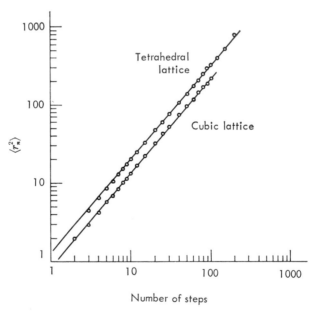

Number of steps

FIGURE 7. Mean square end-to-end separation vs. number of steps on log-log grid
[After Wall, Hiller, and Wheeler, 1954, Figure 4]

Table I shows the empirical results obtained by fitting appropriate constants to an equation suggested by Figure 7, namely,

$$\langle r_n^2 \rangle = an^b.$$

TABLE I

Mean Squares of End-to-End Separations
in Terms of Number of Steps

Tetrahedral lattice	$\langle r_n^2 \rangle = 1.25 n^{1.20}$
Three-choice square lattice	$\langle r_n^2 \rangle = 0.80 n^{1.50}$
Unrestricted (both lattices)	$\langle r_n^2 \rangle = 2n$

The significant thing is b, the power of n, which equals unity for unrestricted walks and exceeds unity for excluded volume walks. As mentioned earlier, the coefficient a depends on the lattice and on the coordination number. Each step is assumed to be of unit length.

Since these results are based on calculations up to about 800 steps, this empirical representation should be useful for many purposes. However, it is tantalizing not to know what happens when n is ten thousand, a hundred thousand, or a million. What happens with large values of n we do not know from our stochastic studies. This is not a practical problem, however, for polymers we are normally concerned with. Recently, Edwards (1965) showed asymptotically that

$$ b = \frac{6}{d + 2} $$

where d is the number of dimensions. For $d = 3$, the value of b should be 1.20 (as observed), and for $d = 2$, the value should be 1.50 (also observed). The empirical results are gratifying in the light of the theory.

Other interesting statistical information about random chains concerns the mean square of the radius of gyration $\langle S_n^2 \rangle$. Table II summarizes some of this information, obtained empirically. The radius of gyration of a molecule about its center of gravity is important, for instance, in connection with the scattering of light. Thus, if light is shone into a polymer solution, some of the light will be scattered by amounts depending, in part, on the radius of gyration. For an unrestricted walk, the mean square

TABLE II

Mean Squares of Radii of Gyration Compared with
Mean Squares of End-to-End Separations

Unrestricted walk	$\langle S_n^2 \rangle = 0.167 \langle r_n^2 \rangle$
Restricted tetrahedral lattice	$\langle S_n^2 \rangle = 0.157 \langle r_n^2 \rangle$
Restricted square lattice	$\langle S_n^2 \rangle = 0.145 \langle r_n^2 \rangle$

radius of gyration is exactly $\frac{1}{6}$ of the mean square end-to-end separation. In chains subject to the restricted volume effect, this ratio is slightly less than $\frac{1}{6}$. However, the actual value of the mean square of the radius of gyration for a restricted chain will be much greater than it is for walks in an unrestricted lattice, because the mean square of the end-to-end separation is much greater for the restricted case. Happily, the ratio $\langle S_n^2 \rangle / \langle r_n^2 \rangle$ does not change much, so, in the absence of knowledge to the contrary, one can assume the unrestricted random walk model for some purposes. One can thus use the ratios, even though the original model is deficient in detail.

Table III summarizes some additional statistical information. The quantity $\langle R_{ij}^2 \rangle$ is the mean square of the intrachain separation between the ith and the jth members of the chain. For the first quarter of the chain $(i = 0, j = n/4)$, the ratio $\langle R_{ij}^2 \rangle / \langle r_n^2 \rangle$ is 0.2047, whereas for an unrestricted walk it is exactly $\frac{1}{4}$. For the second quarter $(i = n/4, j = n/2)$, the ratio is 0.2203. For the first half $(i = 0, j = n/2)$, the ratio is 0.4607. For the middle half $(i = n/4, j = 3n/4)$, the ratio is 0.4893. For the first three-quarters $(i = 0, j = 3n/4)$, the ratio is 0.7370.

TABLE III

Ratios $\langle R_{ij}^2 \rangle / \langle r_n^2 \rangle$ for Tetrahedral Lattice

i, j:	0, n/4	n/4, n/2	0, n/2	n/4, 3n/4	0, 3n/4
ratio:	0.2047	0.2203	0.4607	0.4893	0.7370

These interesting results can be readily explained on a qualitative basis. If we generate, say, one-fourth of a walk and then randomly add to make up the remaining three-fourths, we will encounter some interferences with the first quarter, thus giving rise to attrition. Accordingly, we end up with walks significantly longer than those corresponding to the first quarter.

Let us now briefly consider the energetics involved (see Wall and Mazur, 1961). With that end in mind, we introduce a rather crude intramolecular potential energy function (see table below).

TABLE IV

Intramolecular Potential Energies

for $r_{ij} = 0$,	$\epsilon_{ij} = \infty$
$r_0 > r_{ij} > 0$,	$\epsilon_{ij} = \epsilon \neq 0$
$\infty > r_{ij} > r_0$,	$\epsilon_{ij} = 0$

If r_{ij} is zero, then ϵ_{ij}, the intramolecular energy of interaction, is infinite, leading to excluded volume. On the other hand, for an intermediate range $(r_0 > r_{ij} > 0)$, the energy is finite and different from zero. For ranges exceeding r_0, the energy is zero. Thus, we have a simple-step potential function. If z is the number of intramolecular interactions of energy ϵ, then $V = z\epsilon$ is the potential energy of the molecule. If N_z is the number of samples generated with z interactions, we can write the partition function Q as follows:

$$Q = \sum_z N_z \exp\left(-z\epsilon/kT\right).$$

In addition, we can write $\langle r_n^2 \rangle$ as a function of temperature:

$$\langle r_n^2 \rangle = \frac{\sum \langle r_n^2 \rangle_z N_z \exp\left(-z\epsilon/kT\right)}{Q}.$$

When $\log\left(\langle r_n^2 \rangle / n\right)$ is plotted against $\log n$ (see Figure 8), we obtain straight lines with slopes depending on ϵ/kT. If $\epsilon/kT = 0$, the problem reduces to the simple one of excluded volume. If ϵ/kT is negative, the polymer

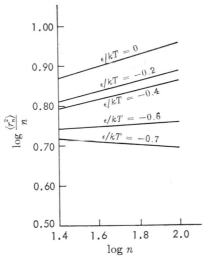

FIGURE 8. $\log\left(\langle r_n^2 \rangle / n\right)$ vs. $\log n$ for different values of ϵ/kT

dimensions do not increase so rapidly with n. If $\epsilon/kT = -0.6$, $\langle r_n^2 \rangle / n$ is independent of n; this corresponds to the Flory temperature (analogous to Boyle temperature for nonperfect gases).

REFERENCES

EDWARDS, S. F. 1965. Proc. Phys. Soc., 85:613.

FLORY, P. J. 1953. Principles of polymer chemistry. Ithaca, N. Y.: Cornell Univ. Press, chap. X.

HAMMERSLEY, J. M., and K. W. MORTON. 1954. J. Roy. Statist. Soc. Ser. B, 16:23–38.

WALL, F. T., and J. J. ERPENBECK. 1959. J. Chem. Phys., 30:634-637.

WALL, F. T., L. A. HILLER, JR., and D. J. WHEELER. 1954. J. Chem. Phys., 22:1036.

WALL, F. T., and J. MAZUR. 1961. Ann. New York Acad. Sci., 89:608.

WALL, F. T., S. WINDWER, and P. J. GANS. 1963, *in* Methods in computational physics, vol. I, ed. B. ALDER, S. FERNBACH, and M. ROTENBERG. New York: Academic Press, 217–43.

DISCUSSION

J. H. GIBBS: When you apply some of these considerations to corrections in, for instance, rubber elasticity, how important are the intermolecular interactions compared with the intramolecular interactions?

F. T. WALL: As for rubber elasticity, we can forget about intramolecular van der Waals forces, but we must take cognizance of the excluded volume. The energy is independent of whether the interactions are intermolecular or intramolecular, although the excluded volume affects the dimensions.

J. H. GIBBS: But in your calculations are the configurations to be thrown out because you have intrachain interactions?

F. T. WALL: That is correct.

J. H. GIBBS: Is that more important or less important than the number that would have to be thrown out because of exclusion between two different chains?

F. T. WALL: If you have two different chains, you will of course run into obvious exclusions, because two different molecules can't occupy the same space. Once a configuration for one molecule is generated, how does that affect the configuration of another molecule in its environment? This is something that we have not determined.

J. H. GIBBS: I know that this was something that you hoped for, but I was wondering if you had done this.

F. T. WALL: This is something we would like to do, to be sure.

S. W. GOLOMB: In 1961, at a symposium on mathematical problems in biology, Max Delbrück of Cal Tech gave a talk (see Delbrück, 1962) in which he proposed the cubic lattice with 90-degree turns at the intersections, and although he had a different chemical structure in mind, the mathematical model was the same. The question in which he was primarily interested was the probability, or the circumstances, under which a chain formed in such a fashion would become knotted. At that time, he had no results other than the size of the smallest knotted chain; but I was wondering if this problem is of any interest to you or if you have had any results on knottedness.

F. T. WALL: We have not given any particular thought to it. Actually, the number of chains with tight knots would be small, because a tight knot is statistically improbable.

QUESTION: In formulating your random walks, you considered only the two lattices?

F. T. WALL: We considered others, too, but these are the only ones I talked about.

QUESTION: Why not assign a random direction with some exclusion, of course, rather than use a lattice?

F. T. WALL: That's a good point. Why constrain the ends of the vectors to be at lattice points? The answer is simply to make the problem amenable to attack. It gets to be exceedingly difficult when you start to subdivide your space and still do all the bookkeeping that's involved with respect to exclusions. The model we used is simple, and we don't have to raise any questions about what is meant by an exclusion. But if you start bending angles a little, then you begin to worry about when you permit a configuration and when you don't permit it. It gets into the question, then, of molecular attractions and repulsions as functions of distance.

QUESTION: So it was for simplicity's sake?

F. T. WALL: Yes. I believe that the use of the lattice model does not render the results invalid. It is certainly valid for the unrestricted chains. The hope is that as the number of steps becomes large enough, even with exclusion, the lattice effect washes out. This is a hope, and it would be extremely distressing if someone were to show that this is wrong.

DISCUSSION REFERENCE

DELBRÜCK, M. 1962. Knotting problems in biology *in* Mathematical problems in the biological sciences (Proceedings of symposia in applied mathematics, vol. XIV), ed. R. E. BELLMAN. Providence, R. I.: Amer. Math. Soc., 55–63.

5

Transmission of Genetic Information

JOSEPH F. SPEYER

New York University School of Medicine[1]

This paper will be a discussion of principles—rather than the technical details or the history—which govern the information transfer in biology. We are talking here about the information for the synthesis of proteins. This is a well-understood process now and may have some features that are of value in thinking about other information transfer processes.

We will not talk about sensory perception or memory storage (also information transfer), about which much less is known, certainly by this author.

Nucleic Acids and Proteins—the Librarians and Executers,
Respectively, of Genetic Information

The molecules of which we and the rest of biology consist contain carbon, hydrogen, oxygen, nitrogen, phosphorus, and sulphur. Nearly all the bonds linking these molecular structures are covalent bonds which involve sharing electron pairs between atoms. These are strong bonds and are not broken nor made spontaneously at the temperatures at which life exists, because the molecules or atoms do not possess sufficient kinetic energy for this. Instead, the making or breaking of these bonds always is catalyzed by proteins (enzymes) which drastically lower the activation energy for a particular reaction. There are also weak interactions (bonds); they are not catalyzed. Thus, enzymes control both the rate and the kind of chemical reactions which go on in life. All this takes place in cells, which are the smallest subunits of life and of which consist more complex creatures such as you and I. For the most part, it is more convenient and scientifically more productive to study single cells or subfractions of cells in order to understand the molecular mechanisms. Nevertheless, the results still apply to higher organisms, because all life appears to have had the same ancestry. All forms appear to employ the same basic molecular mechanism for making proteins and for storing and transmitting the information for this synthesis. Proteins, since they are catalysts,

---

[1] Presently at Cold Spring Harbor Laboratory of Quantitative Biology, Cold Spring Harbor, Long Island, N. Y.

represent the capability of a cell. Proteins can exist in infinite varieties, but they all have this in common: Each protein is a polymer consisting of amino acid subunits.

There are, in all, 20 different amino acids. An average protein contains a specific linear sequence of about 200 of these. This linear array is folded into a specific three-dimensional shape which then has the particular catalytic properties associated with that protein.

There are proteins which have only 100 subunits, while others are known which contain several thousand. These large proteins are usually specific combinations of shorter chains, usually different kinds, containing several hundred amino acids each. The variety of possible chains is obviously staggering. Thus there are 20^{200} possible proteins whose chain length is 200 amino acids. Since the median molecular weight of the various amino acids is 100 times that of hydrogen, there is not enough mass in the solar system to make even a single molecule of each possible kind.

The situation isn't that chaotic or immense. In a bacterial cell there are perhaps a couple of thousand different kinds of protein: one kind of protein for each of the chemical reactions that this cell carries out and other kinds for regulating the rate of production for the various catalytic proteins as well as their location and cellular environment.

How Are Proteins Made?

The breakdown of proteins into subunits releases energy; thus the reversal of this process requires energy. This energy is supplied by combining the amino acids—at the expense of other high-energy chemical bonds—with specific carrier molecules called transfer ribonucleic acid (t-RNA). This is a high-energy combination, the energy residing in the chemical bond that links the t-RNA to the amino acid.

All amino acids have this structure:

R denotes the various differing types of side chain—20 varieties

$$
\begin{array}{c}
\text{R} \\
| \\
\text{H}_2\text{NC}-\text{C}-\text{OH} \\
\text{H} \quad \| \\
\text{O} \quad \text{carboxyl group} \\
\text{amino group}
\end{array}
$$

A protein is a peptide chain $\rightarrow$

$$
\text{H}_2\text{N}-\underset{\underset{1}{\text{H O}}}{\overset{\text{Rx}}{\text{C}}}-\text{C}-\text{N}-\underset{\underset{2}{\text{H O}}}{\overset{\text{Rm}}{\text{C}}}-\text{C}-\text{N}-\underset{\underset{3}{\text{H O}}}{\overset{\text{Ra}}{\text{C}}}-\text{C}-\text{N}-\underset{\underset{4}{\text{H O}}}{\overset{\text{Rd}}{\text{C}}}-\text{C}-\text{N}-\underset{\underset{5}{\text{H O}}}{\overset{\text{Rl}}{\text{C}}}-\text{C}-\text{OH}
$$

The synthesis of protein begins at the amino terminal end and proceeds (left to right above) to the carboxyl end.

The amino acid sequence of the proteins involves a selection of the correct order in arraying these amino acids. Could this be done by copying a parental protein to produce a replica? First, the facts are that proteins are *not* made on parental proteins. The reason for this may be that, to copy a linear array, the parental strand needs to be accessible. However, proteins are folded into compact coils within coils, often with secondary cross-linkage between adjacent coils. This hardly makes for a readable tape of instructions. In any case, Nature has made the job of protein-synthesis instructions that of a second class of biological polymers, the nucleic acids. There are two chemically distinct types: deoxynucleic acid (DNA) and ribonucleic acid (RNA). These have a simpler structure than do the proteins and consist of linear arrays of four different types of subunits, the nucleotides. These linear arrays do not fold into complex shapes and are literally information tapes. The size of these linear structures is impressive. Thus, bacteria contain a single chromosome which is an enormously long molecule of deoxynucleic acid.

This is 1 mm long or 1000 times longer than the bacteria in which it is coiled. Its length-to-width ratio is 500,000:1, similar to 2 miles of $\frac{1}{4}$-inch rope. In it are the instructions for the synthesis of a new bacterium. However, these instructions are useable only by a parental cell which has all the machinery for translating this information. If all the information is for making proteins (we believe that 99% of it is used for this purpose), then it has information for making 5000 different proteins of average 200-amino-acid chain length.

Before considering how this information is translated, consider how it is stored.

Molecular Storage of Information

Nucleic acid subunits, the four nucleotides referred to above, have the property of forming weakly bonded complementary pairs. The four subunits (A, T, G, C) form these pairs: A = T, G = C. DNA contains two strands which run in opposite directions—there is polarity to the inter-nucleotide linkage from which this direction is derived.

The two strands contain different sequences of bases, but they both have the same information, since the bases in each strand complement those in the other strand. This means if one sequence has

A–G–T–T–C–G–G–A–C
: : : : : : : : :
: : : : : : : : :
T–C–A–A–G–C–C–T–G   is in the other strand.

The organism derives the following advantage from this duplication.

If one strand is damaged—as the result of radiation, for instance—the cell is able to repair this damage by rebuilding the damaged strand, using the opposite strand as the source of information for rebuilding the sequence. (There are viruses which have but single-stranded nucleic acid, and they are much more radiation-sensitive than those in which the information is duplex.)

In a human cell the information is in 23 chromosome pairs. Here the information is quadruplicate, since the DNA double strands which carry the genetic information in each chromosome are duplicated by virtue of having pairs of chromosomes.

We are all familiar with information stored in writing or on magnetic or punched tape or on phonograph records. How does the storage of genetic information differ from this? In two obvious ways: (a) it is much, much more compact; (b) it can be replicated quickly and with virtually no errors. These attributes derive from having the information stored in a molecular form rather than as a change in physical state.

The bacterial chromosome contains 3×10^6 base pairs, while a human cell has perhaps 1000 times more. The compactness of this information storage is such that the informational content of human DNA (which is equivalent to 300 books of 1000 pages each) can be stored in a space less than a ten-millionth of a pinhead. In its replication virtually no errors occur. The copy produced has all the attributes of the original. There is no loss of definition, as there is in all physical replication processes.

The DNA has information in a 4-symbol alphabet which must be translated into the 20-symbol alphabet of the amino acids that make up the proteins. The code of the DNA is translated in groups of three at a time. This means that there are $4^3 = 64$ combinations possible. It seems that all are used for specifying amino acids or punctuation marks between different proteins, i.e., start and stop. Most of the 20 amino acids have more than one symbol in this triplet code. The general arrangement of the code is such that most mutations (errors) will cause amino acid changes that have a minimum effect. Similar amino acids generally have similar triplet representation. Also, synonym triplets representing the same amino acid are closely related in that they differ by one base only. Thus Nature has evolved a system in which all information is redundant, by having a second copy (the *two* strands of DNA) and a molecular code that minimizes error. The read-out of the code is sequential and non-overlapping, and the nucleic acid and the protein are, as a result, colinear in information. There is no known (or expected) backward flow of information from the protein to the nucleic acid.

Lastly, the code is universal; the same combinations of symbols are used for the same amino acids in all forms of life. This is the best evidence for a common origin of creation. It is hard to see how the code can change by mutations. Of course, individual proteins do change with evolution due to natural selection, but the basic machinery has remained unchanged.

GENERAL REFERENCE

WATSON, J. D. 1965. Molecular biology of the gene. New York and Amsterdam: W. A. Benjamin, Inc.

6

Mathematical Problems in Crystallography[1]

A. L. PATTERSON

The Institute for Cancer Research

INTRODUCTION

A crystal consists of a regular three-dimensional periodic arrangement of atoms or groups of atoms in space. The atoms or groups of atoms take up their positions in the crystal primarily on account of the intrinsic properties of the atoms themselves and of the interaction of these atoms one with another. In many cases, but with notable exceptions, the atoms combine with one another to form molecules or complexes, and it is the object of the science of chemistry to understand these configurations. Crystallography then assumes the task of finding out how these objects of chemical study pack themselves in regular periodic arrays. Chemistry is basically a topological science. It tells what atoms are attached to a given atom and has very little to say about the way in which these atoms are arranged in space. But crystallography is also a metric science. It measures the exact positions of atoms in the process of finding out how the molecules pack together periodically in space, and it must of necessity learn a great deal about the metric nature of the molecules themselves. Thus, our science obtains a great deal of chemical information that cannot be obtained by standard chemical methods.

That a discussion of crystallography belongs in a symposium on combinatorial problems is not at all strange, because crystallography does consist of a study of the arrangements of balls in boxes. The only strange thing is that the shape and arrangement of the boxes, which are of course imaginary, is specified by the interactions of the atoms which we put in the boxes. If we had a clear picture of the way in which atoms react with one another, we could sit down at a desk (preferably the console of a large computer) and predict how a certain number of atoms satisfying a few incidental chemical conditions would combine themselves into molecules and how in turn these molecules would then pack together

---

[1] This work is supported by U. S. Public Health Service grants A 2884 and CA 06927.

into crystals. We might be driven to several alternative solutions, but we would there be on common ground with other, more orthodox combinatorial problems.

In case you have a mistaken idea of the nature of this paper, I must say bluntly that no one has ever come near to the combinatorial approach that I have outlined, except in the simplest possible cases. I believe that the actual structure of rock salt appeared in the writings of Barlow and of Nernst before the discovery of X-ray diffraction, but the Braggs had several possibilities to choose between when they actually analyzed this structure.

Since we do have an extremely complicated combinatorial problem under review, it may be profitable to consider some of the methods which have been used to get around the fact that we do not have the knowledge to approach the combinatorial problem directly. We shall also consider how by other means, mostly very far from combinatorial, we try to obtain information which one day might permit us to solve the basic problem.

PERIODICITY

A triply periodic structure in three dimensions is defined by the three noncoplanar vectors a_1, a_2, a_3 (see Figure 1). If these are appropriately chosen (and they can be with the aid of X-ray diffraction), they define a *primitive cell* for the crystal. This can then be considered as built up of a very large number of identical cells stacked together. In such an arrangement, any two points separated by a vector

$$\mathbf{P} = p^1\mathbf{a}_1 + p^2\mathbf{a}_2 + p^3\mathbf{a}_3 \qquad (6.1)$$

will have identical properties, provided that the quantities p^i are integers (positive, negative, or zero).

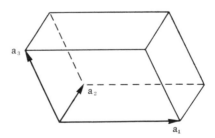

FIGURE 1. Crystallographic unit cell

The physical properties of the crystal can then be described in terms of an arbitrary origin O and a vector $\mathbf{x}$ drawn from the origin and defined by

$$\mathbf{x} = x^i \mathbf{a}_i, \qquad (6.2)$$

with the usual summation convention. The local physical properties within the crystal can then be expressed as functions of $\mathbf{x}$, and the addition of integers to any one or all of the x^i can be expected to produce reference vectors to physical situations identical to that at $\mathbf{x}$.

In addition to the repetition from unit cell to unit cell implied by the translations $\mathbf{a}_i$, there may be additional repetitions *within* the unit cell due to rotation and reflection symmetry. Thus, there may be a number of different points within the cell defined by the $\mathbf{a}_i$ in which identical physical situations occur.

The picture of a three-dimensional periodic structure for a crystal was a long time in developing, and I am sorry that I do not have the time to go into the full history. I can only mention the way in which these ideas arose from the planeness of the faces of crystals and the constancy of the angles between them. The fact that rational relations exist between the intercepts which these faces make on suitably chosen axes led to the idea of the 32 crystal classes which we now know as the point groups. This happened long before the abstract notion of a group had taken form. The story is familiar and can be found in detail in many texts of crystallography, such as those listed in the bibliography. For the present, we need only know that in the last decade of the 19th century a complete lattice theory of crystal structure was available, 20 years before the discovery of X-ray diffraction showed that crystals were indeed lattice structures. Even then it was known that there were 14 different symmetrical lattices with 32 point groups and 230 space groups isomorphous with them.

The experiment which was the foundation both for modern crystallography and for X-ray spectroscopy was performed in 1912 by Friedrich, Knipping, and Laue. Friedrich and Knipping were the experimenters, and Laue (later von Laue) was the *Theoretiker* and expert in wave optics. At that time, it was a matter of controversy whether X-rays were waves or particles. Those who thought they were waves estimated their wavelength as 10^{-8} to 10^{-9} cm. From knowledge of the density of a crystal and of the number of molecules in a gram molecule, one could estimate the lattice dimensions, which turned out to be of the order of 10^{-8} cm (1 Å). Von Laue saw that if X-rays were a form of wave motion and crystals were periodic structures, crystals would diffract X-rays. The success of the experiment thus demonstrated the wave nature of X-rays and the periodic structure of crystals at the same time.

For the sake of brevity, we shall bypass a great deal of very agonizing struggle to understand the results of these brilliant experiments of von Laue and his collaborators and to express the problem as we now see it.

KINEMATIC THEORY OF X-RAY DIFFRACTION

The following is an account of X-ray diffraction which could in physical content have been written by von Laue in 1912. However, in writing it, I have made use of advances (largely in the field of nomenclature) that have been made since that time.

At first, we talk entirely in terms of the classical electron theory of J. J. Thomson and H. A. Lorentz, and we are fortunate to be able to validate this discussion in a later section by a brief remark.

Consider a distribution of classical electrons $\rho(\mathbf{x})$, where

$$\mathbf{x} = x^i \mathbf{a}_i \tag{6.2}$$

and where $\mathbf{a}_i$ is again a system of three noncoplanar vectors which describe a parallelepiped of volume V. If a monochromatic parallel beam of X-rays of wavelength λ is incident on this distribution in the direction of the unit vector $\mathbf{s}_0$ (see Figure 2), and if the Fraunhofer diffracted radiation is observed in the direction $\mathbf{s}$, the diffracted radiation will have an amplitude $F(\mathbf{u})$ given by

$$F(\mathbf{u}) = V \iiint \rho(\mathbf{x}) \, e^{2\pi i (\mathbf{u}\mathbf{x})} \, dx^1 \, dx^2 \, dx^3, \tag{6.3}$$

in which

$$\mathbf{u} = (\mathbf{s} - \mathbf{s}_0)/\lambda = u_i \mathbf{b}^i, \tag{6.3a}$$

where $\mathbf{b}^i$ is the reciprocal triplet related to $\mathbf{a}_i$ by the relationship

$$(\mathbf{a}_i \mathbf{b}^k) = \delta_i^k. \tag{6.3b}$$

This calculation is not much more than the usual Fresnel construction. In this approach, every point on an optical wavefront becomes a new source of radiation whose radiating power depends on the density function $\rho(\mathbf{x})$. The function $F(\mathbf{u})$ is clearly the Fourier transform of the density

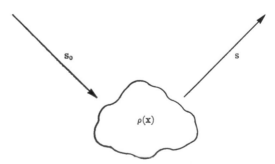

FIGURE 2. Scattering from a distribution $\rho(\mathbf{x})$

function $\rho(\mathbf{x})$, and the coordinate vector $\mathbf{u}$ in the transform space is related to vectors $\mathbf{s}_0$ and $\mathbf{s}$ describing the incident and diffracted directions by (6.3a). We can visualize this relation by an ingenious construction due to Ewald (see Figure 3). We describe a sphere of radius $1/\lambda$ about the origin S of the vector $\mathbf{s}_0/\lambda$ and locate the head of the vector $\mathbf{s}_0/\lambda$ at the origin O of the transform space. The vector $\mathbf{s}/\lambda$ drawn from S will then lie on the surface of the sphere at some point P. It then follows from (6.3a) that

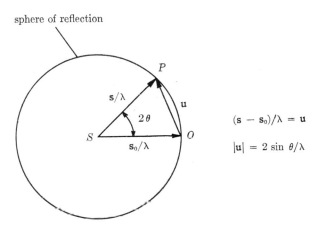

$$(\mathbf{s} - \mathbf{s}_0)/\lambda = \mathbf{u}$$

$$|\mathbf{u}| = 2 \sin \theta/\lambda$$

FIGURE 3. Ewald's construction. Center S is free to rotate about the vector $\mathbf{u}$.

the vector $\mathbf{u}$ is OP. In Figure 4, we see that the X-rays scattered from one crest of the electron density sinusoid are exactly one wavelength ahead of those scattered by the next crest.

We see also from Ewald's construction in Figure 3 that we have considerable freedom in locating $\mathbf{s}$ and $\mathbf{s}_0$ to study a given point $\mathbf{u}$ in the transform space. The three vectors must be in the same plane and must satisfy Ewald's construction, but the center of the sphere of reflection is perfectly free to rotate about $\mathbf{u}$. This freedom must be kept in mind for discussion in a later section.

Returning to (6.3), we see that if we could measure $F(\mathbf{u})$ for all points $\mathbf{u}$ in transform space, we could simply invert the Fourier transform (6.3) in the form

$$\rho(\mathbf{x}) = \frac{1}{V} \iiint F(\mathbf{u}) \, e^{-2\pi i (\mathbf{u}\mathbf{x})} \, du_1 \, du_2 \, du_3 \tag{6.4}$$

to obtain a map of the electron density. Unfortunately, we are unable to measure $F(\mathbf{u})$ and can at best obtain values of $|F(\mathbf{u})|^2$.

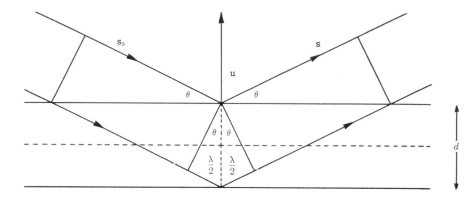

$$\frac{\lambda}{2} = d \sin \theta \qquad |\mathbf{u}| = \frac{1}{d} = \frac{2 \sin \theta}{\lambda}$$

FIGURE 4. Diffraction from a sinusoid. Solid lines are maxima; dotted lines are minima.

For a crystal in which the structure is strictly periodic, the electron density $\rho(\mathbf{x})$ will be representable by a Fourier series

$$\rho(\mathbf{x}) = \frac{1}{V} \sum_{\mathbf{h}} F(\mathbf{h}) \, e^{-2\pi i (\mathbf{h}\mathbf{x})}, \tag{6.5}$$

and the transform $F(\mathbf{u})$ will be zero everywhere except where

$$\mathbf{u} = \mathbf{h} = h_1 \mathbf{b}^1 + h_2 \mathbf{b}^2 + h_3 \mathbf{b}^3, \tag{6.5a}$$

in which h_1, h_2, h_3 are integers (positive, negative, or zero) and are the Miller indices of classical crystallography. At these whole-numbered points, delta functions will be located, and the integral over the delta function will have the value $F(\mathbf{h})$ of the corresponding Fourier coefficient.

Of course, in the case of a real crystal, the delta functions will be replaced by very high peaks whose volume will depend on many things, including X-ray line breadth, instrumentation, crystal perfection, etc., and again all we can measure is $|F(\mathbf{h})|^2$.

CALCULATED STRUCTURE FACTORS

If there are N atoms in the unit cell located at known points defined by the N vectors $\mathbf{x}_i$, we can clearly write the calculated Fourier coefficients, or "structure factors" as they are called, in the form

$$F_c(\mathbf{h}) = \sum_{i=1}^{N} f_i(|\mathbf{h}|)\, e^{2\pi i(\mathbf{h}\mathbf{x}_i)}, \tag{6.6}$$

where $f_i(|\mathbf{h}|)$ is the transform of a given atom. This is a real function which depends only on $|\mathbf{h}|$ if the atom is assumed to be spherically symmetrical. If we know the crystal symmetry, we can simplify (6.6) in accordance with the symmetry and enter it only with the coordinates of the atoms of the basic pattern which is repeated by the symmetry operations.

In the form in which (6.6) is usually used, an extra factor $T_i(\mathbf{h})$ is included for each atom, and the equation becomes

$$F_c(\mathbf{h}) = \sum_{i=1}^{N} f_i(|\mathbf{h}|)T_i(\mathbf{h})\, e^{2\pi i(\mathbf{h}\mathbf{x}_i)}. \tag{6.7}$$

The function $T_i(\mathbf{h})$ allows for the thermal motion of the atoms in the crystal and is the transform of the probability density function for the distribution of a given atom during its thermal motion. In the less sophisticated stages of analysis, this distribution is taken as "isotropic," that is,

$$T_i(\mathbf{h}) = e^{-C_i |\mathbf{h}|^2}. \tag{6.8}$$

In the days before computers, one value of the constant C_i served for all atoms. Nowadays, every atom must at least have its own individual isotropic thermal factor, and in a really topflight analysis, individual "anisotropic" thermal distributions are used for each atom. Then $T_i(\mathbf{h})$ becomes

$$T_i(\mathbf{h}) = e^{-\beta_i^{mn} h_m h_n}, \tag{6.8a}$$

where β_i^{mn} is a symmetric tensor, and each atom thus has six parameters describing its thermal motion.

If we have a crystal structure model which for some reason we think is reasonably close to the structure under study, we can use (6.7) to calculate $F_c(\mathbf{h})$ and hence $|F_c(\mathbf{h})|$ for all the reflections we have observed. We express the agreement between the observed $|F_o(\mathbf{h})|$ and the calculated $|F_c(\mathbf{h})|$ in terms of the residual

$$R = \sum_{\mathbf{h}} w\{|F_o(\mathbf{h})| - |F_c(\mathbf{h})|\}^2, \tag{6.9}$$

which is a function of the atomic coordinates x_i and of the thermal parameters C_i or β_i^{mn}. There are thus four or nine parameters for every atom in the isotropic or anisotropic cases, respectively. The residual R is not linear in the parameters, but it can be linearized by expanding in Taylor's series; in this form, R can be minimized by a standard Gaussian least-squares process. The catch here is the size of the matrix for the canonical equations. For a structure containing ten atoms (which is a very small structure) with anisotropic temperature factors, the symmetric canonical matrix will be 90 × 90 and will thus contain 4,095 terms, every one of which has a contribution from each of 1,000 to 2,000 reflections. These terms will then have to be handled in an equation-solving process or in a matrix inversion. Such an operation for a structure containing 50 or 60 atoms is clearly beyond all but the largest computers. Fortunately, a block diagonal matrix, including the most important coupling terms (which I shall not enumerate here), produces effective convergence of the successive stages of least-squares refinement necessitated by the nonlinearity of (6.9) and makes it possible to squeeze a 50-atom refinement into an IBM 1620 with 20K memory.

Thus, even when one has a good approximation to a crystal structure, the process of refinement is complicated and still has some unsolved problems (which I shall not discuss here). But it is very straightforward compared with the process of finding the approximate structure.

COMMENTS ON THEORY

Most of the rest of my paper will be devoted to discussing the various methods which have been suggested and used in finding an approximate structure. But we must first go back and examine the nature and shortcomings of the assumptions which were made in deriving (6.3). The first point is that although this expression was derived in terms of a density of classical electrons, it has been shown to be equally valid for the electron density derived from quantum mechanics. The second, more serious point is that the incident and diffracted rays have been treated independently of one another. We have assumed that the incident beam is of uniform intensity throughout the crystal and that at every point a certain part of this energy is transferred to the equally uniform diffracted beam. It is very fortunate for X-ray diffraction analysis that this is a good approximation for the rather imperfect crystals which we usually meet. For perfect crystals, it is easy to see by qualitative argument that the theory cannot be very good. First, the incident beam arriving at any point in a crystal will be attenuated by the diffraction from it and should, at first sight, decrease. However, the diffracted beam is in the correct position to feed back diffracted energy into the incident beam. As a still further complication, it is possible to adjust the direction of the incident beam (see Figure 3) so that two, and sometimes three, beams are diffracted at the same time. Under such circumstances, it becomes necessary to solve the equations of electromagnetic theory within the crystalline medium, applying appropriate conditions at the boundary of the medium to couple the waves inside the crystal with those outside it. It is fortunate that the expression (6.3) is adequate for most of the cases which arise in crystal analysis.

THE PHASE PROBLEM

We have seen that X-ray diffraction measurements lead to a knowledge of the square of the absolute value of the Fourier transform of the electron density distribution. The transform may be real, as in the case of a distribution which has a center of symmetry, and then the ambiguity is simply that of the sign to be allotted to a square root. In the general case, however, one has to determine a phase angle for every Fourier coefficient, and it is this necessity which constitutes the "phase problem" of crystallography.

In the beginning of X-ray analysis, when the elements and simple salts were under investigation, the procedure was quite simple. One measured a few intensities, guessed a configuration for the crystal which would seem consistent with one's measurements, and calculated the intensities for the measurements. If they agreed, one measured and calculated a few more intensities to "confirm" the structure. If the first guess did not give agreement between observed and calculated intensities, another guess had to be made.

This trial-and-error procedure was extremely fruitful in providing hundreds of simple structures and was carried to an extreme by the early experts—W. L. Bragg, Linus Pauling, Ralph Wyckoff, and many members of their schools, such as B. E. Warren, W. H. Zachariasen, R. W. James, and J. West. The guessing game became very sophisticated when it was possible to recognize certain structural principles, as, for example, in the oxides and some silicates where the structure depends very largely on the packing of oxygens with other elements filling in the holes between the oxygens. It soon become apparent, however, that this sophistication in guessing was not going to keep up with the more complicated minerals and with all but a very few organic compounds.

PRIOR KNOWLEDGE

If we knew nothing of the properties of the distribution $\rho(\mathbf{x})$, it would seem hopeless to attempt to find anything about it from the squared absolute values of its Fourier coefficients. We do know several things about a distribution in a crystal. Some of these are so obvious that it seems trivial to give them a place in a list, but the fact is that in the early days we had no notion we could make any use of them in solving structures. These properties are:

1. *Atomicity:* Crystals are made up of atoms. We usually also know how many and of what kind, but the most important point is that they are atoms.

2. *Atomic Shape:* In all atoms the electron density is largest near the nucleus and falls off as one departs from the nucleus. All atoms have

a bell-shaped distribution which varies only in size and minor features of shape as we go from atom to atom.

3. *Positivity:* We know that the probability of finding an electron anywhere in the crystal is nonnegative.

4. *Democracy:* If there is a large peak anywhere in a Fourier series plot, a great many Fourier terms must make a positive contribution to this peak. This indicates that if in a partial Fourier series a peak of considerable size develops, it can be expected that additional terms will also be added to that peak when the analysis is complete.

CHEMICAL METHODS

We first consider two closely related methods of phase determination which are really of chemical nature and do not involve much mathematical analysis. These are the "heavy-atom" method and the method of "isomorphous replacement." In the first method, it is necessary that one or two of the atoms of a crystal be "heavy atoms," that is, atoms with more electrons than the others. Let us assume that the structure is centrosymmetrical. We must first find where the heavy atom is in the crystal. In some special cases, it is fixed by symmetry, but in the general case, it can be located by vector methods to be discussed in the next section. The procedure is then very simple. We calculate the contribution F_H of the heavy atom to all of the observed reflections. Then, for a given reflection, the contribution of the rest of the molecule is F_R, and we have

$$F = F_H + F_R. \tag{6.10}$$

Clearly, if F and F_H are both large in magnitude, it is probable that F_H and F have the same sign. If F_H is large and F is small, there is a chance that the sign of F is specified by either F_H or F_R, but then if F is small, the contribution it will make to a Fourier series is small. One therefore computes a series giving the sign of F_H to F_o for all the terms for which F_H is large and leaving out all the rest of the Fourier coefficients. This Fourier map will have a large peak at the location assumed for the heavy atom and a number of smaller peaks. A few of the new peaks of this Fourier map are chosen as possible sites for lighter atoms, on the basis of the principle of democracy, and are used in combination with the heavy atom to form an F_H' in an expression similar to (6.10). If F_H' is greater than F_H or not much less, the sign is probably right. If F_H' is very much less than F_H, the sign determination should probably be discarded and replaced by one or more of the terms for which F_H' has been notably increased by the additional atoms. A new series is then computed. Any peaks which are higher in the new series than they were in the old series are considered for inclusion as atomic sites. Those peaks whose height in the second series is markedly lower should probably be abandoned as atomic sites. We hope that this process will add peaks which are assured as atomic sites and will subtract misassignments. It has done this in many practical cases.

In the method of isomorphous replacement, an atom which we call H_1, although it may not necessarily be heavy, is replaced by an atom H_2 without materially changing the positions of the atoms in the rest of the crystal. In this case, our F values will be of the form

$$F_1 = F_{H_1} + F_R,$$
$$F_2 = F_{H_2} + F_R. \qquad (6.11)$$

The sign of F_{H_1} will be the same as the sign of F_{H_2}. It then follows that if an increase in magnitude of F_{H_1} to F_{H_2} results in an increase from F_1 to F_2, then the sign of F_1 must be the same as that of F_{H_1}. If the reverse is the case, we enter a doubtful area in which the sign determination may depend on the sign of F_R. Even in this area, some signs can be determined. The process of refinement then follows the same course as the one indicated for the heavy-atom approach.

When a crystal does not have a center of symmetry, the heavy-atom method may not be so effective, nor will the method of isomorphous replacement be very effective with only one substituent. However, in the hands of Max Perutz and John Kendrew, the method of isomorphous replacement with five or more different heavy-metal substituents in myoglobin and hemoglobin has resulted in a very complete determination of these very complex structures.

VECTOR METHODS

An early approach had its basis in the suggestion by Zernike and Prins in 1926 that the local order in a liquid should give rise to diffraction effects. In a monatomic liquid such as mercury, the nearest neighbors would never be less than two atomic radii apart, and seldom much more. The set of second neighbors would be less exactly specified, and by the third or fourth neighbors, the distribution should be essentially uniform. Debye and Menke wrote out the details of the theory and, by qualitative experiments on mercury, showed it to be essentially correct. Warren placed the experimental methods on an absolute basis and, with his co-workers, made quantitative measurements of the number of nearest neighbors in various liquids. He also applied the same technique to powdered crystals of sulfur and showed that each sulfur atom has two neighbors. This indicated that sulfur is either in rings or in long chains. At that time, I was working at M. I. T. in Warren's group, and it occurred to me that if one could find the radial average distribution about the atoms of a liquid or of a powdered crystal, one ought to be able to do something similar for a single crystal. If one omitted the part of Debye's calculation in which he averaged over all directions of space, one came to the expression for the vector distribution

$$A(\mathbf{v}) = \iiint_{\text{cell}} \rho(\mathbf{x})\rho(\mathbf{x} + \mathbf{v}) \, dx_1 \, dx_2 \, dx_3 = \frac{1}{V^2} \sum \sum \sum |F(\mathbf{h})|^2 \, e^{-2\pi i (\mathbf{h}\mathbf{v})}.$$

$$(6.12)$$

This was familiar to me because I had heard of a Faltung from Norbert Wiener but had not been able to interpret it until the idea of a distribution function came from the liquid work. We now see from (6.6) that

$$|F(\mathbf{h})|^2 = \sum_{i=1}^{N} f_i^2 + \sum_i \sum_j f_i f_j \, e^{2\pi i \mathbf{h} \cdot (\mathbf{x}_i - \mathbf{x}_j)}. \qquad (6.13)$$

We know that the transform of the convolution of two functions is the product of the two transforms. By looking at the integral in (6.12), we can see that the convolution of every atomic peak function with every atomic peak function will appear somewhere in the cell of the function $A(\mathbf{v})$; from (6.13), we can see that the convolution of atom i with atom j will appear twice, once at $\mathbf{u} = +(\mathbf{x}_i - \mathbf{x}_j)$ and once at $\mathbf{u} = -(\mathbf{x}_i - \mathbf{x}_j)$, and that there will be $\frac{1}{2}N(N - 1)$ such pairs. In addition, there will be N peaks at the origin, each corresponding to the self-convolution of one of the atoms.

Because the original atomic peaks are bell-shaped, the convoluted peaks will also be bell-shaped, and the width of the convoluted peak will be the sum of the widths of the contributors to the convolution. Thus, it was clear in the beginning that things will be quite crowded in a cell, supposed to contain N peaks in fairly close packing, when N^2 peaks of twice the size are crowded into it. For this reason, the peaks of the $|F|^2$-series were sharpened by dividing the $|F|^2$ values by an average squared atomic-scattering factor $\bar{f}^2$. This had the effect of making the atoms in the original series and in the $|F|^2$-series more pointed. It was also possible to alleviate the congestion by the removal of the peak at the origin and of the peaks due to atoms in known positions.

But the congestion is still extremely bad, and many peaks overlap one another. Matters are improved by the presence of a single heavy atom in the asymmetric unit. The vectors from heavy atom to heavy atom will stand out in the map, enabling one to locate the heavy atom immediately, as, for example, in the use of the heavy-atom or isomorphous-replacement methods. Then too, the peaks from the heavy atom to the lighter atoms will stand out above the peaks between light atoms, and one may be able to see the rest of the molecule imaged in the heavy atom.

With the advent of three-dimensional methods made possible by computers, the situation was improved considerably. In two-dimensional projections, it is only the exceptional Fourier map that does not overlap itself, and the $|F|^2$-map is even more so.

In 1936, Harker made a major step in the interpretation of $|F|^2$-series in that he recognized that the peaks due to symmetry-related atoms in the crystal would appear in special positions in the $|F|^2$-map. Thus, an atom at x, y, z which has an atom at $\bar{x}$, y, $\bar{z}$ related to the first by a two-fold axis would result in peaks at $2x$, 0, $2z$ and $2\bar{x}$, 0, $2\bar{z}$. Thus, peaks in the Harker plane $v = 0$ of the $|F|^2$-map could well arise from a twofold axis, and the corresponding $2x$, 0, $2z$ values could be read off the map. In the case of a twofold screw axis, x, y, z would give rise to $\bar{x}$, $y + \frac{1}{2}$, $\bar{z}$ and to peaks in the $|F|^2$-map at $2x$, $\frac{1}{2}$, $2z$ and $2\bar{x}$, $\frac{1}{2}$, $2\bar{z}$. Thus, we can say that for a twofold axis parallel to the y axis, Harker peaks are to be found in the Harker plane $y = \frac{1}{2}$, etc. It is not difficult to extend the idea to planes and glide planes, which give rise to Harker lines in the $|F|^2$-map. Since Harker's discovery of the symmetry properties of the $|F|^2$-series, many papers have been written on the interpretation of $|F|^2$-series, and many partial and complete structure analyses have been carried out by these methods. Almost all of these methods involve the recognition of pairs or more complicated groups of atoms, and then proceed, by super-position of one part of the $|F|^2$-map on another, to produce a deconvolution of the map. With these developments are associated many names, among which are Wrinch, Beevers, Robertson, Clastre, Gay, and, above all, Buerger. It is not inappropriate that the latter, who has perhaps con-tributed more than anyone to this field, should have written a complete monograph on the subject, to which the interested reader is referred in the bibliography.

INEQUALITIES

The next stages in the discussion of the phase problem came from the consideration of the mathematical form of the structure factor (6.6), that is,

$$F_c(\mathbf{h}) = \sum_{i=1}^{N} f_i(|\mathbf{h}|)\, e^{2\pi i (\mathbf{h}\mathbf{x}_i)}. \tag{6.6}$$

Harker and Kasper in 1948 assumed that all atoms in the crystal have the same shape, so that all electrons in the crystal can be assumed to have the same distribution $\hat{f}(|\mathbf{h}|)$. They could then write

$$f_i = n_i Z \hat{f}, \tag{6.14}$$

in which the atom i contains a fraction n_i of the total number of electrons Z in the crystal unit cell, and so (6.6) becomes

$$F(\mathbf{h}) = \sum_{i=1}^{N} n_i Z \hat{f}\, e^{2\pi i (\mathbf{h}\mathbf{x}_i)}. \tag{6.6a}$$

If then we define a normalized $F(\mathbf{h})$ by

$$\hat{F}(\mathbf{h}) = F(\mathbf{h})/Z\hat{f} = \sum_{i=1}^{N} n_i \, e^{2\pi i (\mathbf{h}\mathbf{x}_i)}. \tag{6.15}$$

The critical advance made by Harker and Kasper was the recognition that (6.15) could be arranged in a form in which the application of the Cauchy inequality

$$\left| \sum a_i b_i \right|^2 \le \sum |a_i|^2 \sum |b_i|^2 \tag{6.16}$$

would give useful results. If in (6.15) one chooses

$$\sqrt{n_i} = a_i, \qquad \sqrt{n_i} \, e^{2\pi i (\mathbf{h}\mathbf{x}_i)} = b_i,$$

then (6.16) gives

$$|\hat{F}(\mathbf{h})|^2 \le \left(\sum n_i \right)^2 = 1. \tag{6.17}$$

This result is trivial in that it simply tells us that we have normalized our $\hat{F}(\mathbf{h})$ in such a way that a given $\hat{F}$ achieves the value 1 if and only if all the electrons in the cell are scattering in phase for that reflection.

However, some very significant results become apparent if one considers the effect of symmetry on (6.15). Thus, one knows that if the crystal has a center of symmetry, then for every atom at $\mathbf{x}_i$ there will be an equivalent atom at $-\mathbf{x}_i$, and so (6.15) becomes

$$\hat{F}(\mathbf{h}) = 2 \sum_{i=1}^{N/2} n_i \cos 2\pi(\mathbf{h}\mathbf{x}_i), \tag{6.18}$$

with

$$2 \sum_{i=1}^{N/2} n_i = 1. \tag{6.18a}$$

We now assume $a_i = \sqrt{2n_i}$, $b_i = \sqrt{2n_i} \cos 2\pi(\mathbf{h}\mathbf{x}_i)$ and find from (6.16) and (6.18) that

$$|\hat{F}(\mathbf{h})|^2 \le \left\{ 2 \sum_{i=1}^{N/2} n_i \right\} \{2 \sum n_i \cos^2 2\pi(\mathbf{h}\mathbf{x}_i)\}. \tag{6.19}$$

The first brace is clearly unity. The second brace can be rewritten in terms of well-known trigonometric formulas as

$$|\hat{F}(\mathbf{h})|^2 \le \tfrac{1}{2}\{2 \sum n_i + 2 \sum n_i \cos 2\pi 2(\mathbf{h}\mathbf{x}_i)\},$$

and one can reinterpret this, using (6.18) and (6.18a), as

$$|\hat{F}(\mathbf{h})|^2 \le \tfrac{1}{2}\{1 + \hat{F}(2\mathbf{h})\}. \tag{6.20}$$

This remarkable formula was a great surprise to crystallographers when it was first presented, for here the sign of a coefficient in the Fourier series depends on the magnitude of another coefficient. It is easy to see here a physical meaning for (6.20). If $F(\mathbf{h})$ produces a series of large peaks, these peaks will be separated by equally large negative troughs. These troughs must be filled in by a large positive contribution from $F(2\mathbf{h})$. In the original paper, Harker and Kasper derived inequalities for all the crystallographic symmetry operations. They were also able to prove inequalities of the type (for a center of symmetry)

$$|\hat{F}(\mathbf{h}) + s\hat{F}(\mathbf{k})|^2 \leq [1 + s\hat{F}(\mathbf{h} + \mathbf{k})][1 + s\hat{F}(\mathbf{h} - \mathbf{k})] \qquad (6.21)$$

for $s = +1$ or -1. Thus, in their first paper, Harker and Kasper were able to show that each space group of crystallography has its own galaxy of inequalities which, for the cases of higher symmetry, sometimes become very potent in their sign-determining properties.

With the aid of these inequalities, Kasper, Lucht, and Harker were able to determine the structure of a decaborane which was previously unknown and for which existing chemistry gave very little in the way of help.

Following the lead of Harker and Kasper, many people produced many inequalities by special and by general methods, and many structures were analyzed, either partially or completely, by the use of inequalities.

One approach which was ingenious and which led to a new and important set of inequalities was due to David Sayre, who observed that since a crystal whose density was $\rho(\mathbf{x})$ consisted of a number of atoms in definite locations, each of which was bell-shaped, then the "squared crystal" whose density was $\rho^2(\mathbf{x})$ would consist of the same number of atoms, each again of a different bell shape, but in the same locations. He then realized that the Fourier coefficients of the squared crystal would be given by convolutions of the Fourier coefficients of the original crystal and that these coefficients for the squared crystal should differ from those of the original crystal only by a factor $S(\mathbf{h})$ which allowed for the change in shape of the squared crystal with respect to the original. Sayre was thus able to write

$$S(\mathbf{h})F(\mathbf{h}) = \frac{1}{V} \sum_{h'} F(\mathbf{h}')F(\mathbf{h} + \mathbf{h}'). \qquad (6.22)$$

Although Sayre's approach did not receive much application in the determination of new structures, it led to the important relationship between signs represented by the formula

$$S(\mathbf{h} + \mathbf{h}') = S(\mathbf{h})S(\mathbf{h}'); \qquad (6.23)$$

that is, if $F(\mathbf{h})$, $F(\mathbf{h}')$, and $F(\mathbf{h} + \mathbf{h}')$ are all large, it is probable that the signs of these quantities are related by (6.23).

PROBABILITY METHODS

From the earliest application of the Harker-Kasper inequalities to structure determination, the notion was implicit that these inequalities were limiting expressions of probabilities. Thus, if we have an inequality which is nearly but not quite satisfied, we are inclined to assume that the sign relation implied by the inequality is "probably" true. The crudest attempts in this direction involved (either intentionally or sometimes unintentionally) scaling up the $\hat{F}$ values. However, many serious attempts were made to estimate the probability that particular sign relationships were valid, and there was a period in which one could not pick up a copy of *Acta Crystallographica* without finding at least one paper on a new "direct method" of structure analysis and perhaps two other papers declaring that someone else's direct method could not be correct.

One of the most important developments of this time is due to Hauptmann and Karle in a long series of papers (which cannot be analyzed in detail here). They recognized that the structure factor formula (6.6) implied that the quantities $F(\mathbf{h})$, or appropriately normalized equivalents of these quantities, were distributed in terms of the random variables $\mathbf{h}$ or $\mathbf{x}_i$ in a manner which was conditioned by the form of the expression (6.6) or its more symmetrical forms as required by the space group symmetry. They found expressions giving the distribution of one of the F's, both as to magnitude and as to phase, in terms of the distributions of the $|F|^2$ of certain other sets of reflections. Since the distributions of the $|F|^2$ could be determined directly from experiment on a given crystal, it then became possible to determine the phase of a given reflection and the probability that this phase was correct. This approach has been applied successfully to a number of centrosymmetrical structures.

Before I conclude, one further point must be brought up, and that concerns structures which are not congruent but which give the same diffraction pattern. The first such structure was found by Pauling and Shappell and is quite complicated. Three very simple structures of this type are shown in Figures 5 through 7. It is clear from the figures that in each of these cases the vector distances are the same but that the arrangements are not congruent. With such structures, which are called "homometric," any direct method such as that of Hauptmann and Karle will lead to multiple solutions. However, the chances are that if such a situation arises in practice, the two solutions will be topologically quite different and will therefore be easy to distinguish on chemical grounds.

Some of the methods which have been tried in crystallography in solving some of its problems have been briefly outlined in this paper. Some of these methods are combinatorial, and others are perhaps akin to combinatorial problems only in their complexity.

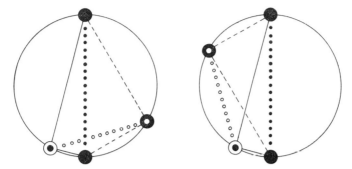

FIGURE 5. Periodic homometric pair on the line. Points marked with different symbols may have different weights.

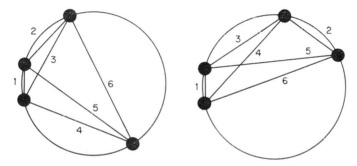

FIGURE 6. Periodic homometric pair on the line: modulo 13

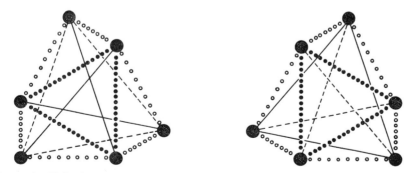

FIGURE 7. Finite homometric pair in the plane. The homometric property is preserved under affine transformation.

SELECTED BIBLIOGRAPHY

This bibliography hits only the high spots of a very broad field. The comments indicate the nature of the references.

Early History of Crystallography

Almost any textbook of crystallography, as, for example:

VON LAUE, M. 1952. *International Tables for X-ray Crystallography, Vol. I*. Birmingham, England: Kynoch.

PHILLIPS, F. C. 1956. *An Introduction to Crystallography*. London: Longmans-Green.

History since Discovery of X-ray Diffraction

EWALD, P. P. 1963. *Fifty Years of X-ray Diffraction*. Utrecht, Netherlands: Oosthoeck.

Early Diffraction Work

BRAGG, W. L. 1937. *Atomic Structure of Minerals*. Ithaca: Cornell Univ. Press.

BRAGG, W. L. 1939. *The Crystalline State*. London: Bell.

X-ray Diffraction Theory Basic for X-ray Crystallography

JAMES, R. W. 1948. *The Optical Principles of the Diffraction of X-rays*. London: Bell.

Modern Methods of X-ray Analysis

LIPSON, H., and W. COCHRAN. 1953. *The Determination of Crystal Structures*. London: Bell.

BUERGER, M. J. 1960. *Crystal Structure Analysis*. New York: Wiley.

Computer Techniques for Crystallography

PEPINSKY, R., J. M. ROBERTSON, and J. C. SPEAKMAN (eds.). 1961. *Computing Methods and the Phase Problem in X-ray Crystal Analysis*. New York: Pergamon.

$|F|^2$-Series and its Interpretation

BUERGER, M. J. 1959. *Vector Space*. New York: Wiley.

See also Lipson and Cochran (1953) above.

Harker-Kasper Inequalities

HARKER, D., and J. S. KASPER. 1948. *Acta Cryst.*, 1:70–75.

See also Lipson and Cochran (1953) above, Buerger (1960) above, and Woolfson (1961) below.

Probability Methods—Hauptmann and Karle

Reference is given to the basic monograph and to the most recent papers, from which earlier papers can be traced:

HAUPTMANN, H., and J. KARLE. 1953. *Solution of the Phase Problem. I: The Centrosymmetric Crystal. American Crystallographic Association Monograph #3*. Brooklyn: Polycrystal Book Store.

HAUPTMANN, H., and J. KARLE. 1962. *Acta Cryst.*, 15:547–50.

HAUPTMANN, H. 1963. *Acta Cryst.*, 16:792–95.

KARLE, I. L., and J. KARLE. 1963. *Acta Cryst.*, 16:969–75.

Direct Methods Generally

WOOLFSON, M. M. 1961. *Direct Methods in Crystallography*. Oxford: Clarendon.

Since the presentation of this paper, an excellent review of the whole phase problem has appeared:

KARLE, J. 1964. "The Determination of Phase Angles" in *Advances in Structure Research by Diffraction Methods, Vol. I*, ed. R. BRILL. New York: Interscience, 55–89.

Homometric Structures

PAULING, L., and M. D. SHAPPELL. 1930. *Z. Krist.*, 75:128–42.

PATTERSON, A. L. 1944. *Phys. Rev.*, 65:195–201.

HOSEMANN, R., and S. N. BAGCHI. 1954. *Acta Cryst.*, 7:237–41.

BULLOUGH, R. K. 1961. *Acta Cryst.*, 14:257–68.

BULLOUGH, R. K. 1964. *Acta Cryst.*, 17:295–308.

Operations Research I

7
Scheduling in Project Networks[1]

D. R. FULKERSON
The RAND Corporation

INTRODUCTION

Problems that involve a schedule or timetable of projected operations or jobs occur very frequently in operations research. Such scheduling problems usually involve optimization in some form or another and, more often than not, turn out to have the unpleasant features of large combinatorial magnitude and apparent lack of structure. The combinatorial magnitude precludes exhaustive enumerative methods of solution, while the lack of structure makes useful analysis difficult. Faced with this situation, the operations researcher frequently resorts to "solution" by computer simulation, rules of thumb, incomplete enumerative schemes, heuristic computer programs, or like devices which distress the mathematician. But the three scheduling problems discussed in this survey do not fall in this category of "bad" problems. Each of these problems poses a question about a finite partially ordered set of jobs, a question that can, in each case, be rephrased in terms of flows in networks. Consequently, there are good algorithms available for solving these problems.

The following section reviews relevant material concerning flows in networks (see Ford and Fulkerson, 1962). The specific scheduling problems are then discussed in the remaining sections. The problem of minimizing the number of machines was proposed by Tompkins (1952). A method of solution (though not the one described in this paper) was later given by Dantzig and Fulkerson (1954). The problems of project scheduling and cost curves have been written about extensively in operations research journals, newspapers, and popular magazines, and are frequently

---

[1] This research is sponsored by the United States Air Force under Project RAND—Contract No. AF 49(638)-700 monitored by the Directorate of Development Planning, Deputy Chief of Staff, Research and Development, HQ USAF. Views or conclusions contained herein should not be interpreted as representing the official opinion or policy of the United States Air Force. This paper appeared as RAND Memorandum RM-4137-PR, June 1964.

identified by such names as PERT (Program Evaluation and Review Technique), CPM (Critical Path Method), and others too numerous to list. The basic model described in the section on project scheduling was formulated and studied by Malcolm *et al.* (1959) and independently by Kelley and Walker (1959) as a means of scheduling large, complicated projects composed of many individual jobs, each of which has a known duration time. The problem of project cost curves (formulated by Kelley and Walker, 1959) deals with the same basic model but introduces further complications concerning cost-time relations for the jobs. Network flow methods of solution for this class of problems have been given by Kelley (1961) and Fulkerson (1961). A related solution method, using longest chains, is described in the section on project cost curves. These models have had widespread industrial impact in the last few years and are currently in extensive use.

FLOWS IN NETWORKS

A *directed network* (graph) $G = [N; \mathcal{C}]$ consists of a finite collection N of elements 1, 2, $\cdots$, n together with a subset $\mathcal{C}$ of the ordered pairs (i, j) of distinct elements of N. The elements of N will be called *nodes*; members of $\mathcal{C}$ are *arcs*. Figure 1 shows a directed network having four nodes and six arcs (1, 2), (1, 3), (2, 3), (2, 4), (3, 2), and (3, 4).

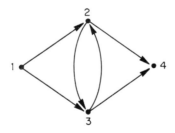

FIGURE 1

Suppose that each arc (i, j) of a directed network has associated with it a nonnegative number c_{ij}, the *capacity* of (i, j), which may be thought of as representing the maximal amount of some commodity that can arrive at j from i along (i, j) per unit time in a steady-state situation. Then a natural question is: What is the maximal amount of commodity flow from some node to another via the entire network? (For example, one might think of a network of city streets, the commodity being cars, and ask for a maximal traffic flow from some point to another.) We may formulate the question mathematically as follows. Let 1 and n be the two nodes in question. *A flow, of amount v, from 1 to n in* $G = [N; \mathcal{C}]$

is a function x from $\mathcal{C}$ to real numbers (a vector x having components x_{ij} for (i, j) in $\mathcal{C}$) that satisfies the linear equations and inequalities:

$$\sum_j x_{ij} - \sum_j x_{ji} = \begin{cases} v, & i = 1, \\ -v, & i = n, \\ 0, & \text{otherwise,} \end{cases} \qquad (7.1)$$

$$0 \le x_{ij} \le c_{ij}, \qquad (i, j) \quad \text{in} \quad \mathcal{C}. \qquad (7.2)$$

In (7.1) the sums are, of course, over those nodes for which x is defined. We call 1 the *source*, n the *sink*. A *maximal flow* from source to sink is one that maximizes the variable v subject to (7.1) and (7.2).

Figure 2 shows a flow from source node 1 to sink node 6 of amount 7. In Figure 2 the first number of each pair beside an arc is the arc capacity, the second number the arc flow.

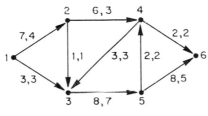

FIGURE 2

To state the fundamental theorem about maximal flow, we need one other notion, that of a cut. A *cut separating 1 and n* is a partition of the nodes into two complementary sets, I and J, with 1 in I, say, and n in J. The *capacity* of the cut is then

$$\sum_{\substack{i \text{ in } I \\ j \text{ in } J}} c_{ij}. \qquad (7.3)$$

(For instance, if $I = \{1, 3, 4\}$ in Figure 2, the cut has capacity $c_{12} + c_{35} + c_{46} = 17$.) A cut separating source and sink of minimum capacity is a *minimal* cut, relative to the given source and sink.

Summing the equations (7.1) over i in the source-set I of a cut and using (7.2), we see that

$$v = \sum_{\substack{i \text{ in } I \\ j \text{ in } J}} (x_{ij} - x_{ji}) \le \sum_{\substack{i \text{ in } I \\ j \text{ in } J}} c_{ij}. \qquad (7.4)$$

In other words, for an arbitrary flow and arbitrary cut, the net flow across the cut is the flow amount v, which is consequently bounded above by the cut capacity. Theorem 1 asserts that equality holds in (7.4) for some flow and some cut; hence the flow is maximal, the cut minimal (see Ford and Fulkerson, 1956).

Theorem 1. For any network the maximal flow amount from source to sink is equal to the minimal cut capacity relative to the source and sink.

Theorem 1 is a kind of combinatorial counterpart, for the special case of the maximal flow problem, of the duality theorem for linear programs and can be deduced therefrom (see Dantzig and Fulkerson, 1956). But the most revealing proof of theorem 1 uses a simple "marking" or "labeling" process (see Ford and Fulkerson, 1957) for constructing a maximal flow, which also yields the following theorem:

Theorem 2. A flow x from source to sink is maximal if and only if there is no flow-augmenting path with respect to x.

Here we need to say what an x-augmenting path is. First of all, a path from one node to another is a sequence of distinct end-to-end arcs that starts at the first node and terminates at the second; arcs traversed with their direction in going along the path are *forward* arcs of the path, while arcs traversed against their direction are *reverse* arcs of the path. A path from source to sink is x-augmenting provided that $x < c$ on forward arcs and $x > 0$ on reverse arcs. For example, the path (1, 2), (2, 4), (5, 4), (5, 6) in Figure 2 is an augmenting path for the flow shown there. Figure 3 indicates how such a path can be used to increase the amount of flow from source to sink.

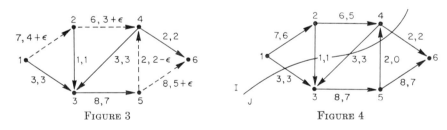

FIGURE 3   FIGURE 4

Taking the flow change ϵ along the path as large as possible in Figure 3 (namely, $\epsilon = 2$) produces a maximal flow, since the cut $I = \{1, 2, 4\}$, $J = \{3, 5, 6\}$ is then "saturated" (see Figure 4—on right above).

The labeling process described by Ford and Fulkerson (1957) is a systematic and efficient search, fanning out from the source, for a flow-augmenting path. If none such exists, the process ends by locating a minimal cut.

The following theorem, of special significance for combinatorial applications, is also a consequence of the procedure sketched above for constructing a maximal flow.

Theorem 3. If all arc capacities are integers, there is an integral maximal flow.

It is sometimes convenient to alter the constraints (7.2) of the maximal flow problem to

$$l_{ij} \leq x_{ij} \leq c_{ij}. \tag{7.5}$$

Here l is a given lower-bound function satisfying $l \leq c$. The analog of theorem 1 is then

Theorem 4. If there is a function x satisfying (7.1) and (7.5) for some number v, then the maximum v subject to these constraints is equal to the minimum of

$$\sum_{\substack{i \text{ in } I \\ j \text{ in } J}} (c_{ij} - l_{ji}) \tag{7.6}$$

taken over all cuts I, J separating source and sink. On the other hand, the minimum v is equal to the maximum of

$$\sum_{\substack{i \text{ in } I \\ j \text{ in } J}} (l_{ij} - c_{ji}) \tag{7.7}$$

taken over all cuts I, J separating source and sink.

Appropriate analogs of theorem 2 are also valid for the construction of maximal or minimal flows satisfying lower and upper bounds on arcs. Hence, if all l_{ij} and c_{ij} are integral, there exist integral maximal and minimal flows, provided that feasible flows exist.

One of the most practical problem areas involving network flows is that of constructing flows satisfying constraints of various kinds and minimizing cost. The standard linear programming transportation problem, which has an extensive literature, is in this category.

We put the problem as follows. Each arc (i, j) of a network $G = [N; \alpha]$ has a capacity c_{ij} and a cost a_{ij}. It is desired to construct a flow x from source to sink of specified amount v that minimizes the total flow cost

$$\sum_{(i,j) \text{ in } \alpha} a_{ij} x_{ij} \tag{7.8}$$

over all flows that send v units from source to sink. In many applications, one has supplies of a commodity at certain points in a transportation network and demands at others; the objective is to satisfy the demands from the supplies at minimum cost. It is easy to convert such a problem to the form described above.

By treating v as a parameter, the method for constructing maximal flows can be used to construct minimal cost flows throughout the feasible range of v. Indeed, the solution procedure can be viewed as one of solving a sequence of maximal flow problems, each on a subnetwork of the original one (see Ford and Fulkerson, 1958). Another, not essentially different, viewpoint is provided by theorem 5 (see Busacker and Gowen, 1961, and Jewell, 1960).

Theorem 5. Let x be a minimal cost flow from source to sink of amount v. Then the flow obtained from x by adding $\epsilon > 0$ to the flow in forward arcs of a minimal cost x-augmenting path, and subtracting ϵ from the flow in reverse arcs of this path, is a minimal cost flow of amount $v + \epsilon$.

Here the *cost* of a path is the sum of arc costs over forward arcs minus the corresponding sum over reverse arcs, that is, the cost of "sending an additional unit" via the path.

Thus, if all arc costs a_{ij} are nonnegative, for example, one can start with the zero flow and apply theorem 5 to obtain minimal cost flows for increasing v. (The cost profile thereby generated is piecewise linear and convex.) All that is needed to make this an explicit algorithm is a method of searching for a minimal cost flow-augmenting path. Various ways of doing this can be described. One such will be given below.

These methods produce integral flows in case the arc capacities (and lower bounds) are integers. Theoretical upper bounds on the computing task, ones that are quite good, are easily obtained in each case. This may be contrasted with the situation for general linear programs, where decent upper bounds on solution methods are unknown.

In order to describe a procedure for locating minimal cost flow-augmenting paths, we begin with the following problem. Consider a directed network in which each arc (i, j) has associated with it a positive number a_{ij}, which may be thought of as the length of the arc or the cost of traversing the arc. How does one determine a shortest chain from some node to another? Here we have used *chain* to mean a path containing only forward arcs, the length of the chain being obtained by adding its arc lengths.

Many ways of locating shortest chains efficiently have been suggested. One such method is described in Ford (1956). Like others, it simultaneously finds shortest chains from the first node to all others reachable by chains.

In this method each node i will initially be assigned a number π_i. These node numbers, which we shall refer to as *potentials*, will then be revised in an iterative fashion. Let 1 be the first node. To start, take $\pi_1 = 0$, $\pi_i = \infty$, for $i \neq 1$. Then search the list of arcs for an arc (i, j) whose end potentials satisfy

$$\pi_i + a_{ij} < \pi_j. \tag{7.9}$$

(Here $\infty + a = \infty$.) If such an arc is found, change π_j to $\pi_j' = \pi_i + a_{ij}$

and search again for an arc that satisfies (7.9), using the new node potentials. Stop the process when the node potentials satisfy

$$\pi_i + a_{ij} \geq \pi_j \qquad (7.10)$$

for all arcs.

It is not hard to show that the process terminates and that, when this happens, the potential π_j is the length of a shortest chain from 1 to j. (Here $\pi_j = \infty$ at termination means that there is no chain from 1 to j.) A shortest chain from 1 to j can be found by tracing back from j to 1 along arcs satisfying (7.10) with equality (see Figure 5).

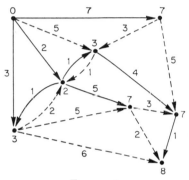

FIGURE 5

While we have assumed positive lengths for the method described above, this assumption can be weakened. Let us call a chain of arcs leading from a node to itself a *directed cycle*. Then it is enough to suppose that all directed cycle lengths are nonnegative.[2]

If directed cycle costs are nonnegative, the minimal cost flow problem can be solved by repeatedly finding cheapest chains in suitable networks. Because of the assumption on the cost function a, we may start with the zero flow. Thus, using theorem 5, it is enough to reduce the problem of finding a cheapest flow-augmenting path with respect to a minimal cost flow x of amount v to the problem of finding a cheapest chain. Define a new network $G' = [N; \alpha']$ from the given one $G = [N; \alpha]$ and the flow x as follows. First note that we may assume $x_{ij}x_{ji} = 0$, since $a_{ij} + a_{ji} \geq 0$. Now put (i, j) in α' if either $x_{ij} < c_{ij}$ or $x_{ji} > 0$, and define a' by

$$a_{ij}' = \begin{cases} a_{ij} & \text{if} \quad x_{ij} < c_{ij} \quad \text{and} \quad x_{ji} = 0, \\ -a_{ji} & \text{if} \quad x_{ji} > 0. \end{cases} \qquad (7.11)$$

---

[2] This assumption appears to be essential in the sense that the problem of finding a shortest (simple) chain from one node to another in a network whose arcs may have arbitrary lengths can be shown to be equivalent to the traveling salesman problem, for which no good solution methods are known.

Thus a chain from source to sink in the new network corresponds to an x-augmenting path in the old, and these have the same cost. Moreover, since x is a minimal cost flow, the function a' satisfies the nonnegative directed cycle condition. Hence the method described above can be used to construct minimal cost flows of successively larger amounts.

If the network is acyclic (contains no directed cycles), the shortest chain method can be modified in such a way that, once a potential is assigned a node, it remains unchanged. One can begin by numbering the nodes so that if (i, j) is an arc, then $i < j$. Such a numbering can be obtained as follows. Since the network is acyclic, there are nodes having no inward-pointing arcs. Number these nodes 1, 2, $\cdots$, k in any order. Next, delete these nodes and all their arcs, search the new network for nodes having no inward-pointing arcs, and number these, starting with $k + 1$. Repetition of this process leads to the desired kind of numbering (see Figure 6).

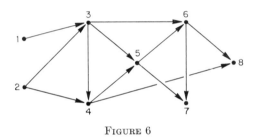

FIGURE 6

If we wish to find shortest chains from node k to all other nodes reachable from k by chains, the calculation is now trivial. Simply define π_k, π_{k+1}, $\cdots$, π_n recursively by

$$
\begin{cases}
\pi_k = 0, \\
\cdots \\
\pi_j = \min_{k \le i < j} (\pi_i + a_{ij}), \qquad j = k + 1, \cdots , n.
\end{cases} \tag{7.12}
$$

Here the minimum is, of course, taken over i such that (i, j) is an arc.

Longest chains in acyclic networks can be computed by replacing "min" by "max" in (7.12).

MINIMUM NUMBER OF MACHINES TO MEET A FIXED JOB SCHEDULE

Suppose that there are n jobs 1, 2, $\cdots$, n with specified start and finish times $a_1, a_2, \cdots , a_n$ and $b_1, b_2, \cdots , b_n$, with $a_i \le b_i$. In other words, the schedule of starting times for the various jobs is fixed in advance, and the duration times $t_i = b_i - a_i$ of the jobs are known. Assume that we have a number of (identical) machines, each of which can perform any job in the specified time, and that the reassignment or setup time required for a machine to go from job i to job j is $r_{ij} \geq 0$ $(i, j = 1, 2, \cdots, n)$. What is the minimum number of machines required to meet the given job schedule? For a concrete example, think of an airline, say, which wants to meet a fixed flight schedule with the minimum number of planes, all of the same type. Start and finish times are known for each flight, and the times r_{ij} to return from the destination point of flight i to the origin point of flight j arc also known.

Making the reasonable assumption that the reassignment times satisfy

$$r_{ij} \leq r_{ik} + r_{ki}, \tag{7.13}$$

for all i, j, k, we may easily check that the jobs can be partially ordered by saying that i precedes j if

$$b_i + r_{ij} \leq a_j. \tag{7.14}$$

We may depict the order relations among the jobs by means of an acyclic directed network whose arcs represent jobs. To take a simple case, suppose that there are five jobs with the ordering: 1 precedes 3, 1 and 2 precede 4, and 1, 2, 3, 4 precede 5. This may be pictured by the network shown in Figure 7. Notice that we have added a "dummy" job, the dotted arc of Figure 7, to maintain the proper order relations among the jobs. It is not difficult to show that the use of dummies permits a network representation of this kind for any finite partially ordered set.

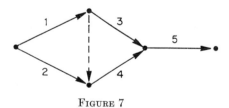

FIGURE 7

Since a chain of arcs in this network represents a possible assignment of jobs to one machine, the problem is to cover all nondummy arcs with the minimum number of chains. By use of the integrity theorem, this can be made into a flow problem as follows. Add a node to the network, the source for flow, and direct dummy arcs from this node to all nodes of the network that have only outward-pointing arcs. Similarly, add a sink node, directing dummy arcs into this from all nodes having only inward-pointing arcs. Now place a lower bound of 1 on each nondummy arc, a lower bound of 0 on each dummy arc, and take all arc capacities infinite. Then an integral flow through the enlarged network of amount v picks out v chains (not necessarily distinct) that cover all nondummy arcs; consequently, we wish to minimize v subject to (7.1) and (7.5). This can be done by a suitable labeling process which locates flow-decreasing paths.

It can also be seen that the second half of theorem 4 implies the following theorem (theorem 6) for acyclic directed networks. This theorem is closely related to a theorem by Dilworth on chain decompositions of partially ordered sets (see Dilworth, 1950).

Theorem 6. The minimum number of chains in an acyclic directed network required to cover a subset of arcs is equal to the maximum number of arcs of the subset having the property that no two belong to any chain.

In terms of the job scheduling problem, theorem 6 asserts that the minimum number of machines required is equal to the maximum number of jobs, no two of which can be done by one machine. For example, in the network of Figure 8, three chains are required to cover the solid arcs (as indicated by the flow shown in the figure); jobs 2, 3, 4, for example, constitute a maximal set of jobs, no two of which can be done by one machine.

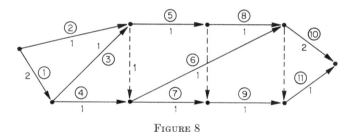

FIGURE 8

Problems of this nature become considerably more complicated if the assumption of a fixed schedule is dropped. For instance, suppose that the times a_i and b_i are at our disposal subject to the restrictions that $b_i - a_i \geq t_i$, with the duration times t_i known, as well as the reassignment times r_{ij}. The problem might then be to arrange a schedule which finishes all jobs by a given time and requires the minimum number of machines, or to finish all jobs at the earliest possible time with a fixed number of machines. For such scheduling problems there is very little known in the way of general theoretical results or good computational procedures. However, some special results have been deduced, notably by Johnson (1954) and Hu (1961).

The problem of this section can also be viewed in terms of matrices of zeros and ones (see Ford and Fulkerson, 1962). For instance, we may form an $n \times n$ (0, 1) matrix $A = (a_{ij})$ by setting $a_{ij} = 1$ if job i precedes job j and setting $a_{ij} = 0$ otherwise. If we let $\rho(A)$ denote the term rank of A, that is, the maximum number of ones of A such that no two lie in the same row or column, then it can be shown that the minimum number of machines required is equal to $n - \rho(A)$. Since the calculation of term rank can also be posed as a flow problem, this provides another flow formulation of the minimum machine scheduling problem.

PROJECT SCHEDULING

As noted in the introduction to this paper, one of the most popular combinatorial applications involving networks deals with the planning and scheduling of large complicated projects. Suppose that such a project (the construction of a bridge, for example) is broken down into many hundreds or thousands of individual jobs. Certain of these jobs will have to be finished before others can be started. Again we depict the partial ordering of jobs by an acyclic directed network, some of whose arcs correspond to actual jobs, as we did in the preceding section.

Assuming that each job has a known duration time (dummies have zero duration times) and that the only scheduling restriction is that all inward-pointing jobs at a node must be finished before any outward-pointing job can be started, it follows that the minimum time to complete the entire project is equal to the length of a longest chain of jobs. Hence the minimum project time can be calculated easily by the recursive method described at the end of the section on flows in networks.

Figure 9 provides an example of such a calculation. The number recorded beside each arc is the job duration time, and the number beside a node is the length of a longest chain from the starting node to the node in question.

The heavy arcs in Figure 9 pick out a longest chain from node 1 to node 9. Such a chain is called *critical*, and the jobs which constitute a critical chain are called *critical jobs*. Some critical job must be expedited if total project time is to be shortened. The nodes of the project network are usually called *events*, and the times recorded by them are *event times*.

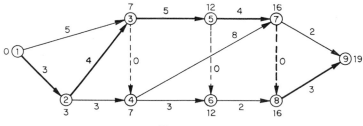

FIGURE 9

For example, node 7 is the "event" of finishing its inward-pointing jobs, which event can occur at time 16. The event times provide a schedule for all jobs in the project.

The PERT model of a project usually assumes independent random variables for job times, instead of deterministic times as we have assumed above. But the usual practice has been to replace these random variables by their expected values, thereby obtaining a deterministic problem. The solution of this deterministic problem always provides an optimistic estimate of the expected length of the project. One method for computing a better lower bound on expected project time has been given in Fulkerson (1962). It appears difficult to obtain very explicit information about the distribution of project duration time from known distributions of job times. In a practical situation, if such information is deemed desirable, one can always Monte Carlo the project on a computer. (See MacCrimmon and Ryavec, 1964, and Van Slyke, 1963, for a fuller discussion of this.)

Although the analysis of a PERT model with fixed job times is trivial from the mathematical point of view, the model itself appears to be a useful one, judging from its widespread acceptance and use throughout industry today. But it should be added that it is difficult to assess the usefulness of PERT on this basis alone, since the model has been the subject of much hard-sell advertising and exaggerated claims.

PROJECT COST CURVES

The PERT model can be complicated in various ways. One of the more interesting of these ways is to assume that a job can be expedited by spending more money on it, thereby raising the question: Which jobs should money be spent on, and how much money, in order that the project can be finished by a given date at minimum cost? In this section we shall assume that the time-cost relation for each job (i, j) is linear. Specifically, we suppose that each arc (i, j) of the project network has associated with it three nonnegative integers

$$a_{ij}, b_{ij}, c_{ij} \qquad (7.15)$$

with $a_{ij} \leq b_{ij}$, the interpretation being that a_{ij} is the crash time for (i, j), that b_{ij} is the normal completion time, and that c_{ij} is the decrease in cost of doing (i, j) per unit increase in time from a_{ij} to b_{ij}. In other words, the cost of doing (i, j) in t_{ij} units of time is given by the known linear function

$$k_{ij} - c_{ij}t_{ij} \qquad (7.16)$$

over the interval

$$a_{ij} \leq t_{ij} \leq b_{ij}. \qquad (7.17)$$

Then, given λ units of time in which to finish the project, the problem is to choose job times t_{ij} and event times t_i satisfying

$$t_{ij} + t_i - t_j \leq 0,$$

$$t_n - t_1 \leq \lambda, \qquad\qquad (7.18)$$

$$a_{ij} \leq t_{ij} \leq b_{ij},$$

and maximizing

$$\sum_{ij} c_{ij} t_{ij}. \qquad\qquad (7.19)$$

For dummy jobs we may take $a_{ij} = b_{ij} = c_{ij} = 0$ in this linear program. We may also assume $t_1 = 0$, of course.

After some simplification, the dual of this linear program can be phrased as the following network flow problem. Find nonnegative numbers x_{ij}, one for each arc of the project network, and a nonnegative v, which satisfy the flow constraints (7.1) and minimize the nonlinear function

$$\lambda v + \sum_{ij} [b_{ij} \max (0, c_{ij} - x_{ij}) - a_{ij} \max (0, x_{ij} - c_{ij})]. \qquad (7.20)$$

The function in brackets in (7.20) is sketched in Figure 10. Since it is piecewise linear and convex, the theory outlined in the section on flows in networks can be applied; i.e., the program (7.1), (7.20) can be solved parametrically in v, and the dual problem (7.18), (7.19) parametrically in λ, either as a sequence of maximal flow problems or as a sequence of extremal chain problems in appropriate networks. Maximal flow approaches were described by Fulkerson (1961) and Kelley (1961). Here we show a longest chain approach, using a small numerical example.

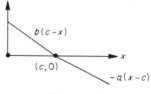

FIGURE 10

Consider the project network and job data shown in Figure 11, where we have recorded the data for arc (i, j) in the order b_{ij}, c_{ij}, a_{ij}. The first step in the computational procedure is to take job times at their upper bounds b_{ij} and find the corresponding event times t_i and the critical chain, as shown in Figure 12. This constitutes an optimal solution for $\lambda = t_4 = 11$.

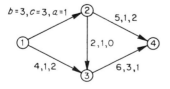

FIGURE 11

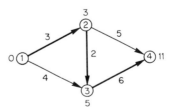

FIGURE 12

We next impose flow along the critical chain, treating the c_{ij} as arc capacities at this step. Here we take a flow of one unit, the bind occurring on arc $(2, 3)$. Using the resulting flow and the problem data, we now form a new network. We consider the following possibilities, corresponding to arc (i, j) of the project network:

(a) $x_{ij} = 0,$
(b) $0 < x_{ij} < c_{ij},$
(c) $x_{ij} = c_{ij},$
(d) $c_{ij} < x_{ij}.$

In case (a), put in an arc (i, j) with length b_{ij}; in case (b), put in an arc (i, j) with length b_{ij} and an arc (j, i) with length $-b_{ij}$; in case (c), put in an arc (i, j) with length a_{ij} and an arc (j, i) with length $-b_{ij}$; in case (d), put in an arc (i, j) with length a_{ij} and an arc (j, i) with length $-a_{ij}$. For the example we have the network shown in Figure 13. Although this network contains directed cycles, such cycles have nonpositive lengths; consequently, we can easily compute a longest chain from source to sink by an iterative procedure analogous to the procedure (discussed in the section on flows in networks) for shortest chains in networks having nonnegative directed-cycle lengths. This has been done for the example in Figure 13, where the node potentials pick out the longest chain 1, 3, 4, which is shown in heavy arcs. This chain corresponds to a flow-augmenting path, and we increase the flow along this path as described below. First note that arcs in Figure 13 which have the same orientation as arcs of the project network correspond to possible forward arcs of the desired flow-augmenting path, whereas arcs having the opposite orientation correspond to possible reverse arcs of the flow-augmenting path. Consequently, if flow in an arc of the project network is to be increased, we treat c_{ij} as a capacity if (i, j) is in state (a) or (b) and take infinite capacity for arcs in state (c) or (d). On the other hand, if flow in arc (i, j) is to be decreased, we take zero as a lower bound if (i, j) is in state (b) or (c) and take c_{ij} as a lower bound if (i, j) is in state (d). In the example, this means that we send one unit of flow along the chain 1, 3, 4, thereby obtaining the flow shown in Figure 14. The potentials of Figure 13 constitute optimal

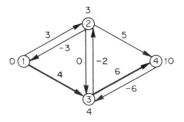

FIGURE 13

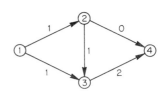

FIGURE 14

event times corresponding to $\lambda = t_4 = 10$. Optimal job times are given by

$$t_{ij} = \min (b_{ij}, t_j - t_i). \tag{7.21}$$

The procedure outlined above is then repeated, using the flow shown in Figure 14. We obtain successively the results shown in Figure 15.

In the last flow network of Figure 15, there is no bound on the flow change ϵ. This signals termination of the computation. The complete minimal cost curve $P(\lambda)$ for the project has now been determined over the range of feasible λ ($3 \leq \lambda \leq 11$), the function $P(\lambda)$ being piecewise

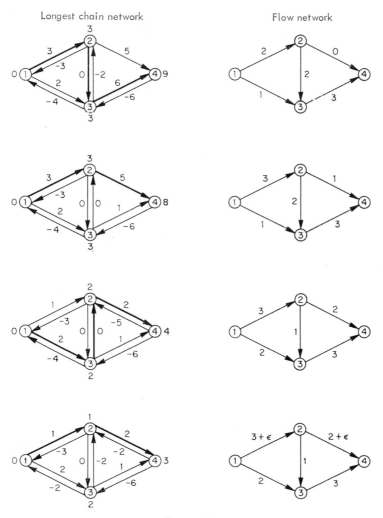

FIGURE 15

linear, with breakpoints at the successive values of $\lambda = t_4$ generated in the computation. Optimal event times for values of λ between two successive breakpoints are given by taking appropriate convex combinations of those corresponding to the two breakpoints; optimal job times are then determined from (7.21).

Note that optimal times for a job (i, j) are not necessarily monotone in λ. For instance, the optimal job times for (2, 3) in the example are

$$2, 1, 0, 0, 0, 1,$$

corresponding to λ-values of

$$11, 10, 9, 8, 4, 3,$$

respectively. In other words, compressing the project time optimally can increase certain job times.

The method of this section can also be applied if job costs are piecewise linear and convex between crash and normal completion times. Such a job cost merely introduces other breakpoints in the function shown in Figure 10, and the solution process is changed only in details.

REFERENCES

BUSACKER, R. G., and P. J. GOWEN. 1961. A procedure for determining a family of minimal cost network flow patterns. Technical paper 15. Operations Research Office.

DANTZIG, G. B., and D. R. FULKERSON. 1954. Minimizing the number of tankers to meet a fixed schedule. Naval Res. Logist. Quart., 1:217–22.

———. 1956. On the max-flow min-cut theorem of networks *in* Linear inequalities and related systems (Ann. of Math. Study No. 38), ed. H. W. KUHN and A. W. TUCKER. Princeton, N. J.: Princeton Univ. Press, 215–21.

DILWORTH, R. P. 1950. A decomposition theorem for partially ordered sets. Ann. of Math., 51:161–66.

FORD, L. R., JR. 1956. Network flow theory. Paper P-923. Santa Monica, Calif.: The RAND Corp.

FORD, L. R., JR., and D. R. FULKERSON. 1956. Maximal flow through a network. Canad. J. Math., 8:399–404.

———. 1957. A simple algorithm for finding maximal network flow and an application to the Hitchcock problem. Canad. J. Math., 9:210–18.

———. 1958. Constructing maximal dynamic flows from static flows. Operations Res., 6:419–33.

———. 1962. Flows in networks. Princeton, N. J.: Princeton Univ. Press.

FULKERSON, D. R. 1961. A network flow computation for project cost curves. Management Sci., 7:167–78.

———. 1962. Expected critical path lengths in PERT networks. Operations Res., 10:808–17.

HU, T. C. 1961. Parallel sequencing and assembly line problems. Operations Res., 9:841–49.

JEWELL, W. S. 1960. Optimal flow through networks with gains. Paper presented at the Second International Conference on Operations Research, Aix-en-Provence, France.

JOHNSON, S. M. 1954. Optimal two- and three-stage production schedules with setup times included. Naval Res. Logist. Quart., 1:61–68.

KELLEY, J. E., JR. 1961. Critical path planning and scheduling: mathematical basis. Operations Res., 9:296–321.

KELLEY, J. E., JR., and M. R. WALKER. 1959. Critical path planning and scheduling. Paper presented at the Eastern Joint Computer Conference, Boston, Mass.

MACCRIMMON, K. R., and C. A. RYAVEC. 1964. An analytical study of the PERT assumptions. Operations Res., 12:16–38.

MALCOLM, D. G., J. H. ROSEBOOM, C. E. CLARK, and W. FAZAR. 1959. Application of a technique for research and development program evaluation. Operations Res., 7:646–69.

TOMPKINS, C. B. 1952. Discrete problems and computers. S3–5. I.N.A.

VAN SLYKE, R. M. 1963. Monte Carlo methods and the PERT problem. Operations Res., 11:839–60.

DISCUSSION

A. J. HOFFMAN: I would like to ask either Dr. Fulkerson or Dr. Kuhn to what extent these ideas were anticipated in the 1920s or the 1930s.

H. W. KUHN: Several of the key ideas can be traced to the work in graph theory of Petersen, Egervary, and König. Surely the first instance of duality in network theory is contained in the theorem of König which asserts that, in any rectangular array of zeros and ones, the maximum number of ones that can be chosen with no two in the same line (row or column) is equal to the minimum number of lines needed to contain all of the ones. Several proofs of this theorem depend on a graph theoretical representation and use the concept of alternating chains which goes back to Petersen.

There is no doubt that Ford and Fulkerson brought a new approach to these problems with their emphasis on flows in networks and the dual concept of cut set. While the cut and flow concepts are closely related to linear programming, Ford and Fulkerson have gone back to the geometry of the network rather than utilizing the algebraical combinatorics of the simplex method.

A. J. GOLDMAN: Have there been any extensions to situations where one regards the spreading out of the flow from the source as taking place over several time periods and where the capacities are also time-varying, so that one might want to hurry the flow along a particular chain to take advantage of a temporarily high link capacity that would be unavailable later on?

D. R. FULKERSON: A dynamic flow problem of this kind can always be posed as a static flow problem in an enlarged network obtained from the given network by expanding it over time.

If each arc capacity is constant over time, a maximal dynamic flow for a given number of time periods can be constructed in a much better way, one that doesn't begin by enlarging the network but works instead with the original network. Ford and I wrote a paper on this topic several years ago (see Ford and Fulkerson, 1958, cited in my paper).

P. A. ZAPHYR: You mentioned in your third example that there are many ways of handling the problem of minimizing the cost by using

CPM and PERT. Would you comment on the efficiency of these computational procedures? I can think of one method that will minimize costs for critical path scheduling, but that is not very fast. Would you comment on the relative speed of cost-minimizing CPM to the speed without minimizing costs?

D. R. FULKERSON: The parametric linear program for constructing project cost curves can be solved in various ways. For example, it can be solved as a sequence of maximal flow problems or as a sequence of longest chain problems. It could also be handled by another network flow method that I described in another paper (see Fulkerson, 1961). Another way would be to use the simplex method, suitably simplified for network flow problems. Of these methods, the first three would be roughly equivalent computationally, I think, and the simplex method would be more time-consuming. We have an IBM 7090 program at RAND based on the out-of-kilter method, and it seems to work very well. For instance, a network having 4,000 to 5,000 arcs usually requires about 4 to 5 minutes of machine time.

H. D. MILLS: Have you formulated any conjectures or rules of thumb about how computational time depends on the size and structure of the network? In particular, how is computational time divided between logic and arithmetic?

D. R. FULKERSON: Good theoretical bounds on the maximum number of steps required to solve minimal cost flow problems are known. For example, if you consider one application of what Ford and I have called the "labeling routine" (a good method of finding a flow-augmenting path) as an elementary step, then a problem in which you want to send v units through an n-node network at minimal cost requires at most vn steps. Thus, if the problem is an $n \times n$ optimal assignment problem, say, then the bound is of the order n^2.

In answer to the second part of your question, most of the time is spent in doing logic rather than arithmetic.

J. EDMONDS: If steps were chosen so that they each involved a constant amount of work in carrying out—that is, if you chose some substeps of your steps to make the steps constant—then would you have an upper bound of n^3 or n^4 steps?

D. R. FULKERSON: Yes.

A. W. TUCKER: Alan Hoffman's question opened a Pandora's box. In the 19th century G. R. Kirchhoff and J. C. Maxwell treated direct-current network problems in a manner not unlike contemporary quadratic programming. In the paper of 1847 in which he introduced his two fundamental laws, Kirchhoff proved that the flow of current in a given network is uniquely determined by the topology, the resistances, and the impressed emf's. Maxwell, in his famous treatise, later introduced the notion of potential, thereby bringing duality into the picture, and showed that the Kirchhoff loop law resulted from minimizing heat loss (a positive-definite quadratic function).

H. W. KUHN: The Pandora's box to which Professor Tucker referred contains other disconcerting historical facts. In particular, there is at least one instance of nonlinear programming duality which goes back at least 100 years before the term "nonlinear programming" was introduced. This duality derives from a classical problem in geometry, known as Steiner's problem, which was first posed by Fermat about 1638. He asked the following question: Given three points in the plane, find a fourth point such that the sum of the distances to the three given points is a minimum. In 1846, the geometer Fasbender found the dual to this problem. Precisely, consider all equilateral triangles circumscribing the three given points. If we choose the triangle of maximum area, the altitude of this triangle has length equal to the minimum sum of distances sought previously. Of course, we also know of the work of Montmort which established a particular instance of the minimax theorem of matrix games in 1713.

S. W. GOLOMB: If we are going back to the 19th century, I know of a nice quotation by Sylvester which König uses in his book on graph theory to the effect that you can't expect merely by looking at the connectivity of the genealogical table to learn the laws of biological reproduction (see Sylvester, 1909, p. 23, and König, 1950, p. 2). Something similar could be said here. We can't expect to learn too much about the actual technology of missile production merely by studying the cohomology of the PERT chart.

J. EDMONDS: I think the most interesting part is the problem where you are given a certain number of machines and asked to minimize the time required for the schedule. Would you care to comment, Dr. Fulkerson?

D. R. FULKERSON: Such problems are interesting and difficult. If there are n jobs with known performance times t_i and known reassignment or setup times r_{ij} to go from job i to job j, and if you are asked to arrange a schedule for a fixed number of machines (of the same type) that minimizes completion time, you have a considerably harder problem than the one I discussed. I don't know of any good ways of solving such a problem. A somewhat related problem, sometimes called the "m-machine problem," involves scheduling jobs on m different machines, each job requiring time on each machine. Except for the case $m = 2$, which has been solved by Johnson (1954), cited in my paper, I know of no good computational methods here either.

A. J. GOLDMAN: In connection with this subject, I recall that there was a lengthy report by Heller at the Courant Institute of Mathematical Sciences which went rather deeply into the details of the Monte Carlo attack on such problems and proved a number of theoretical results. It struck me as one of the more profound treatments of large scheduling problems of this type (see Heller and Logemann, 1962).

DISCUSSION REFERENCES

FULKERSON, D. R. 1961. An out-of-kilter method for minimal cost flow problems. J. SIAM, 9:18–27.

HELLER, J., and G. LOGEMANN. 1962. An algorithm for the construction and evaluation of feasible schedules. Management Sci., 8:168–83.

KÖNIG, D. 1950. Theorie der endlichen und unendlichen Graphen. New York: Chelsea.

SYLVESTER, J. J. 1909. The collected mathematical papers of James Joseph Sylvester, vol. III, ed. H. F. BAKER. Cambridge, Eng.: Cambridge Univ. Press.

8

The Traveling Salesman Problem

R. E. GOMORY

IBM *Corporation*

The traveling salesman of the traveling salesman problem is interested in only one thing—money. He sets out to pass through a number of points, usually called cities, and then returns to his starting point. When he goes from the ith city to the jth city, he incurs a cost $c_{i,j}$. His problem is to find that tour of all the points (cities) that minimizes the total cost.

Now this problem, although easy to state, turns out to be an extremely difficult one to solve. This is surprising, because the traveling salesman problem is almost indistinguishable from a very easy problem—the assignment problem.

The assignment problem is illustrated in Figure 1. That figure shows a situation in which there are n nodes, or men, which can be assigned to n other nodes, or jobs. If the ith man is assigned to the jth job, there is a cost for that assignment $c_{i,j}$. The problem here is simply to find a permutation, or assignment, which assigns to every job a man and minimizes the total cost of the assignment. One assignment or permutation, ϕ, is illustrated in the top of the figure.

Another way of illustrating the assignment problem, which makes the connection with the traveling salesman problem more obvious, is not to have two sets of nodes representing jobs but only one set. When the ith man is assigned to the jth job, an arrow is drawn from the ith node to the jth node, and the cost $c_{i,j}$ is incurred. The problem is, of course, unchanged. It is to find a permutation ϕ which assigns to each node i a successor $\phi(i)$ such that the total cost is minimized. Now, as the lower part of Figure 1 shows, the only difference between the assignment problem and the traveling salesman problem is that we allow small closed loops in the assignment problem. The traveling salesman problem, as can

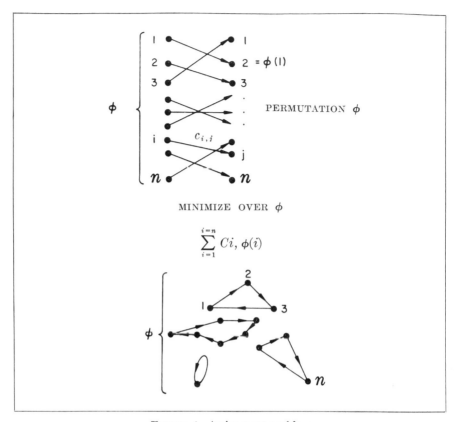

FIGURE 1. Assignment problem

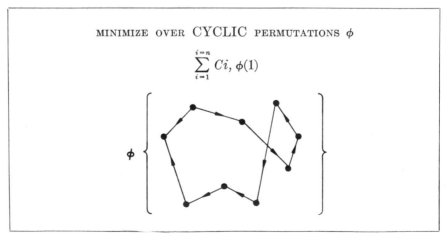

FIGURE 2. Traveling salesman problem

be seen from Figure 2, is almost exactly the same. We are looking for a permutation ϕ that gives to every node i a successor j and which minimizes the total cost. In the traveling salesman problem, we must have a cyclic permutation; the diagram must not break up into little loops.

The two problems, the assignment problem and the traveling salesman problem, may not seem to be very different; but they are, and we cannot really ignore either of them. They both have a considerable number of applications. I will not try to list these applications in general. However, for the traveling salesman problem, there is one very important application that I will outline. This is the problem of sequencing jobs on a machine. Let us assume that there are a number of jobs to be run in succession on the machine. After the ith job is run, the machine is set up to run the jth job, and a certain cost $c_{i,j}$ is incurred by this setup. The problem is to run the jobs on the machine one after the other so that the total changeover or setup cost is minimized. Now this is very close to the traveling salesman problem because one must run through all of the jobs, incurring a cost $c_{i,j}$ going from i to j. If the jobs are represented by points, this is the same as asking for a path that runs through all these points (jobs) with the least total cost. One difference is that we are not now asking to come back to the starting point. Actually, this is of very little consequence, and there are tricks that transform the sequencing problem, just described, into the traveling salesman problem. The two problems are essentially the same, and the traveling salesman problem is easier to work with, since one deals with complete permutations.

If we take these two problems, the assignment problem and the traveling salesman problem, which appear to be only slightly different, and if we ask how much work must be done to obtain the optimal permutation, the answers are tremendously different in the two cases. In the assignment problem, the optimal assignment can at present be obtained in $O(n^4)$ elementary steps. The corresponding bound in the traveling salesman problem is $O(n^2 2^n)$ elementary steps. So these two problems which seem to be so close are, at least at the present time and so far as our bounds are concerned, radically different.

One of the ways that this difference could be investigated is to take a look at the polyhedra associated with these problems to see if they look more or less alike. This is a reasonable procedure because there has been considerable success on the assignment problem by using vertex-to-vertex searches on polyhedra—this is in fact the linear programming approach. Since we have to specify which polyhedron is under discussion, let us first take the assignment problem. Any permutation ϕ provides a feasible solution to it, and any permutation ϕ can be represented as an $n \times n$ matrix with a 1 in the ij position if i goes to j and with a 0 otherwise. Thus, with every permutation there is an associated $n \times n$ matrix, which can then be regarded as a point in n^2-dimensional space. Taking the convex hull of these points gives a certain polyhedron. For the assignment problem, the associated polyhedron is the convex hull of all permutations. For the traveling salesman problem, it is the convex hull of those permutations that are cyclic. In any case, to solve our problem, we try to maximize a linear form $\sum c_{i,j} x_{i,j}$ over these polyhedra.

A number of facts about these polyhedra were assembled by Heller (1954 and 1955), by Motzkin (1956), and by Kuhn (1955), and are illustrated in Figure 3. First, what about the dimension of the polyhedron? Although these points are in n^2-dimensional space, they could perfectly well all be in a lower-dimensional subspace; in fact, they are. The dimension of the polyhedron P of permutations is $(n-1)^2$, and that of the polyhedron Q of cyclic permutations is $(n-1)^2 - n$. So the convex of all tours is a little bit smaller in dimension, which suggests, rather misleadingly, that this problem might be the easier one. Something further, that is perhaps more relevant to a vertex-to-vertex search, is the question of the neighborliness of the points on the polyhedra. Should one expect to travel a long distance to get from a starting vertex to the optimal one in doing a vertex-to-vertex search? To answer this, some measure of the neighborliness of points on the polyhedra is needed.

Two measurements of neighborliness will be discussed here.

One way to measure neighborliness is to say that two points are very close if they have a one-dimensional face in common. That is about as neighborly as vertices can be on a polyhedron. Let us also say that they are fairly near if they have a two-dimensional face on which both vertices lie, and so on up. In fact, we will say that points are n-neighbors if they both lie on the same n-dimensional face. According to this index of neighborliness, all vertices on these polyhedra are very close to each other because the most unneighborly pair of points are neighbors of order $[n/2]$; in other words, there is a face of dimension $[n/2]$, or lower, containing any pair of points on the polyhedra. This is a very low dimensional face compared with the dimension of the space in which the polyhedron is, and this is just as true for Q, the convex of tours, as it is for the polyhedron P. In fact, it is slightly more so for Q, since it is known that on Q, for $n \leq 5$, each vertex is a one-dimensional neighbor of every other vertex; it is only for $n = 6$ that it takes two steps to get from one point to another.

This suggests another measure of neighborliness, which is the number of edges to be traversed to get from one vertex to another. In the case of P, this number is known, because two vertices are one-step neighbors if their difference, the difference permutation, contains only one cycle. The number of steps to get from one vertex to another is the number of cycles in the corresponding difference permutation. Therefore, the maximum distance on P in this sense is again an integer part of $n/2$,

$$\phi \equiv \begin{bmatrix} & 1 & & & & \\ & & 1 & & & \\ & & & 1 & & \\ & 1 & & & & \\ & & & & 1 & \\ & & & 1 & & \end{bmatrix} \qquad x_{i,j} = \begin{Bmatrix} 1 & \text{asigned} \\ 0 & \text{not assigned} \end{Bmatrix}$$

$$x \; \varepsilon \; E_{n^2}$$

P   Convex of Permutations
Q   Convex of Cyclic Permutations

	P	Q		
DIMENSION	$(n-1)^2$	$(n-1)^2 - n$		
NEIGHBORLINESS				
A) Maximum lowest-dimension face in common	$[n/2]$	$n/2 - 1$	if $n = 4m + 2$	$n \geq 8$
		$[n/2]$	if $n \neq 4m + 2$	$n \geq 8$
		0, 0, 1, 1, 1, 2, 2.		
B) Edges to be traversed (neighbors differ by 1 cycle)	$[n/2]$	?		

FIGURE 3. Polyhedra

namely, $([n/2])$; so this measure of neighborliness comes out the same as the other measure. For Q, however, no facts about this type of distance or neighborliness are known, and this is the first place that the two polyhedra seem to look different, but, of course, this difference is not certain.

We now come to another way of looking at the polyhedra in which they definitely do look different; this is again suggested by a linear programming approach. For the linear programming approach, the number of faces is relevant, as each one of these represents an inequality of the linear programming method. So it is relevant to ask: If we had to write down all the equations describing these polyhedra for a linear programming approach, how many would have to be written?

Let us first consider the assignment problem. The permutations of the assignment problem satisfy the two sets of equations shown in Figure 4. These are the equations that cut the dimension of the polyhedron P down from n^2. In addition, in this lower-dimensional face, there are the nonnegativity conditions, also shown in Figure 4, which actually provide the faces. There are $(n-1)^2$ of these. This then is the number of faces. (One can show that these inequalities each give faces; none is redundant or misses the polyhedron entirely.) When we consider the convex Q, the story is very different. First of all, there are the sets of equations which cut down the dimension. There are a few more of these than there are

ASSIGNMENT PROBLEM

$$x_{i,j} \geq 0 \qquad\qquad \left\{\begin{array}{l} \sum_i x_{i,j} = 1 \\[2mm] \sum_j x_{i,j} = 1 \end{array}\right\} \quad \begin{array}{l} j = 1, \cdots, n \\[2mm] i = 1, \cdots, n \end{array}$$

TRAVELING SALESMAN

$n = 5$

I (20) $x_{i,j} \geq 0$ (i, j) I $\left[\begin{array}{l}\sum_i x_{i,j} = 1\end{array}\right.$ $j = 1, \cdots, n$

II (10) $x_{i,j} + x_{j,i} \leq 1$ $i \neq j$ II $\left\{\begin{array}{l}\sum_j x_{i,j} = 1 \\[2mm] x_{i,i} = 0\end{array}\right.$ $i = 1, \cdots, n$

III $\left\{\begin{array}{l} (60)\ x_{i,j} + x_{j,i} + x_{r,s} - x_{s,t} - x_{t,r} \leq 1 \qquad i, j, r, s, t \text{ distinct} \\[3mm] (120)\ 2(x_{i,j} + x_{j,i}) - x_{i,r} + x_{j,r} - x_{s,i} + x_{s,j} - x_{r,s} \leq 2 \\[1mm] \hspace{5cm} i, j, r, s \text{ distinct} \\[3mm] (60)\ x_{i,j} + x_{j,i} + x_{i,r} + x_{r,i} + x_{s,j} + x_{r,s} + x_{j,t} + x_{t,r} \geq 1 \\[1mm] \hspace{5cm} i, j, r, s, t \text{ distinct} \end{array}\right.$

In general, faces *include* three classes:

I $n(n-1)$, $x_{i,j} \geq 0$

II $P_1 \geq 2^{n-1} - n - 1$ (elements of $k \times k$ principal

III $P_2 \geq \dfrac{(n-1)!\,n!}{2^n}$ minor $= k - 1,\ 2 \leq k \leq [n/2]$)

FIGURE 4. Faces

in the case of the assignment problem. When we come to the inequalities, we have the nonnegativity conditions, just as in the assignment problem, and then another group (group II in Figure 4), which says that we cannot have an assignment both from i to j and from j to i, because then we would have a two-step loop and not a tour. In Figure 4 these inequalities are illustrated for the case $n = 5$, where there are ten of them. There is a third set (group III), which contributes 240 more inequalities in the case $n = 5$; the origin of this group is too complicated to be given here. There is also a fourth set of 120 more inequalities not shown in Figure 4.[1] Together, the four groups give 390 faces in contrast with the 20 faces of the assignment problem, so we start to see a difference. The assignment problem yields a very simple polyhedron; the traveling salesman problem yields a multifaceted one. As Figure 4 shows, the traveling salesman problem in general yields a polyhedron whose faces from class II are almost 2^{n-1} in number, while in class III they are even more numerous. Those of class II that extend the notion of eliminating two-step tours, which appeared in the case $n = 5$, are the inequalities that eliminate subtours or lengths less than $[n/2]$.

This very large number of faces would discourage most people from trying to use the linear programming approach on the traveling salesman problem, but it did not discourage Dantzig, Fulkerson, and Johnson, who tried it anyway. They were, perhaps, a little encouraged by the fact that the number of faces does not seem to be quite so excessively large in the symmetric case ($c_{i,j} = c_{j,i}$). In the symmetric problem, groups I and II of the inequalities (Figure 4) are sufficient for $n = 5$, but not for $n = 6$. For $n = 7$, there are already 2,177 inequalities. So the symmetric situation, although better, is not good. However, Dantzig, Fulkerson, and Johnson worked on a traveling salesman problem involving 42 cities and obtained the solution shown in Figure 5. This was quite a remarkable achievement and I would like to indicate, roughly, what they did. They would start with some tour x and a starting convex made up of a subset of the inequalities. (For instance, one could take just the nonnegativity conditions.) Call this the convex C_1. Our tour x is an extreme point of C_1. Use the simplex method to move to an adjacent extreme point e in C_1 which gives a better value. If e is a tour, repeat from it. If it is not a tour, then among the unwritten inequalities there must exist a hyperplane separating the starting point from e. Find one of these which passes through x, and add it to the problem, making a new convex C_2. Start with x again, and repeat the procedure until a tour x^* and a convex C_m are found over

---

[1] This group was overlooked in the original presentation of my paper. I would like to thank H. W. Kuhn for bringing to my attention his paper which corrects earlier work on this topic (see Kuhn, 1955).

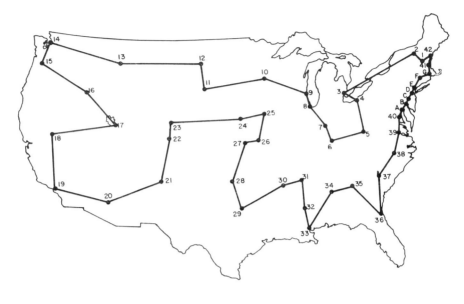

FIGURE 5

which x^* maximizes the linear form $\sum c_{i,j} x_{i,j}$ according to the usual simplex criteria.

Using this method, Dantzig, Fulkerson, and Johnson managed to solve the problem. They found that they encountered very few inequalities from the third or complicated family. Apparently, in practice, the relatively easy types, one and two, are predominant. The method they used has a very large artistic component; the way that the inequalities were produced to cut off the non-tour points was not routine but had to be invented at each step. Also, the procedure was not certain of being terminated, and there was also the problem of maintaining a basis in a compact way that I would describe as artistic rather than algorithmic. Nevertheless, they solved a traveling salesman problem of a size comparable to the best that can be solved today.

I do not see why this particular approach stopped where it did. It should be possible to use the same approach today, but in an algorithmic manner. We no longer have to be artistic about generating the separating hyperplanes or cuts, since this is now done automatically in integer programming. It seems likely that one can get over the difficulties of maintaining the basis as well. So it should be possible to do the whole thing now systematically. This is an approach one might not expect to work, but we already know that it does.

Now we will turn to an entirely different approach, one based on dynamic programming. The approach I am going to describe was invented by Bellman (1960) and, later, independently by Held and Karp (1962). Their procedure is illustrated in Figure 6.

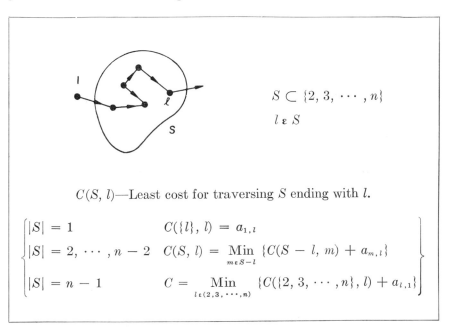

$$S \subset \{2, 3, \cdots, n\}$$

$$l \varepsilon S$$

$C(S, l)$—Least cost for traversing S ending with l.

$$
\left[
\begin{array}{lll}
|S| = 1 & C(\{l\}, l) = a_{1,l} \\[2mm]
|S| = 2, \cdots, n-2 & C(S, l) = \underset{m \varepsilon S - l}{\text{Min}} \{C(S - l, m) + a_{m,l}\} \\[2mm]
|S| = n - 1 & C = \underset{l \varepsilon (2,3,\cdots,n)}{\text{Min}} \{C(\{2, 3, \cdots, n\}, l) + a_{l,1}\}
\end{array}
\right]
$$

FIGURE 6.   Dynamic programming

Let us introduce a function $C(S, l)$. This is defined as the least cost associated with any path that starts from node 1, traverses all the elements of the set S, and ends with the element l belonging to S. The function $C(S, l)$ is easy enough to calculate if S consists of a single element; then as Figure 6 shows, $C(\{l\}, l)$ is simply $a_{1,l}$. Now let us suppose that we have $C(S, l)$ for all sets l containing some number of elements p, where p is greater than one and less than $n - 2$. Then we can find the $C(S, l)$ for a set containing $p + 1$ elements by a second recursion. For the cost $C(S, l)$ is the minimum over all m of the cost of the path that starts out at node 1, traverses all the elements of $S - l$, and ends up at m, plus the cost of then getting from node m to node l. Finally, for sets of $n - 1$ elements, there is a similar recursion which allows the computation of the cost of a complete tour. So it is clear that the various $C(S, l)$ can be computed successively, starting with the one-element sets, going to the two-element sets, and so forth, until finally a cost for the entire tour is obtained.

The main question is how much arithmetic will have to be done to get this answer.

There are $\binom{n-1}{k}$ ways to pick a subset of k elements, and in every such subset there are k elements that can serve as the last element; therefore, the minimization in the second recursion will have to be done $k\binom{n-1}{k}$ times, and the minimization can be regarded as having about $k - 1$ moves, a move being an add or a compare. If this is then summed over the various-sized subsets, we get the formula

$$\sum_{k=2}^{k=n-1} k\binom{n-1}{k}(k-1) = (n-1)(n-2)2^{n-3} + n - 1,$$

so the computation is $O(n^2 2^{n-3})$. All that this work gives us is the cost of the minimal tour, and there would be a certain amount of extra computation involved in going back to find out which tour gave that minimal value. However, this is negligible by comparison with the rest of the work. As far as storage is concerned, we can assume one location for each of the $C(S, l)$ values, which gives us the formula shown below and something of the order of $n2^{n-2}$ locations for the n-city problem.

Storage one location for each $C(S, l)$

$$\sum_{k=2}^{k=n-1} k\binom{n-1}{k} = (n-1)2^{n-2}$$

IBM 7090 — 13 cities — 17 seconds

Roughly speaking then, what the dynamic programming does is to replace a roughly $n!$ problem with one of the order of 2^n. On a computer one can get up to about 13 cities without too much difficulty. At that point we begin to get a little short on storage, and times start to go up by a factor of 2 each time, roughly speaking.

Now Held and Karp did not stop at 13 cities. They took the same technique and applied it to bigger problems to obtain approximate solutions. The sort of thing they did is illustrated in Figure 7. They supposed that they had some sort of a starting solution—good, bad, or indifferent— which they would break up into little sequences of a few cities each. Then they would regard these pieces themselves as being cities. The cost of going from this piece to some other piece is the cost of going from the last node in the first piece to the first node of the second piece. This then gives the $c_{i,j}$ for a new problem.

This new problem is, of course, smaller than the original and, in fact, is usually broken up into a 13-city problem, because that can be done with reasonable rapidity by the dynamic programming technique. If one particular way of cutting up does not work, in the sense of producing

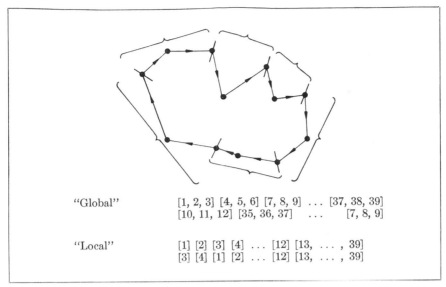

"Global"	[1, 2, 3] [4, 5, 6] [7, 8, 9] ... [37, 38, 39]
	[10, 11, 12] [35, 36, 37] ... [7, 8, 9]
"Local"	[1] [2] [3] [4] ... [12] [13, ... , 39]
	[3] [4] [1] [2] ... [12] [13, ... , 39]

FIGURE 7. Iterating the procedure

a better tour, there are other methods of cutting up that can be tried. Held and Karp called the procedure of cutting up into approximately 13 equal pieces the "global" approach:

$$[1, 2, 3] [4, 5, 6] [7, 8, 9] \cdots [37, 38, 39]$$

$$[10, 11, 12] [35, 36, 37] \cdots [7, 8, 9].$$

They have also a "local" approach, where a tour is divided into 12 one-unit stretches and one very long stretch:

$$[1] [2] [3] [4] \cdots [12] [13, \cdots , 39]$$

$$[3] [4] [1] [2] \cdots [12] [13, \cdots , 39].$$

Here we are looking for a local improvement because most of the tour will be unchanged, while the tours within a short stretch are rotated.

Held and Karp have a number of rules for how many times to try the various methods of cutting up, and they seem to get fairly good results on problems up to about size 50, that is, either the correct answer (known to be optimal by some other means) or a good approximation.

The large-scale Dantzig, Fulkerson, and Johnson problem was solved five times, with five different starting solutions. Two of the answers came out optimal (699); the others were quite close (704, 704, 705). For a 20-city problem, devised by Croes, three starting solutions gave optimal answers. A highly structured problem (a knight's tour on an

8 × 6 chess board) was attempted. The optimal solution is known to be 48. The answers obtained were 56, 52, 54, and 56.

Roughly speaking, the sort of computational results that were obtained by Held and Karp were: in the range of 20 to 25 cities, they almost always got the optimal solution, with running times of 2 to 5 minutes; in the range of 25 to 50 cities, they seemed to get good results, nearly optimal. Of course, "nearly optimal" is a little hard to define, but it suggests what the results look like. They are optimal about one out of every five times. The running times in this range are approximately five to fifteen minutes. Now this sort of result takes the traveling salesman problem, computationally, further than it has been taken before. It does not tie in very much with the polyhedral approach or with methods for the assignment problem. The next method to be described is a little more in that direction.

This is the branch-and-bound method, due to Little *et al.* (1963). The relevant figure here is Figure 8, which shows a node marked "all tours."

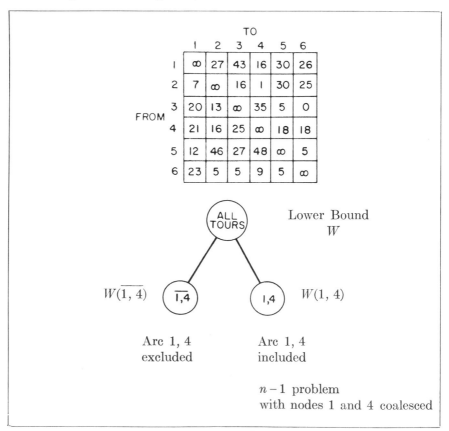

FIGURE 8.   Branch and bound

By some scheme not yet specified, we find a lower bound W on the cost of all tours; that is, the optimal tour must be at least W. Then we select a particular arc—the arc 1, 4 is an example—and divide the tours up into two groups: those which use the arc 1, 4 and those which do not, that is, those from which the arc in question is excluded. Again, for each of these new groups of tours, each one of which is indicated by a node, a new lower bound is computed. Any tour in the group will have a cost equal to or exceeding the associated lower bound. The idea is to go on branching in this way. As a convention, we will say that when we branch to the right we go to a new node in which an arc is included, and when we branch to the left we go to a new node from which an arc is excluded.

Once we have branched n times to the right, there is only one tour remaining in the node at the end of that branch. If the cost of that tour is less than the bound appearing on all the other nodes of the tree, that tour must be optimal. So the idea is to develop the tree until it reaches this state. There are two kinds of choices that can be made in the development of the tree: (1) deciding which node, or group of tours, is to be broken up next and (2) once the node has been specified, deciding which arc is the one on which inclusion and exclusion are to be based. Before making these decisions, we will briefly discuss the bound that is used.

This bound comes from doing the first few steps of the Hungarian method for the assignment problem. It is well known that if a constant is subtracted from any row or any column of the cost matrix, the solution doesn't change, in the sense that the same permutation is still the solution, although the *cost* associated with the solution does change. In fact, the cost of the optimal solution is reduced by the amount subtracted from the row or column. Therefore, if one subtracts numbers from rows and columns in such a way that what remains is nonnegative so that a tour using the remaining costs will still have a nonnegative cost, the total amount taken off will be a lower bound on the cost of any tour. This is the idea that is used to provide the bounds here and which is illustrated in Figure 9. The cost matrix is obtained from the cost matrix of Figure 8, taking as much as possible away from each row and each column. One takes the smallest element in the row and subtracts that from all of the other elements. Everything remaining is nonnegative, and the total amount taken off in this fashion from the original cost matrix is 48. This then is the lower bound for the node representing all tours.

Let us now consider branching. We will explain later why the particular node 1, 4 was chosen for branching. On the assumption that we do branch on node 1, 4, the tours split up into two groups: those using the arc 1, 4 and those in which its use is not permitted. Now once it is decided that a particular arc must be used, you may coalesce the two cities involved; so you are now dealing with an $(n - 1)$-dimensional traveling salesman

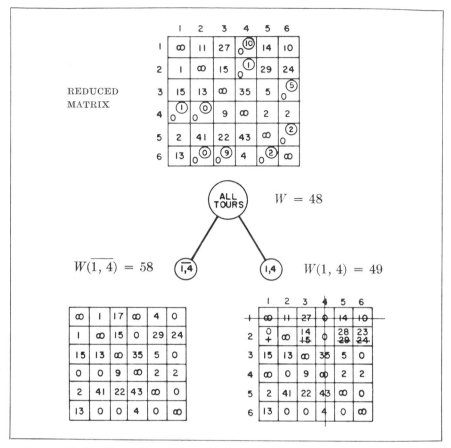

FIGURE 9. Two branching choices, branch to produce max change in left bound

problem. This means that in the new cost matrix for the $(n-1)$-dimensional matrix, one can strike out, in our case, row 1 and column 4. Furthermore, since we are using the arc 1, 4, we will not use the arc 4, 1, which would complete a loop. So the arc 4, 1 can receive a cost of infinity. It may now be possible in this new, smaller matrix with changed costs to make further reductions and thus get a new lower bound. In this particular case (Figure 9), the new lower bound is 49. Similarly, on the other side in the other branch, the cost formerly attributed to the arc 1, 4 is changed to infinity, since that arc is now forbidden. This makes it possible to take 10 off the top row and still preserve the nonnegativity. Thus, the bound associated with this node goes from 48 to 58. One goes on in this fashion, updating the bound by using the new cost matrices obtained after each branching operation.

Let us now consider how to decide which arc to branch on. It is plausible to try to choose the branching arc so that the new bound associated with the lefthand node goes up as much as possible. The idea behind this is that we would like to find our optimal solution down one of the righthand paths, for that leads us into smaller and smaller problems and gets to a solution. We do not want to have to pursue lefthand branches, because the problem size there remains large. So the idea is to do the branching in such a way that the bound on the left goes up, and this branch is unlikely to obtain the optimal solution.

It is quite easy to check through a matrix and find out which branch gives the biggest increase in the lefthand bound (see Little *et al.*, 1963). It turns out that we want to branch only on those arcs that have zeros, and it is not hard to pick from among those the one that does the most for the bound. We have branched according to that rule in the procedures shown in Figures 8 and 9.

There is still the question of which branches of the tree should be developed and which branches should be left alone. A very plausible thing to do is to pursue that branch that has the lowest bound associated with it. That would be where the low-cost tours can be found. So one rule to follow would be to branch on the node currently having the lowest bound. We may, of course, run into the problem that the tree becomes too large and that there may be too many nodes to hold in memory. This difficulty can be avoided by a different approach. This is to proceed by always branching to the right until we have reached a point where no further right branching is possible. Then back up and take one left, and then back up again and stay, so to speak, as far right in the tree as possible. This scheme would not be expected to be as fast as the one in which the choice of node is made on the basis of the lower bound, but it has the advantage that we can keep the number of stored nodes down to a small multiple of n. So there are two things we can do with the node choice. We can use it to promote a rapid calculation or to conserve memory. This second use is also illustrated in Figure 10.

Figure 11 shows some of the computational results. They are very good. The problems on which the test runs were made were random problems with costs drawn from a uniform distribution of three-digit numbers. The first column shows the number of cities in the problem, the second column shows the number of problems run, the third column shows the time in minutes of IBM 7090 time, and the fourth column shows the standard deviation of the running times. These results are very good because we are getting answers up to 40 cities; this is an area where people have not previously obtained optimal solutions. Even an incomplete calculation gives both a tour and a lower bound. A good rule of thumb for the running times involved here is that adding 10 cities multiplies the running time

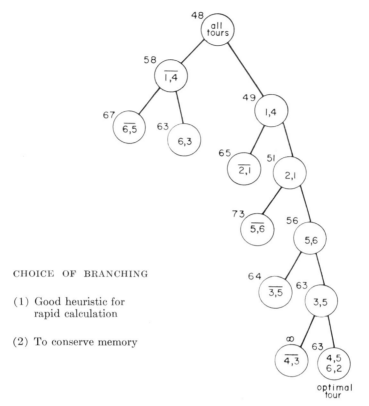

CHOICE OF BRANCHING

(1) Good heuristic for
    rapid calculation

(2) To conserve memory

FIGURE 10

| | Uniformly distributed three-digit random distances | | |
No. of cities	No. of problems	Mean T (IBM 7090 minutes)	Standard deviation
10	100	0.012	.007
20	100	0.084	.063
30	100	0.975	1.280
40	5	8.37	10.2

FIGURE 11. Computational results

by 10. So, as far as computing is concerned, we are still dealing with an exponentially increasing method.

In view of this, it is especially comforting to note that this computation has the feature that if we do not finish, we can still leave it. This is because we have bounds on each node. The smallest of these bounds is an underestimate of the cost of the optimal solution. Thus, the gap between the smallest bound and the best solution we have at that point is an overestimate of the error we would make in accepting our current best tour as the optimal one.

So far I have discussed the general traveling salesman problem. I am not aware of much work having been done on special cases of the problem. Nevertheless, in sequencing problems, it is not true that we have to deal with every possible cost matrix. For example, here is one very special case. Consider making sandpaper in a sandpaper-making machine (Maxwell, 1962). When the machine finishes making coarse sandpaper, there is a great deal of coarse sand in the machine. If fine sandpaper is made next, the coarse sand must be taken out. On the other hand, if coarser sandpaper is made next, it doesn't matter that much. The changeover cost in this problem is the cost of taking the sand out of the machine. Clearly, here the problem is easily solved. You should start with the fine sandpaper and work steadily up to the coarser types. This situation is very special and very simple, but it is a solvable special case. What else can we do with special traveling salesman problems?

We next come to some work of P. C. Gilmore and myself on a special traveling salesman problem (Gilmore and Gomory, 1964). I will start by giving a particular example. Suppose that there are a number of jobs to be done on a furnace. Each job is loaded into the furnace at a certain starting temperature, is cycled through various different temperatures, and is taken out at a certain ending temperature. For example, in the problem of Figure 12, job 1 starts at a temperature of 500°, and at a later time it comes out leaving the furnace at 611°. The next job must be started at a temperature of 750°. So the furnace has to be heated up from 611° to 750° before the next job can go in. Job 2 ends at 400°, and we must now heat the furnace to 550° for job 3. The problem here is to arrange the jobs in such an order that the cost of changing the furnace temperature is minimized. That cost may be a delay in time, it may be the total energy involved, or anything of that sort. The general problem of this type, which we call the problem of sequencing a one state-variable machine, is quite similar to this special case. There is one variable which characterizes the state of the machine, and moving this variable up and down is what incurs changeover cost. More precisely, we will assume that we have n jobs, $J_1, \cdots, J_n$. Each J_i is characterized by two numbers, A_i and B_i; A_i can be regarded as the starting state of the machine and

FURNACE   Job 1   Starts $T = 500°$
                    Ends $T = 611°$
           Job 2   Starts $T = 750°$
                    Ends $T = 400°$
           Job 3   Starts $T = 550°$
                      .   .
                      .   .
                      .   .

Cost of changing T between jobs is to be minimized

GENERAL PROBLEM

Jobs $J_1, \cdots J_n$

$$J_i = (A_i, B_i)$$

$$\begin{cases} c_{i,j} = \displaystyle\int_{B_i}^{A_j} f(x)\, dx & \text{if } A_j \geq B_i \\[2mm] c_{i,j} = \displaystyle\int_{A_j}^{B_i} g(x)\, dx & \text{if } A_j < B_i \end{cases}$$

$$f(x) + g(x) \geq 0$$

FIGURE 12.   Sequencing a one state-variable machine

B_i as the state in which the machine is left. If $A_j \geq B_i$, the cost $c_{i,j}$ of following i with j is given by

$$c_{i,j} = \int_{B_i}^{A_j} f(x)\, dx.$$

In other words, if we must go to a higher state, there is a cost $f(x)$ for every infinitesimal increase in the state variable. There is a similar cost if the state variable must be changed downward (that is, if $A_j < B_i$), and we can have a separate cost variable $g(x)$ for a downward change. Then,

$$c_{i,j} = \int_{A_j}^{B_i} g(x)\, dx.$$

The only important condition is that the sum $f(x) + g(x)$ be nonnegative.

One state-variable machines are not always as obvious as a furnace. Here is a different example of a one state-variable machine. Let us imagine a long ribbon of glass that is being cut up by a cutting device, Figure 13. The device consists of two axles and round knives on each axle. There

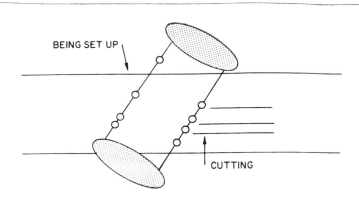

BEING SET UP

CUTTING

Job is a cutting pattern

$J_i = (A_i, B_i) =$ (setup time, run time)

if j follows i and $A_j \geq B_i$, delay $A_j - B_i$

if j follows i and $A_j < B_i$, no delay

FIGURE 13

is a succession of patterns for knife positions which must be used for cutting the correct amounts and the correct widths of glass. Each pattern must be set up on an axle; then, while this axle is actually running and cutting glass, another pattern can be set up on the other axle. The problem is to sequence the patterns so that there is always time to set up the next pattern while the previous one is running. All patterns have different running times and different setup times. The setup time is the A_i associated with the ith job, and the run time is the B_i. If we try to minimize the delay that is incurred when there is an inadequate setup time, then the cost equations given in the preceding paragraph assume the following forms:

$$f(x) = 1, \qquad g(x) = 0;$$

hence, when $A_j \geq B_i$ (delay),

$$c_{i,j} = \int_{B_i}^{A_j} 1 \, dx = A_j - B_i,$$

and when $A_j < B_i$ (no delay),

$$c_{i,j} = \int_{A_j}^{B_i} 0 \, dx = 0.$$

The one state-variable here is actually the amount of time that the cutting pattern currently being used for cutting has already been running. Thus, we can regard this cutting machine as a one state-variable machine just like the furnace, although in this case what the one state-variable should be is not quite as obvious.

Next we turn to a description of how the one state-variable sequencing problem can be solved. As you will see, this is a throwback, in a way, to the polyhedral systems which we discussed earlier.

The first step in this calculation is to solve the corresponding assignment problem. This will give us a point, in fact a vertex, on the polyhedron P. Next (Figure 14), we consider some interchanges $\alpha_{i,j}$ which will modify this permutation. Figure 14a shows the assignment problem. The interchange $\alpha_{i,j}$ is itself a permutation which sends node i into j, node j into i, and leaves all other nodes the same. The effect of applying α to a permutation ϕ is shown in Figure 14b. The effect of using $\alpha_{i,j}$ to modify ϕ is the same as adding a four-arc loop which is directed forward along the dashed lines and backward along the two connecting straight lines. Since ϕ and the modified permutation ϕ' differ only by this single cycle, they are neighboring points on the polyhedron P. The cost equation becomes

$$c(\alpha_{i,j}) = c(\phi\alpha_{i,j}) - c(\phi).$$

Thus, a series of such modifications will be a vertex-to-vertex exploration scheme. It is also clear that if such an interchange is effected on two nodes i and j in different subtours of the permutation ϕ, the result is to unite the two subtours into a single larger tour. Thus, we are moving closer to a single tour.

Next, we can associate costs with each interchange $\alpha_{i,j}$. The cost of $\alpha_{i,j}$ is the cost of $\phi\alpha_{i,j}$ less the cost of ϕ. Of course, this cost depends on ϕ as well as on $\alpha_{i,j}$. If $\alpha_{i,j}$ were applied to a different permutation, the cost would also be different.

[*Text resumes on page 114*]

(a)   Solve Assignment Problem

ϕ

(b)   Consider Interchanges $\alpha_{i,j}$ and Their Costs

$\phi' = \phi\alpha_{i,j}$

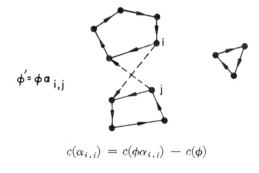

$$c(\alpha_{i,j}) = c(\phi\alpha_{i,j}) - c(\phi)$$

FIGURE 14.   Method

We now consider a set of interchanges that will convert these permutations into a tour (Figure 15). If we simply drop the directions on the arcs in Figure 15a, we get Figure 15b, and if we put in a dark line whenever an interchange is applied, then the corresponding interchange connects the directed components in Figure 15a, just as the dark line connects the undirected components in Figure 15b. Consequently, a set of arcs that would connect up the components in Figure 15b corresponds to a set of interchanges which, if executed, would transform the permutation

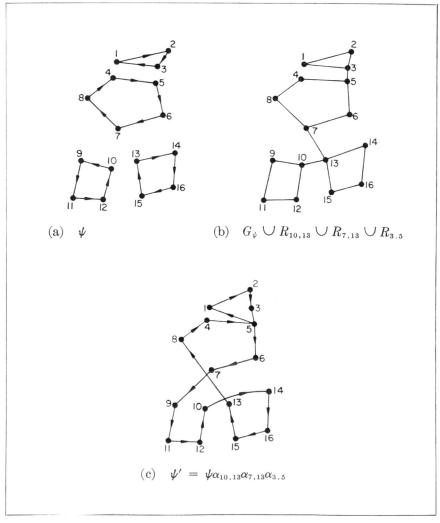

(a) ψ

(b) $G_\psi \cup R_{10,13} \cup R_{7,13} \cup R_{3,5}$

(c) $\psi' = \psi \alpha_{10,13} \alpha_{7,13} \alpha_{3,5}$

FIGURE 15

in Figure 15a into a tour such as that illustrated in Figure 15c. Now this suggests the following procedure: Put in the costs on all the arcs, and then choose the minimal-cost set of arcs that connect up the graph. Then perhaps the corresponding set of interchanges will, at least cost, transform the original permutation into a tour. This idea is illustrated in Figure 16, where the original arcs of the permutation appear as dashed lines. A number of interchanges are drawn as solid lines with their costs attached, and the bold solid lines are the minimal-cost interconnecting set. Fortunately, picking the minimal interconnecting set is a very slight modification on the well-known problem of picking a minimal-cost spanning tree. For this problem there is a well-known solution due to Kruskal (1957). So this is a solvable problem and one which can be done, in fact, extremely rapidly.

What we have said so far can be summarized as follows: It is plausible to pick a set of interchanges by a minimal spanning-tree argument and

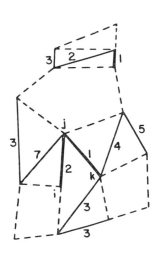

$$\alpha_{i,j}\,\alpha_{j,k} \neq \alpha_{j,k}\,\alpha_{i,j}$$

Cost depends on order
as well as set of interchanges

FIGURE 16

then to execute these interchanges to get what we hope will be a minimal-cost tour.

There are only two things wrong with this approach. First, the costs are generally wrong. When the interchange marked with a cost 7 is executed, it will not generally change the permutation cost by an amount 7. This is because, in general, the interchanges affect each other; the cost 7 was computed on the basis of the original permutation ϕ and will be different if the interchange is executed later, after several other interchanges have modified ϕ. Second, merely picking a set of interchanges, even if they are the right ones, does not specify a tour, because different tours will be obtained by executing the set of interchanges in a different order. Since, in general, these different resulting tours will have different costs, merely specifying a set of interchanges cannot possibly specify the optimal tour. It is necessary to have both a set of interchanges and a specified order in which to execute them before it is even possible to reach an answer.

These, then, are the difficulties which, in general, apply to this approach to the traveling salesman problem. However, in our particular case, we can get over these difficulties. In our case, the following three statements are correct, provided that the jobs are renumbered so that their final states B_i are numbered in increasing size:

First, the set of interchanges chosen by the minimal spanning-tree algorithm is correct and contains only interchanges of the form $\alpha_{i,i+1}$. Thus, it is meaningful to talk about the ith interchange, meaning $\alpha_{i,i+1}$.

Second, the minimal-cost tour will be obtained if this set of interchanges is executed in the correct order, that is, if we divide the interchanges into two groups. The ith interchange goes into group 1 if under the original assignment the ith job left the state variable so that it had to be increased for the start of the succeeding job. An interchange goes into group 2 if under the original assignment the corresponding job left a state variable that had to be decreased. Then a permutation ψ^* is obtained by applying to ϕ the interchanges of group 1 with the largest-indexed interchange first, the second-largest interchange second, etc., and then applying the interchanges of group 2, starting with the lowest-numbered interchange, following with the second interchange, etc. The resulting permutation ψ^* will be a cycle and will be the minimal-cost tour. The correct order is given by

$$\underbrace{\psi^*(i) = \phi \quad \alpha_{i_1,i_1+1}\alpha_{i_2,i_2+1}}_{\text{group 1: } A_{\phi(i)} \geq B_i} \quad \underbrace{\cdots \alpha_{j_i,j_1+1}\alpha_{j_2,j_2+1} \cdots \alpha_{j_m,j_m+1}}_{\text{group 2: } A_{\phi(i)} < B_i}(i),$$

where $i_1 > i_2$ and $j_1 < j_2$.

Third, the amount of computing that has to be done is very slight; it is $O(n^2)$.

By way of summary, we can see that the methods reviewed in this paper can be divided into three categories. First, there was a part where we dealt with linear programming and polyhedra. Then there was a part dealing with the work of Held and Karp and the branch-and-bound method. And finally there was a method that dealt with special $c_{i,j}$. Actually, I think that in all three areas which have been represented here, there is a great deal more work that can be done. In the area of linear programming and polyhedra, there are now methods available which should enable us to extend the more artistic, less systematic work already done. Certainly in the branching and dynamic programming area there are many more possibilities to be explored that could put us into a new range of practical applications, now that we know that present methods already take us into the range of 20 to 50 cities. In this area people will be producing one method after another, now that they know that a certain degree of success has already been obtained along these lines. Finally, it is hard to believe that there should be only one special case in the traveling salesman problem. This is an area which deserves to be looked at in more detail; a good look will probably reveal a variety of important and solvable special cases.

REFERENCES

BELLMAN, R. 1960. Combinatorial processes and dynamic programming *in* Combinatorial analysis (Proceedings of symposia in applied mathematics, vol. X), ed. R. BELLMAN and M. HALL, JR. Providence, R. I.: Amer. Math. Soc., 217–49.

GILMORE, P. C., and R. E. GOMORY. 1964. Sequencing a one state-variable machine: a solvable case of the traveling salesman problem. Operations Res., 12:655-79.

HELD, M., and R. M. KARP. 1962. A dynamic programming approach to sequencing problems. J. Soc. Indust. Appl. Math., 10:196–210.

HELLER, I. 1954. The travelling salesman's problem. Part I: Basic facts. Washington, D. C.: George Washington Univ., Logistics Research Project.

———. 1955. On the travelling salesman's problem *in* Proceedings of the second symposium in linear programming, vol. II. Washington, D. C.: Nat. Bur. Standards, 643–65.

KRUSKAL, J. B. 1957. On the shortest spanning subtree of a graph and the travelling salesman problem. J. Soc. Indust. Appl. Math., 5:32–38.

KUHN, H. W. 1955. On certain convex polyhedra. Abstract 59-6-664. Bull. Amer. Math. Soc., 61.

LITTLE, J. D. C., K. G. MURTY, D. W. SWEENEY, and C. KAREL. 1963. An algorithm for the traveling salesman problem. Operations Res., 11:972–89.

MAXWELL, W. L. 1962. The scheduling of economic lot sizes. Ithaca, N. Y.: Cornell Univ., Department of Industrial and Engineering Administration.

MOTZKIN, T. S. 1956. The assignment problem *in* Numerical analysis (Proceedings of symposia in applied mathematics, vol. VI), ed. J. H. CURTISS. New York: McGraw-Hill, 109–25.

[*Discussion begins on page 118*]

DISCUSSION

H. W. KUHN: I would like to make a correction to the number of faces cited in Dr. Gomory's paper for the nonsymmetric traveling salesman problem with five cities.

The correct enumeration, found by me in 1953, and presented at the summer meeting of the American Mathematical Society in Ann Arbor in 1955, includes 390 faces. That is to say, the miserable polyhedron has 24 vertices, is situated in eleven-dimensional space, but has 390 faces.

To turn this quibble in a more positive direction, let me describe an experiment that was run in 1953 with the help of Alan Hoffman. Imagine yourself sitting at the center of gravity of the polyhedron with a pistol. If you fire at random, the distance the bullet travels inside the polyhedron can be calculated by solving a linear program—namely, maximize the distance subject to the condition that the coordinates of the bullet be a convex combination of the vertices. In general, the vertices in the optimal basis will span a face, and thus, if you fire enough shots, you should find all types of faces.

In the actual experiment, the random directions were taken from a Los Angeles telephone book; the problems were sent to the National Bureau of Standards and solved by Saul Gass on the SEAC. Strangely enough, no matter how many times we tried it, we always hit the faces $x_{ij} = 0$. That is, out of 390 possible faces, our bullets always passed out through one class of 20 faces. This means to me that these are the "walls" of the polyhedron and that all the rest of the faces are small irregularities in the "corners" where these join. This is an empirical fact that has never received any theoretical explanation.

Of course, the same technique can be used to construct new constraints in any integer program in which the vertices are known explicitly.

S. H. CHASEN: I would like to compare the concept of randomness with its extreme opposite. I know that this will be repulsive after all of this fine analytical work, but let us introduce a little of the concepts of statistics. I think this is necessary for completeness. Suppose we take a number of nodes—for example, the 42 indicated cities of the United States. We pass through the cities randomly. With all of the different combinations, there are 42 factorial, which we might regard as infinite, for all practical purposes. It occurs to me that if we completely randomize our selection of tours from city to city, which is not elegant by any means, it does not take the computer very long to traverse around. We can do literally tens of thousands of tours with very nominal expenditure of computer time. Again, for the sake of completeness, how would this procedure, if we picked the minimum route or the minimum cost, compare with the optimal solution in terms of percentage of error?

R. E. GOMORY: I can only say that I do not know.

S. H. CHASEN: Could certain empirical investigations be done on a low scale?

R. E. GOMORY: Yes.

S. H. CHASEN: This is very important because, as the density of points increases, we might expect that there are a number of solutions which are very close to optimal—not optimal, of course, but, for all practical purposes, adequate.

R. E. GOMORY: This is an approach which people have tried on numerous scheduling problems. Sometimes it seems to be pretty good, and sometimes it seems to be pretty bad. I do not know of any experiments in this way on the traveling salesman problem. This does not mean that it would not work.

D. W. SWEENEY: There are some experiments going on now at the University of Rochester. Professor J. W. Gavett informed me that he is comparing the optimal solutions of job-shop setup problems with the rule-of-thumb solutions gained by taking as the next job the one with the shortest setup time. On a 25-city problem, less than 1,000 branches (partial or complete tours) were followed, using the branch-and-bound procedure to find an optimal tour. I would say that this is a far more hopeful approach than the use of random-walk techniques.

R. E. GOMORY: I would not be very optimistic about a scheme that went randomly from one city to another, because the salesman is then going to go to very distant points and ruin the tour.

S. H. CHASEN: A lot will depend on the confines of the area involved, will it not?

R. E. GOMORY: Yes, but there are bound to be some points that are distant.

A. J. GOLDSTEIN: I personally did the experiment that you have mentioned. I took an 11-city problem and exhibited all of the 1.8 million possible tours in numerical order. This took a minute and a half on the IBM 7094. The interval between the minimum and the median tours was divided into ten intervals, and I asked how many tours were in the first interval. I took several random 11-point examples from the unit square and found that this first interval had between 15 and 50 of the 1.8 million tours.

May I mention some results in the competition for speed and size of problem. Shen Lin at the Bell Telephone Laboratories has modified the dynamic programming approach so that on the IBM 7094 (which is 40% faster than the 7090) he has cut the time for a 13-city problem from 17 to 3.5 seconds. He has also used an iterative approach on the 20-, 25-, and 48-city problems discussed in the Held and Karp paper that you cited. The 25-city problem takes about 8 seconds to run, and the optimum is found in 50% of the runs. For 48 cities the figures are 30 seconds and 30%. The running time is proportional to the cube of the number of cities.

J. EDMONDS: I have a comment on the polyhedral approach to complete analysis, supplementing Professor Kuhn's remarks. I do not believe there is any reason for taking as a measure of the algorithmic difficulty of a class of combinatorial extremum problems the number of faces in the associated polyhedra. For example, consider the generalization of the assignment problem from bipartite graphs to arbitrary graphs. Unlike the case of bipartite graphs, the number of faces in the associated polyhedron increases exponentially with the size of the graph. On the other hand, there is an algorithm for this generalized assignment problem which has an upper bound on the work involved just as good as the upper bound for the bipartite assignment problem.

H. W. KUHN: I could not agree with you more. That is shown by the unreasonable effectiveness of the Norman-Rabin scheme for solving this problem. Their result is unreasonable only in the sense that the number of faces of the polyhedron suggests that it ought to be a harder problem than it actually turned out to be. It is not impossible that some day we will have a practical combinatorial algorithm for this problem.

J. EDMONDS: Actually, the amount of work in carrying out the Norman-Rabin scheme generally increases exponentially with the size of the graph.

The algorithm I had in mind is one I introduced in a paper submitted to the Canadian Journal of Mathematics (see Edmonds, 1965). This algorithm depends crucially on what amounts to knowing all the bounding inequalities of the associated convex polyhedron—and, as I said, there are many of them. The point is that the inequalities are known by an easily verifiable characterization rather than by an exhaustive listing—so their number is not important.

This sort of thing should be expected for a class of extremum problems with a combinatorially special structure. For the traveling salesman problem, the vertices of the associated polyhedron have a simple characterization despite their number—so might the bounding inequalities have a simple characterization despite their number. At least we should hope they have, because finding a really good traveling salesman algorithm is undoubtedly equivalent to finding such a characterization.

What amazes me is that the known successful examples of the philosophy I am propounding are so scarce. Perhaps a reason for the scarcity is the lack of attention which has been given to the theoretical distinction between finite algorithms and "better-than-finite" algorithms.

Practically the only other successful example that I know is the problem, mentioned by Dr. Gomory, of finding a minimum spanning tree in a graph which has a real numerical weight on each of its edges. The well-known, very easy algorithm for the problem is not usually regarded as an instance of linear programming. However, the justification of the algorithm can be used to prove a simple characterization of the bounding planes of the polyhedron whose vertices correspond to the spanning trees of the graph. The number of these planes increases exponentially with the size of the graph. However, the algorithm can be interpreted as a refinement of a linear programming method operating on this polyhedron.

Dr. Gomory's general algorithm for integer programming may be regarded as a characterization of the bounding inequalities of the convex hull of the integer points in a prescribed convex polyhedron. The work involved in carrying out his algorithm depends not so much on the number of these inequalities as on the complexity of using the characterization to identify them.

R. E. GOMORY: I think it is clear that the faces have nothing to do with it, particularly if we are not going to try something like a linear programming approach, which usually presupposes that we list all of the faces and equalities. In the spanning tree, we do not go at it in that way. It is not a measure of the inherent difficulty so much as it is a measure of what we have to face if we take the linear programming approach. Sometimes even the sheer number of faces is not a deterrent if we have some systematic way of getting at them. For example, if we took the cutting stock problem, which has millions of columns, and dualized that, we would have millions of faces; but if we generated the faces of the new problem by knapsack methods, we would get the same good computational results that we have on the primal problem. So the number of faces is not the problem. The question is whether we can get them. And the trouble with the traveling salesman problem is that we have not, up to now (I still think it can be done), been able to produce enough of them easily enough, whereas, if we have a thing with only a few faces, we can list them once and for all and then unleash the linear program.

DISCUSSION REFERENCE

EDMONDS, J. 1965. Paths, trees, and flowers. Canad. J. Math., 17:449–67.

9

Convex Polytopes and Linear Programming

Victor Klee

University of Washington and
Boeing Scientific Research Laboratories

INTRODUCTION

The development of linear programming, designed to solve a wide variety of practical optimization problems, has also had a strong influence on several branches of pure mathematics—especially matrix theory, graph theory, and the theory of convexity. The present report contains a survey of past discoveries and current knowledge concerning the facial structure of convex polytopes, including some connections with linear programming. Details of proofs seem relatively unimportant for our purpose; we rely on statements of definitions and theorems and on references to the literature, along with an account of unsolved problems and a few historical remarks.

The next section describes four "landmarks" of the theory, which are treated in more detail in subsequent sections on polytopal d-tuples, polytopal graphs, paths in polytopes, and additional results and problems. Bibliographic notes refer to the list of about 150 publications which appears at the end of the paper.

It should be emphasized that we are mainly concerned with convex polytopes and their facial structure; linear programming enters because of its background in the theory of convexity and its influence on that theory. In addition, we hope that some of the remaining puzzles in linear programming—for example, "Why does the simplex method work so efficiently?"—may be successfully attacked in terms of the geometric notions described here. Our attention is not confined to problems which are directly related to linear programming. Perhaps this is just as well, even from a linear programmer's viewpoint, for combinatorial complexities are often best understood in settings more general than those in which they first appear.

The combinatorial study of convex polytopes may be traced to Euler's formula of 1752, and perhaps even to Euclid's study of the Platonic solids more than 2,000 years ago. Nevertheless, the subject abounds in unsolved problems, and even some of its most basic questions appear to be very difficult. We hope that this report will arouse interest in the subject and will contribute to its development by suggesting avenues for future research. For some shorter expository accounts which overlap somewhat with this one, see Grünbaum (1966*a*) and Klee (1966*b*).

FOUR LANDMARKS

A subset P of a finite-dimensional real vector space will be called here a *polyhedron* provided that P is the intersection of a finite number of closed halfspaces. A polyhedron P will be called a *pointed polyhedron* provided that P contains no line, and a *polytope* provided that P is bounded. Equivalently, a polytope is the convex hull of a finite set of points.[1] The *dimension* of a polyhedron is that of the smallest affine subspace (or *flat*) containing it. A *face* of a polyhedron P is the intersection of P with a supporting hyperplane; in addition, P itself and the empty set are counted as (improper) faces of P. A polyhedron has only finitely many faces; in fact, this property characterizes the polyhedra among the closed convex sets.

The dimension of a set will often be indicated by a prefix. Thus, we shall speak of d-polyhedra, s-flats, s-faces, etc. The 0-faces, 1-faces, $(d-2)$-faces, and $(d-1)$-faces of a d-polyhedron will be called, respectively, its *vertices, edges, subfacets,* and *facets.*[2]

The number of s-faces of a polyhedron P will be denoted by $f_s(P)$, or simply by f_s when P is understood. In its three-dimensional form, the first landmark of our theory was presented by Euler (1752) to the St. Petersburg Academy. It was apparently known to Descartes more than a century earlier.[3] The d-dimensional form was discovered by Schläfli about 1850 (see Schläfli, 1901) and proved by Poincaré (1893).[4]

---

[1] For a proof of the equivalence, see Weyl (1935). For related results concerning polyhedra and polyhedral cones, see Gale (1951), Gerstenhaber (1951), Goldman (1956), Goldman & Tucker (1956), Klee (1959), Motzkin (1936), and Tucker (1955). (A *cone* is a set which is the union of rays issuing from the origin 0.) Like most of the material presented here, these results are valid in a finite-dimensional vector space over an arbitrary ordered field.

For other basic information on polytopes, see Brückner (1893 and 1900), Coxeter (1948), Eberhard (1891), Lyusternik (1963), Minkowski (1897), Schläfli (1901), Schlegel (1883), Schoute (1905), Sommerville (1929), Steinitz (1922), Steinitz & Rademacher (1934), and especially Grünbaum (1966*b*).

[2] The literature contains a variety of terms for the simple notions which are employed in this report; so the reader should take careful note of our terminology.

[3] See Steinitz (1922, p. 19).

[4] The results of Poincaré (1893 and 1899) were for more general figures, but we are concerned here only with their application to polytopes. For elementary proofs of theorem (1), see Hadwiger (1955) and Klee (1963). The result applies more generally to an arbitrary pointed d-polyhedron P, provided that f_s is replaced by the number of bounded s-faces of P.

Theorem (1). If P is a d-polytope and f_s denotes the number of s-faces of P, then

$$f_0 - f_1 + f_2 - \cdots + (-1)^{d-1}f_{d-1} = 1 - (-1)^d.$$

For other results which are related to (1), see the next section.

Our second landmark is concerned with the *graph of a polytope P*, where this is merely the 1-complex formed by the vertices and edges of P. An abstract graph will be called *d-polytopal* provided that it is isomorphic with the graph of a d-polytope. It is natural to ask for conditions, expressed in purely graph-theoretic terms, which characterize the d-polytopality of a graph. For $d = 2$, the answer is trivial; a graph is 2-polytopal if and only if it is a simple circuit. For $d = 3$, the problem was essentially solved in Steinitz & Rademacher (1934), and their result is our second landmark. Actually, their characterization was in terms of two-dimensional cell-complexes rather than graphs, but it can be translated in several ways into graph-theoretic terms. The simplest of these, noted by Grünbaum & Motzkin (1963a), may be stated as follows:

Theorem (2). A graph is 3-polytopal if and only if it is planar and 3-connected.

Recall that a graph is called *planar* provided that it can be topologically embedded in the plane or, equivalently, provided that it does not contain a refinement of a complete-5-graph or a double-3-graph. A graph is called *d-connected* provided that it has at least $d + 1$ nodes and cannot be separated between any two nodes by the removal of $d - 1$ nodes; equivalently, each pair of its nodes can be joined by d independent paths.[5]

For other results which are related to (2), see the section on polytopal graphs.

The next landmark is not a specific theorem but rather the development of a new area of mathematics which has led to renewed interest in the facial structure of polyhedra. This is the subject of linear programming, especially the simplex algorithm of Dantzig (1951) and its many variants.[6] Here we are concerned with the general idea of the simplex method rather than with its technical details.

In a linear programming problem, one seeks to maximize or minimize a linear form φ (the *objective function*) over a set P (the *feasible region*) which is defined by means of a finite system of linear inequalities (the

---

[5] These equivalences are due to Kuratowski (1930) and Whitney (1932), respectively. For additional proofs and for references to others, see Berge (1958).

[6] Among the many descriptions of the simplex method, we mention especially Dantzig (1951, 1960, and 1963), Dantzig, Orden, & Wolfe (1955), Ficken (1961), Tucker (1962), and Wolfe (1962). Many other references will be found in Dantzig (1963).

constraints). The constraints generally require, in particular, that each of the n variables shall be nonnegative, and then P is a pointed polyhedron contained in the positive orthant O^n in R^n. If they are finite, the extreme values of φ are attained at vertices of P, so the problem is to find an optimum vertex or to show that φ is unbounded on P. When P is presented in terms of linear constraints, it is not practical to determine all its vertices simultaneously by means of a global inspection.[7] However, there are computationally practical ways of looking at P locally so that once a vertex is known we may inspect also all of the other vertices which are *adjacent* (joined by an edge) to it. This suggests the possibility of various search processes which entail moving along the edges of P from one vertex to another and searching for a vertex at which the objective function attains its optimum value. Assuming that the objective function is to be maximized, we shall describe as a *variant of the simplex method* any rule for carrying out the search which necessarily leads to a maximizing vertex and which does not at any stage involve a decrease in the value of the objective function.

A *path* in a polyhedron P is a sequence $(x_0, \cdots , x_l)$ of consecutively adjacent vertices, and the integer l is the *length* of the path. If φ is a function on P, the path $(x_0, \cdots , x_l)$ will be called a *φ-path* provided that $\varphi(x_0) < \varphi(x_1) < \cdots < \varphi(x_l)$. The success of the simplex method rests on the facts which are stated in the following theorem:

Theorem (3). Suppose that P is a pointed polyhedron, φ is a linear form on the containing space, and F is the set of all points $x \; \varepsilon \; P$ such that $\varphi(x) = \sup \varphi P$. Then F is a face of P, and exactly one of the following statements is true:

(a) F is nonempty; each φ-path $(x_0, \cdots , x_k)$ in P can be extended to a φ-path $(x_0, \cdots , x_k, \cdots , x_l)$ such that $x_l \; \varepsilon \; F$;

(b) F is empty; each φ-path $(x_0, \cdots , x_k)$ in P can be extended to a φ-path $(x_0, \cdots , x_k, \cdots , x_l)$ such that x_l is the endpoint of an edge of P on which φ is unbounded.

The section on paths in polytopes contains some results which were suggested by variants of the simplex method or by other search processes which arise in the study of polyhedra.

In connection with the simplex method, one is led inevitably to consider the facial structure and, in particular, the graph structure of polyhedra. This fact has been largely responsible for the rediscovery of the area of combinatorial geometry to which this report is devoted. The aptness of the term *rediscovery* is illustrated by the history of our fourth and last landmark, which might alternatively have been placed second.

---

[7] Algorithms for finding all the vertices of a polytope are given by Balinski (1961*a*), Charnes, Cooper, & Henderson (1953), Goldstein (1963), and Motzkin *et al.* (1953).

Since the simplex method involves moving from a vertex of a polyhedron to an adjacent vertex, it is natural to wonder how many adjacent vertices there might be. This question was considered by H. W. Kuhn for a polytope connected with a linear programming formulation of a traveling salesman problem. His polytope was 11-dimensional with 24 vertices, and he was shocked to find that every one of its vertices was adjacent to every other vertex. Let us call a polytope *m-neighborly* provided that each set of m of its vertices determines an $(m - 1)$-face. Thus, every polytope is 1-neighborly, and Kuhn's 11-polytope was 2-neighborly. He asked for the maximum number of vertices which a 2-neighborly d-polytope could have, and the surprising answer was provided by Gale (1956); see also Motzkin (1957):

Theorem (4). For $d/2 < m \leq d$, the d-simplices are the only m-neighborly d-polytopes. But if $m \leq d/2$, then for each $n > d$ there exist m-neighborly d-polytopes having n vertices.

This theorem's chronology is no less striking than its mathematical content. Since the appearance of Gale's paper in 1956, it has been discovered that the existence of neighborly polytopes in $\mathbf{R}^d$ was known to Carathéodory (1911) and in $\mathbf{R}^4$ to Brückner (1909). Steinitz (1922) refers to the work of both Brückner and Carathéodory, but their results were later forgotten or neglected for many years. Sz.-Nagy (1941) noted that neighborly polytopes other than simplices could be obtained as the joins of simplices and asked whether this was the only way. Results claimed by Chabauty (1952a and 1952b) were invalidated by the existence of neighborly polytopes, and his later correction (Chabauty, 1953) contained a claim which is invalidated by the fact that neighborly polytopes may be constructed so as to have all their vertices on a sphere (Carathéodory, 1911, and Gale, 1963).

A *cyclic d-polytope* is one whose vertices all lie on the moment curve M_d in $\mathbf{R}^d$, where $M_d = \{(r, r^2, r^3, \cdots, r^d) : r \in \mathbf{R}\}$. These are the simplest $[d/2]$-neighborly d-polytopes, and the proof in Gale (1963) of their neighborliness is especially to be recommended. Other results on neighborly or cyclic polytopes have been obtained by Derry (1956), Fabricius-Bjerre (1962), Gale (1956 and 1963), Grünbaum (1966b), Karlin & Shapley (1953), Klee (1964b, 1964c, and 1966a), and Shashkin (1963). Neighborly polytopes will reappear in the remaining sections of this report.

POLYTOPAL d-TUPLES

A d-tuple $(\nu_0, \nu_1, \cdots, \nu_{d-1})$ of positive integers will be called *polytopal* provided that there exists a d-polytope P such that $f_s(P) = \nu_s$ for $0 \leq s \leq d - 1$. Such a d-tuple must satisfy the Euler-Poincaré relation $\sum_{s=0}^{d-1} (-1)^s \nu_s = 1 - (-1)^d$, and it is natural to ask what other algebraic properties it must have. The present section is devoted to this question and to some of its relatives.

The complete characterization of polytopal d-tuples is trivial for $d = 2$, and for $d = 3$ it was accomplished by Steinitz (1906):

Theorem (5). The pair (ν_0, ν_1) is polytopal if and only if $\nu_0 = \nu_1 \geq 3$. The triple (ν_0, ν_1, ν_2) is polytopal if and only if $\nu_0 - \nu_1 + \nu_2 = 2$ and $3\nu_0 \leq 2\nu_1 \geq 3\nu_2$.

The general characterization problem appears to be hopelessly complicated, but certain special aspects have been successfully treated. Most of them involve simplicial polytopes in one way or another, where a d-polytope is called *simplicial* provided that each of its facets is incident[8] to exactly d subfacets or, equivalently, provided that every proper face is a simplex. Dually, a *simple* d-polytope is one in which each vertex is incident to exactly d edges. (Of course, every 2-polytope is both simplicial and simple.) A d-tuple $(\nu_0, \cdots, \nu_{d-1})$ will be called *simplicially polytopal* (or merely *simplicial*) provided that it corresponds to a simplicial d-polytope; the *simply polytopal* (or *simple*) d-tuples are similarly defined. Because of the polar correspondence between simple polytopes and simplicial polytopes, it is evident that a d-tuple $(\nu_0, \nu_1, \cdots, \nu_{d-2}, \nu_{d-1})$ is simple if and only if the d-tuple $(\nu_{d-1}, \nu_{d-2}, \cdots, \nu_1, \nu_0)$ is simplicial.[9]

Steinitz's theorem (5) implies that a triple (ν_0, ν_1, ν_2) is simplicial if and only if $\nu_0 - \nu_1 + \nu_2 = 2$ and $2\nu_1 = 3\nu_2$. The simplicial 4-tuples have not been characterized in algebraic terms.

An easy consequence of (5) is the fact that no 3-polytope has exactly seven edges. This has been discussed by Euler (1752), Steinitz (1906), Cairns (1951), and Buck & Starke (1951), and the analogous result for the d-dimensional case was obtained by Klee (1964c):

Theorem (6). For all s and for each d-polytope P which is not a simplex,

$$f_s(P) \geq \left\lceil \frac{d+1}{s+1} \right\rceil + \left\lceil \frac{d-1}{s} \right\rceil.$$

---

[8] Two faces of a polyhedron are said to be *incident* provided that one contains the other.

[9] Suppose that the finite-dimensional real vector space E is self-dual with respect to a bilinear form $\langle \, , \, \rangle$. With each subset X of E, associate the *polar* set $X^\circ = \{y \in E : \sup_{x \in X}\langle x, y \rangle \leq 1\}$. Then, for each of the following three classes of sets, the mapping $X \to X^\circ$ is an involution which carries the class onto itself: polyhedra which include the origin 0; polyhedral cones; polytopes which have 0 as an interior point. Now suppose that P is in the third class, and for each proper face F of P let $F^* = \bigcap_{f \in F}\{y \in P^\circ : \langle f, y \rangle = \sup_{x \in X}\langle x, y \rangle\}$. Then F^* is a proper face of P° and dim F + dim $F^* = d - 1$. Further, $F_1 \subset F_2$ if and only if $F_1^* \supset F_2^*$. Thus, if P is a polytope which has 0 as an interior point, there is an incidence-preserving dimension-complementing correspondence between the proper faces of P and those of its polar P°. The situation for polyhedral cones is similar. For more details, see the references listed under footnote 1.

Further, there is a d-polytope P_d such that

$$f_s(P_d) = \begin{bmatrix} d+1 \\ s+1 \end{bmatrix} + \begin{bmatrix} d-1 \\ s \end{bmatrix}$$

for all s.

Some considerable refinements of this result have been obtained by Grünbaum (1966b).

It is a common occurrence in mathematics that the easiest way of solving a particular problem may involve the solution of a much more general problem. This seems to be especially true of combinatorial problems and of those in which mathematical induction is a natural tool. Along these lines, I feel that some of the unsolved problems concerning polytopes can best be attacked in terms of cell-complexes. A *cell-complex* (or simply a *complex* when there is no danger of ambiguity) is a finite family $\mathcal{K}$ of polytopes (the *cells* of $\mathcal{K}$) such that every face of a cell of $\mathcal{K}$ is itself a cell of $\mathcal{K}$ and such that the intersection of any two cells of $\mathcal{K}$ is a face of both.[10] A complex is called *simplicial* provided that each of its cells is a simplex. If P is a polytope and $\mathcal{B}(P)$ is the set of all faces of P other than P itself, then $\mathcal{B}(P)$ is a complex and will be called the *boundary complex* of P.

For any complex $\mathcal{K}$, let $f_s(\mathcal{K})$ denote the number of s-cells of $\mathcal{K}$. The *dimension* of $\mathcal{K}$ is the largest integer n for which $f_n(\mathcal{K}) > 0$, and the *Euler characteristic* of $\mathcal{K}$ is the integer

$$\chi(\mathcal{K}) = \sum_{s=0}^{\dim \mathcal{K}} (-1)^s f_s(\mathcal{K}).$$

For a cell K of $\mathcal{K}$, the *linked complex* $\mathcal{L}(K, \mathcal{K})$ is the set of all cells C of $\mathcal{K}$ such that C is disjoint from K but some cell of $\mathcal{K}$ has both C and K as faces. An *Eulerian n-manifold* is defined as a simplicial n-complex $\mathfrak{M}^n$ such that for each s-cell K^s of $\mathfrak{M}^n$ the linked complex has the same Euler characteristic as an $(n-s-1)$-sphere, that is, $\chi(\mathcal{L}(K^s, \mathfrak{M}^n)) = 1 - (-1)^{n-s}$. For each simplicial d-polytope P, the boundary complex $\mathcal{B}(P)$ is an Eulerian $(d-1)$-manifold (Klee, 1964a).

In studying the polytopal d-tuples, we natually ask whether they must satisfy some linear relations in addition to the Euler-Poincaré relation and its multiples. The answer is negative for the set of *all* polytopal d-tuples but usefully affirmative for the set of *simplicial* d-tuples. This matter has been considered successively by Dehn (1905), Sommerville (1927), Fieldhouse (1961 and 1962), Klee (1964a), and Grünbaum (1966b). Perles (1966) has studied the related problem for polytopes having a

---

[10] For a discussion of cell-complexes, see Alexandroff & Hopf (1935).

given group of symmetries. Klee's reasoning applied to arbitrary Eulerian manifolds and led to the following results:

Theorem (7). Suppose that M is an Eulerian n-manifold of Euler characteristic χ, and let f_s denote the number of s-cells of M. Then $\chi = 0$ and

$$f_n = \sum_{i=0}^{u-1} (-1)^{u+1+i} \frac{i+1}{u} \begin{bmatrix} n-1-i \\ u-1 \end{bmatrix} f_i$$

if $n = 2u - 1$, and

$$f_n = (-1)^u \begin{bmatrix} n \\ u \end{bmatrix} \chi + 2 \sum_{i=0}^{u-1} (-1)^{u+1+i} \begin{bmatrix} n-1-i \\ u \end{bmatrix} f_i$$

if $n = 2u$.

Fieldhouse and Grünbaum were concerned only with polytopes, but their results can be extended to Eulerian manifolds. There are formulas for f_{n-1} and f_u in terms of $f_{u-1}, \cdots, f_0$ which are similar in form to those of (7), but for $u < r < n - 1$ the situation is more complicated. The following result is due to Fieldhouse (1962) and Grünbaum (1966b).

Theorem (8). Suppose that P is a simplicial d-polytope, and let f_s denote the number of s-faces of P, with $f_{-1} = 1$. Then, for $v = [d/2]$ and $v \leq r < d$, it is true that

$$f_r = \sum_{i=-1}^{d-v-2} \left[\sum_{j=0}^{d-v-1} (-1)^{1+i+j} \begin{bmatrix} d-1-i \\ d-j \end{bmatrix} \begin{bmatrix} j \\ d-1-r \end{bmatrix} \right] f_i$$

$$+ \sum_{i=-1}^{v-1} (-1)^{1+v+i} \begin{bmatrix} d-1-i \\ d-1-r \end{bmatrix} \begin{bmatrix} r-1-i \\ r-v \end{bmatrix} f_i.$$

The formula of (7) is useful in the determination of $\mu(d, n)$, where (for $n > d$) this denotes the maximum number of facets of d-polytopes having n vertices. By polarity, $\mu(d, n)$ is also the maximum number of vertices of d-polytopes having n facets. Determination of the function μ leads also to determination of

$$\lambda(d, n) = \min \{k : \mu(d, k) \geq n\},$$

and, of course, $\lambda(d, n)$ is the *minimum* number of vertices of d-polytopes having n facets. If a compact subset P of $\mathbf{R}^d$ has nonempty interior and is determined by a system of n linear inequalities in d real variables, then P is a d-polytope which may have as many as n facets but which cannot have more, and the vertices of P are the basic solutions of the system of inequalities. Thus, the function μ is important in estimating the size of the computational problem which is involved in solving a system of linear inequalities.

Theorem (9). If $n > d$, then

$$\mu(d, n) \geq \left[\frac{n - \left[\frac{d + 1}{2} \right]}{n - d} \right] + \left[\frac{n - \left[\frac{d + 2}{d} \right]}{n - d} \right],$$

with equality if $d \leq 8$, or $n \leq d + 3$, or $n \geq (d/2)^2 - 1$.

The inequality in (9) is implied by the fact that its righthand side is equal to the number of facets of a cyclic d-polytope having n vertices. This was noted by Motzkin (1957) and by Jacobs & Schell (1959), and a proof was published by Gale (1963).[11] The equality was established by Fieldhouse (1961) for $d \leq 6$, by Gale (1964) for $n \leq d + 3$, and by Klee (1964c) for $n \geq (d/2)^2 - 1$. The gap left by Gale's and Klee's results was filled for $d = 7$ by Grünbaum (1966b) with the aid of a theorem of Kruskal (1963), and the result for $d = 8$ follows from that for $d = 7$ by reasoning of Fieldhouse (1961 and 1962). See also Saaty (1955) for $d = 4$ and Maghout (1963) for a theorem implying that

$$\mu(d, n) \leq \left[\frac{n - d}{2n - 2d - 1} \right] \binom{n}{d}$$

for all $n > d$. The conjecture that equality always holds in (9) will be referred to here as the *MJSG conjecture* [Motzkin (1957), Jacobs & Schell (1959), Gale (1963 and 1964)].

Gale (1964) showed that the MJSG conjecture is implied by a stronger purely combinatorial conjecture, and he established the latter for the situations corresponding to the cases $n = d + 2$ and $n = d + 3$. For $n = d + 3$, the combinatorial result [attributed by Gale to A. Clark but proved much earlier by Kendall & Babington Smith (1940)—see also Kendall (1955)] asserts that the maximum number of cyclic triangles in an oriented complete graph with n vertices is equal to

$$2 \left[\frac{\frac{1}{2}(n + 2)}{3} \right]$$

for even n and to

$$\left[\frac{\frac{1}{2}(n + 3)}{3} \right] + \left[\frac{\frac{1}{2}(n + 1)}{3} \right]$$

for odd n.

---

[11] Gale's proof is only for even d, but the same reasoning applies to odd d.

It was proved by Klee (1964c), and more simply by Eggleston, Grünbaum, & Klee (1965), that if a d-polytope has the maximum number of facets among those d-polytopes which have a given number n of vertices, then it is simplicial,[12] and hence its boundary complex is an Eulerian manifold. This shows that the problem of determining $\mu(d, n)$ is related to the problem of maximizing the function f_{d-1} over the class $\mathsf{E}(d - 1, n)$ of all Eulerian $(d - 1)$-manifolds which have n vertices and Euler characteristic $1 - (-1)^d$. Suppose that $d = 2u + 1$ or $d = 2u$. Using the existence of the linear relations of (8), Klee (1964c) showed that, for all sufficiently large n, each of the functions $f_{d-1}, \cdots, f_u$ attains its maximum on $\mathsf{E}(d - 1, n)$ exactly for those members in which each set of u vertices determines a $(u - 1)$-cell.[13] For f_{d-1} itself, this holds for $n \geq (d/2)^2 - 1$ [as was deduced with the aid of (7)] and is conjectured for all $n > d$.

There are applications of theorem (9) to polytopal graphs (see Grünbaum, 1964a; Klee, 1964d, 1965c, and 1966a; and the next two sections) and to other matters which are relevant to linear inequalities and linear programming (Klee, 1966c). The following consequence of (9) derives its special interest from the fact that when a linear programming problem is put in standard form, its feasible region is the intersection of a flat with a positive orthant. The theorem appears in Klee (1964c) and partially solves a problem of Dantzig (1962).

Theorem (10). Suppose that the polyhedron P in R^n is the intersection of the positive orthant O^n with a flat of deficiency m in R^n, where $m > n - 2\sqrt{n + 1}$ (a restriction which is unnecessary if the MJSG conjecture is correct). Then the number of vertices of P is at most

$$\frac{2n}{m + n} \left\lfloor \frac{\frac{m + n}{2}}{m} \right\rfloor$$

when $n - m$ is even and at most

$$2 \left\lfloor \frac{\frac{m + n - 1}{2}}{m} \right\rfloor$$

when $n - m$ is odd. These upper bounds are attained if and only if P is a simple $(n - m)$-polytope such that, for all $j \leq [(n - m)/2]$, each set of j facets of P intersects in an $(n - m - j)$-face of P.

---

[12] Gale (1964) also made use of this fact but did not publish a proof of it.
[13] I did not know the exact form of (8), so my result was only qualitative in nature. With the aid of (8), some specific bounds can be given. See Grünbaum (1966b).

As the reader has seen from our account, very little progress has been made toward a complete algebraic characterization of the polytopal d-tuples or even of the simplicial or simple d-tuples. The general problem appears to be hopelessly difficult, and it seems that even if characterizations could be found, they would probably be so complex that they would be of little utility or interest. However, the general problem suggests many smaller problems which are of considerable interest. We shall end this section by mentioning three of these which appear to be especially attractive.

First, there is the problem of characterizing the polytopal 4-tuples and simplicial 4-tuples in algebraic terms. It seems that for this relatively small number of dimensions such characterizations might be simple enough for their geometric significance to be comprehensible; then they would be very useful in augmenting our too-limited intuition concerning the structure of 4-polytopes.

The second problem is an old one. We have seen that, of all the d-polytopes which have a given number of vertices, the *maximum* number of facets is achieved only by certain simplicial d-polytopes; the numerical value of the maximum is given by (9) or by the MJSG conjecture. It is natural to ask also for the *minimum* number $\sigma(d, n)$ of facets that is achieved by *simplicial* d-polytopes having n vertices. The solution is evident for $d = 3$, since $f_2(P) = 2f_0(P) - 4$ for every simplicial 3-polytope P. The four-dimensional case (or rather, its polar equivalent) was treated by Brückner (1909), but Steinitz (1922) noted that Brückner's argument was incorrect. It is evident that

$$(*) \qquad \sigma(d, n) \leq (d - 1)n - (d + 1)(d - 2).$$

Indeed, let $P(d, d + 1)$ be a d-simplex, and for $n > d + 1$ let $P(d, n)$ be obtained from $P(d, n - 1)$ by adding a pyramidal cap over one of the facets of $P(d, n - 1)$. Then $P(d, n)$ is a simplicial d-polytope which has n vertices and $(d - 1)n - (d + 1)(d - 2)$ facets. The conjecture is that equality always holds in (*), but this has not been proved, even for $d = 4$.

The third unsolved problem, by far the most interesting from the viewpoint of linear programming, is that of settling the MJSG conjecture. Note that, in the absence of the MJSG conjecture, the restriction $n \geq (d/2)^2 - 1$ of (9) is reflected in the restriction $m > n - 2\sqrt{n + 1}$ of (10).

POLYTOPAL GRAPHS

For $d \leq 3$, the d-polytopal graphs have been characterized in combinatorial terms; this was the second landmark in our discussion. For $d \geq 4$, no combinatorial characterization is known, but some necessary conditions have been established. The first was that of Balinski (1961*b*), who showed that a d-polytopal graph must be d-connected. In order to state a refinement of his theorem, we must introduce some more terminology.

For a graph $\mathcal{G}$ and a nonnegative integer k, let $\sigma_k(\mathcal{G})$ denote the largest integer m such that some set of m nodes of $\mathcal{G}$ is totally separated by some set of k nodes of $\mathcal{G}$, where this means that the two sets are disjoint and that in every path joining any two of the m nodes there appears at least one of the k nodes. Thus, $\mathcal{G}$ is connected if and only if $\sigma_0(\mathcal{G}) \leq 1$; if $\mathcal{G}$ has at least $d + 1$ nodes, it is d-connected if and only if $\sigma_{d-1}(\mathcal{G}) = 1$. Balinski's theorem was extended in the following way by Klee (1964d):

Theorem (11). For $n > d$, let $\mu(d, n)$ denote the maximum number of facets of d-polytopes which have n vertices. Then,

$$\max \ \{\sigma_n(G)\colon G \ \text{a} \ d\text{-polytopal graph}\} = \begin{cases} 1 & \text{if} \ \ n < d \\ 2 & \text{if} \ \ n = d \\ \mu(d, n) & \text{if} \ \ n > d \end{cases}.$$

Balinski's theorem has been generalized in some other directions by Sallee (1966), who studies connectivity properties of the bipartite graphs representing the incidence between r-faces and s-faces of a polytope. Balinski's result corresponds to the case in which $r = 0$ and $s = 1$.

Note that a graph may be d-polytopal for more than one value of d.[14] Such a graph was called *dimensionally ambiguous* by Grünbaum & Motzkin (1963a), who raised some interesting questions which are still unanswered. In particular, must a graph be d-polytopal if it is both m-polytopal and n-polytopal with $m < d < n$? For each d-polytope P with $d \geq 3$, let $\mathcal{K}^*(P)$ denote the graph of a d-polytope which is obtained from P by adding a pyramidal cap over each facet of P in such a way that none of the original edges or vertices of P is disturbed. Klee (1964d) used (9) and (11) to establish the following result, and then Grünbaum (1964a) gave a shorter proof avoiding (11).

Theorem (12). For each $d \geq 3$, there exist d-polytopes P such that the graph $\mathcal{K}^*(P)$ is not dimensionally ambiguous.

For n sufficiently large, the polytope P of (12) may be taken as one which has n vertices and $\mu(d, n)$ facets. Grünbaum (1964a) conjectured that (12) is valid for every choice of the d-polytope P. It would be instructive to determine the smallest integer k such that there is a graph with k nodes which is 5-polytopal but not 4-polytopal. An example of Grünbaum (1964a) shows that $k \leq 11$.

---

[14] For example, the existence of neighborly polytopes shows that when $k \geq 4$, the complete-$(k + 1)$-graph is d-polytopal for $4 \leq d \leq k$.

The other necessary condition for d-polytopality is that of Grünbaum & Motzkin (1963a) as follows:

Theorem (13). Each d-polytopal graph contains a refinement of a complete-$(d + 1)$-graph.

Equivalently, in every d-polytope there exist $d + 1$ vertices and an independent set of $\binom{d + 1}{2}$ paths[15] such that each pair of the $d + 1$ vertices is joined by one of the $\binom{d + 1}{2}$ paths.

As shown by examples of Grünbaum & Motzkin (1963a), the combined conditions of (11) and (13) do not guarantee the d-polytopality of a graph. Thus, further conditions must be sought. Some insight might result from a study of those sequences $(\sigma_d(G), \sigma_{d+1}(G), \cdots, \sigma_{n-2}(G))$ which can be obtained from d-polytopal graphs G having n nodes.

Let us depart briefly from polytopal graphs in order to describe a recent achievement of Grünbaum (1965). Recall the notion of *complex* employed in the preceding section. The *s-skeleton* of a complex is the subcomplex formed by all of its s-cells and their faces. For each complex $\mathcal{K}$, let $|\mathcal{K}|$ denote the union of the cells of $\mathcal{K}$. A complex $\mathcal{C}$ is said to be a *refinement* of a complex $\mathcal{K}$ provided that there exists a homeomorphism h of $|\mathcal{C}|$ onto $|\mathcal{K}|$ such that for each $K \in \mathcal{K}$ there is a subcomplex $\mathcal{C}_K$ of $\mathcal{C}$ for which $h|\mathcal{C}_K| = K$. Grünbaum's theorem and two of its corollaries are as follows:

Theorem (14). For every d-polytope P, the boundary complex $\mathcal{B}(P)$ is a refinement of the boundary complex of a d-simplex;

Corollary (14a). If P is a d-polytope and $0 \leq s \leq d$, the s-skeleton of P contains a refinement of the s-skeleton of a d-simplex;

Corollary (14b). The s-skeleton of a $(2s + 1)$-polytope is not homeomorphic with that of a d-polytope for any $d > 2s + 1$.[16]

Of course, (14a) is an extension of (13).[17] The result (14b) follows from (14a) in conjunction with a theorem of Flores (1933–1934) and van Kampen (1932) to the effect that the s-skeleton of a $(2s + 2)$-simplex cannot be

---

[15] A set of paths is said to be *independent* provided that any vertex common to two of the paths is an endpoint of both.

[16] By the *s-skeleton* of a polytope we mean that of its boundary complex. Here we should refer, more properly, to sets $|S|$ spanned by the skeletons S.

[17] Grünbaum (1965) notes that the proof of (13) given by Grünbaum & Motzkin (1963a) is incomplete. But, on the one hand, the proof can be repaired, and, on the other hand, the theorem itself follows from the different approach of (14).

topologically embedded in $\mathbf{R}^{2s}$. This brings us back to polytopal graphs, for when $s = 1$ the assertion of (14b) is part of the nonambiguity of 3-polytopal graphs noted by Grünbaum & Motzkin (1963a) and discussed in the next paragraph.

Two polytopes P and Q are said to be *combinatorially equivalent* provided that there exists a biunique correspondence between their vertices such that a set of vertices of P determines a face of P if and only if the corresponding vertices of Q determine a face of Q. A similar definition applies to complexes. Grünbaum & Motzkin (1963a) call a polytopal graph $\mathcal{G}$ (1) *dimensionally ambiguous*, (2) *strongly ambiguous*, or (3) *weakly ambiguous* provided that there exist realizations of $\mathcal{G}$ by means of polytopes P and Q such that the following conditions are respectively satisfied:

1. P and Q are of different dimensions;
2. P and Q are of the same dimension but are not combinatorially equivalent;
3. P and Q are combinatorially equivalent (and hence of the same dimension), but for some set of nodes of $\mathcal{G}$ the corresponding vertices of P determine a face of P while the corresponding vertices of Q do not determine a face of Q.

The following was proved by Grünbaum & Motzkin (1963a):

Theorem (15). If a graph $\mathcal{G}$ is d-polytopal for $d \leq 3$, then $\mathcal{G}$ is neither dimensionally, strongly, nor weakly ambiguous.[18]

They asked whether (for larger values of d) the three types of ambiguity are totally independent and gave some relevant examples.[19]

The remainder of this section will be devoted exclusively to 3-polytopal graphs. A path $(x_0, \cdots, x_l)$ in a graph will be called a *simple path* provided that the x_i's are pairwise distinct, and a *simple circuit* provided that $x_l = x_0$ but that otherwise the x_i's are pairwise distinct. The set of all vertices and edges corresponding to a simple circuit will be called a *polygon*. A polygon $\{x_0, \{x_0, x_1\}, x_1, \cdots, x_{l-1}, \{x_{l-1}, x_l\}, x_l\}$ will be called *non-separating* provided that each pair of the remaining vertices of the graph can be joined by a path which misses all of the x_i's and that no two of the x_i's are joined by an edge which does not appear on the polygon.

---

[18] Grünbaum (1966b) has a generalization of part of (15) as follows: If two d-polytopes are such that their $(d-2)$-skeletons are combinatorially equivalent, then the polytopes themselves are combinatorially equivalent.

[19] Grünbaum (1964a) erred in claiming his graphs $\mathcal{K}^*(P)$ to be strongly unambiguous, although they are that within the class of simplicial polytopes. For $n > d \geq 4$, M. Perles (in a private communication) has produced strongly unambiguous d-polytopal graphs having n vertices, but their dimensional ambiguity is undecided.

The following result (16) can be proved by an extension of the reasoning of Steinitz & Rademacher (1934). [see also Lyusternik (1963), Grünbaum & Motzkin (1962) and (1963a), and Grünbaum (1966b)]. It subsumes our second landmark, theorem (2), and also part of theorem (15).

Theorem (16). For a graph G with v nodes and e edges, the following four conditions are equivalent:

1. G is 3-polytopal;
2. G is planar and 3-connected;
3. If $\mathcal{F}$ is the set of all nonseparating polygons in G and f is the cardinality of $\mathcal{F}$, then (a) $v - e + f = 2$, (b) each edge of G belongs to exactly two members of $\mathcal{F}$, and (c) if two members of $\mathcal{F}$ have more than a single node in common, their intersection consists of a single edge and its endpoints;
4. G contains a set $\mathcal{F}$ of polygons which satisfy (a), (b), and (c).

Further, if G is 3-polytopal and $\mathcal{F}$ is as in the fourth condition, then $\mathcal{F}$ is the set of all nonseparating polygons in G. In every realization of G by means of a 3-polytope P, the members of $\mathcal{F}$ correspond to the boundaries of the facets of P.

Motivated by (16), we define a *facet* of a 3-polytopal graph G as a nonseparating polygon of G. There are several useful operations which can be applied to 3-polytopal graphs in order to generate other 3-polytopal graphs. These were discussed in detail by Steinitz & Rademacher (1934), and some of them were treated also by Lyusternik (1963), Tutte (1961), and Grünbaum (1966b). Here we are concerned only with facet-splittings and vertex-splittings of types 1, 2, and 3.

The three types of facet-splitting are depicted in Figure 1. In a *facet-splitting of type 1*, two nonadjacent vertices of a facet F are joined by an edge. The new graph has the same vertices as the old, but it has one more edge, and the facet F in which the new edge is introduced is "split into" (meaning "replaced by") two new facets, each consisting of the

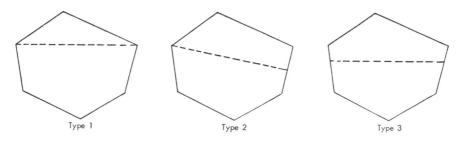

Type 1   Type 2   Type 3

FIGURE 1. Three types of facet-splitting

new edge together with certain edges of F. A *facet-splitting of type 2* involves a facet F, an edge $\{y, z\}$ of F, and a vertex x of F which is not on the edge. By the addition of a new vertex v, the edge $\{y, z\}$ is split into two new edges $\{y, v\}$ and $\{v, z\}$, and the facet F is split into two new facets by the introduction of a new edge $\{x, v\}$. A *facet-splitting of type 3* involves two edges of a facet F. By the addition of new vertices, each of the edges is split into two new edges, and F is split into two new facets by the introduction of an edge joining the two new vertices.

The three types of vertex-splitting are dual to the three types of facet-splitting, both in the duality theory for planar graphs and in the polarity theory for convex polytopes. Consider an edge σ of a 3-polytopal graph G; let x be a vertex of σ, and let F be a facet of G which includes σ. On the one hand, there are two other edges of F which are adjacent to σ in the sense that they have a vertex in common with σ. Dually, there are two other edges incident to x which are adjacent to σ in the sense that they share a facet with σ. The first sort of adjacency is involved in the three types of facet-splitting, for the adjacency relations determine the division of the edges of F between the two new facets into which F is split. Dually, the second sort of adjacency is involved in the three types of vertex-splitting. For a *vertex-splitting of type 1*, the edges incident to x are arranged in a sequence $(\sigma_1, \cdots, \sigma_m, \sigma_{m+1}, \cdots, \sigma_n)$ such that consecutive edges are adjacent, σ_n and σ_1 are adjacent, $m \geq 2$, and $n - m \geq 2$. (Type 1 splitting does not apply to trivalent vertices or triangular facets.) The vertex x is split into two new vertices x' and x'', and a new edge $\{x', x''\}$ is introduced. The vertex x is replaced by x' in its incidence with $\sigma_1, \cdots, \sigma_m$ and by x'' in its incidence with $\sigma_{m+1}, \cdots, \sigma_n$. A vertex-splitting of type 1 is depicted in Figure 2. The other types of vertex-splitting are similarly described.

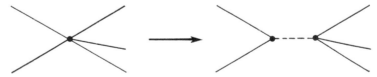

FIGURE 2. Vertex-splitting of type 1

The following theorem is due to Steinitz & Rademacher (1934), and an exposition of their proof was given by Lyusternik (1963):

Theorem (17). A graph $\mathcal{G}$ is 3-polytopal if and only if there is a sequence of graphs $\mathcal{G}_0, \cdots, \mathcal{G}_n$ such that $\mathcal{G}_0$ is isomorphic with $\mathcal{C}_4$ (the graph of a tetrahedron), $\mathcal{G}_n$ is isomorphic with $\mathcal{G}$, and (for $1 \leq i \leq n$) $\mathcal{G}_i$ is obtained from $\mathcal{G}_{i-1}$ by means of a facet-splitting of type 1, 2, or 3.[20]

---

[20] Compare this result with theorem (14).

(The same is true when facet-splitting is replaced by vertex-splitting.) Note that for *simple* 3-polytopal graphs it suffices to employ facet-splitting of type 3. This fact was used by Grace (1965) in writing a computer program for generating combinatorial types of simple 3-polytopes and preparing a list of all those having at most eleven facets.

For $k \geq 3$, let $\mathcal{W}_k$ denote a 3-polytopal graph which looks like a wheel with k spokes; it has $k + 1$ vertices and $2k$ edges and is isomorphic with the graph of a pyramid over a k-gonal base. In particular, $\mathcal{W}_3$ is the same as $\mathcal{C}_4$. The following result is due to Kirkman (1857) and was proved also by Steinitz & Rademacher (1934):

Theorem (18). A graph $\mathcal{G}$ is 3-polytopal if and only if there is a sequence of graphs $\mathcal{G}_0, \cdots, \mathcal{G}_n$ such that $\mathcal{G}_0$ is isomorphic with some $\mathcal{W}_k$, $\mathcal{G}_n$ is isomorphic with $\mathcal{G}$, and (for $1 \leq i \leq n$) $\mathcal{G}_i$ is obtained from $\mathcal{G}_{i-1}$ by means of a facet-splitting of type 1 or a vertex-splitting of type 1.

Alternatively, the third condition of (18) may be replaced by the following: for $1 \leq i \leq n$, $\mathcal{G}_i$ is obtained from $\mathcal{G}_{i-1}$ by dualizing or by means of a facet-splitting of type 1. With this replacement, the theorem was proved by Tutte (1961), to whom it had been communicated by C. J. Bouwkamp. Bouwkamp and his colleagues used the theorem in the tabulation of all 3-polytopal graphs having fewer than 20 edges (Bouwkamp, Duijvestijn, & Medema, 1960). Suppose that G_e is a complete list of (the isomorphism types of) 3-polytopal graphs having exactly e edges. Let G_e' be a list of all graphs which can be obtained from those in G_e by means of a single facet-splitting of type 1, and let G_e'' be a list of the duals of the members of G_e'. Let $G_{e+1} = G_e' \cup G_e''$ when e is even, and let $G_{e+1} = G_e' \cup G_e'' \cup \{\mathcal{W}_{(e+1)/2}\}$ when e is odd. Then G_{e+1} is a complete list of 3-polytopal graphs having exactly $e + 1$ edges.

The three basic problems concerning 3-polytopal graphs may be described as those of *characterization, construction,* and *classification.* The first of these problems is solved by theorem (16) and the second by theorems (17) and (18). The third problem has been studied by many mathematicians, including L. Euler, T. P. Kirkman, A. Cayley, A. F. Möbius, E. Catalan, V. Eberhard, M. Brückner, and E. Steinitz. Yet it remains unsolved and in fact appears to be hopelessly difficult. For a progress review, see Eberhard (1891), Brückner (1900), Steinitz (1922), and Grünbaum (1966b).

Part of the classification problem requires an efficient algorithm for determining whether two given 3-polytopal graphs are isomorphic. A desirable solution would consist in the discovery of a sequence $(\gamma_1, \gamma_2, \cdots)$ of easily computed, isomorphism-invariant, integer-valued functions defined on the class of all 3-polytopal graphs such that two graphs $\mathcal{G}$ and $\mathcal{H}$ are isomorphic if $\gamma_i(\mathcal{G}) = \gamma_i(\mathcal{H})$ for all i. The second part of the problem requires a characterization of the sequences which have the form $(\gamma_1(\mathcal{G}),$ $\gamma_2(\mathcal{G}), \cdots)$ for some 3-polytopal $\mathcal{G}$. Natural candidates for the γ_i's are the functions $\pi_3, \pi_4, \cdots$ and $\varphi_3, \varphi_4, \cdots$, where $\pi_i(\mathcal{G})$ is the number of i-valent vertices of $\mathcal{G}$ and where $\varphi_i(\mathcal{G})$ is the number of i-valent facets (facets with exactly i edges). But, on the one hand, the values of these functions do not suffice to determine the combinatorial type of a 3-polytopal graph, and, on the other hand, it seems exceedingly difficult to characterize the sequences of the form $(\pi_3(\mathcal{G}), \varphi_3(\mathcal{G}), \pi_4(\mathcal{G}), \varphi_4(\mathcal{G}), \cdots)$ for 3-polytopal $\mathcal{G}$.

Euler's theorem leads at once to the well-known fact that

$$\pi_3 + \varphi_3 \geq 8$$

and

$$3\pi_3 + 2\pi_4 + \pi_5 \geq 12 \leq 3\varphi_3 + 2\varphi_4 + \varphi_5.$$

Refinements of these inequalities have been obtained by several authors; for some relatively recent efforts, see Lebesgue (1940) and his references.

Another consequence of Euler's theorem is that if the numbers φ_i are associated with a *simple* 3-polytopal graph, then

$$3\varphi_3 + 2\varphi_4 + \varphi_5 = 12 + \sum_{k \geq 7} (k - 6)\varphi_k.$$

Eberhard (1891) proved that for each sequence $(\varphi_3, \varphi_4, \varphi_5, \varphi_7, \cdots)$ satisfying this condition there exists a value of φ_6 such that the sequence $(\varphi_3, \varphi_4, \varphi_5, \varphi_6, \varphi_7, \cdots)$ is associated with some simple 3-polytopal graph. His proof was very long and complicated, but an understandable proof has been found by Grünbaum (1966b).

A remark of Eberhard (1891) suggested that in a simplicial 3-polytope in which the valence of each vertex is a multiple of 3, the total number of vertices should be even. A partial result was obtained by Grünbaum & Motzkin (1963b), and more recently the conjecture of Eberhard was proved in sharpened form by Motzkin (1964), Grünbaum (1964b), and Kotzig (1965). A recent result of Grünbaum (1966b) asserts that if a simplicial 3-polytope has exactly two vertices of odd valence, then these two vertices cannot be adjacent.

It would be of great interest to know the number of different isomorphism-types of the 3-polytopal graphs having a given number of edges. Results related to this problem have been obtained by Tutte (1963a). For some additional results which are related to 3-polytopal graphs, see W. G. Brown (1963), Brown & Tutte (1964), Dirac (1961 and 1963), Mullin (1964 and 1965), Rademacher (1965), Tutte (1960b, 1962a, 1962b, 1962c, and 1963b), Ungar (1963), and other papers cited in these references or in the next section.

We end this section with two unsolved problems on 3-polytopal graphs which seem to be of interest in connection with linear programming. By an *ordered graph* we mean a graph together with an antisymmetric total ordering of its nodes. One problem is to find a combinatorial characterization of the ordered 3-polytopal graphs which can be realized by means of a 3-polytope in R^3 in such a way that the given ordering of the nodes corresponds to the ordering of the vertices induced by some linear form on R^3. There is a similar unsolved problem which concerns a graph with a consistent system of *local orderings*, where a local ordering involves only a certain vertex and all those adjacent to it. Settling these problems would amount to describing, in combinatorial terms, the structures which underlie the search processes employed in solving three-dimensional linear programming problems by certain variants of the simplex method. Of course, the same questions may be posed for ordered d-polytopal graphs, but this seems premature, since the d-polytopal graphs themselves have not been characterized in combinatorial terms.

PATHS IN POLYTOPES

Of the various sections in this report, the present section is the most technical in nature and at the same time the most closely related to linear programming. We consider several functions of polytopes, each defined in terms of the lengths of certain paths. Some of these are directly related to various search processes which might be employed in solving a system of linear inequalities or in finding an optimal solution. Others are not so immediately related to practical problems but are included for their geometric interest. For each such function g, we should like to have sharp upper and lower bounds for the possible values of $g(P)$ in terms of the dimension of the polytope P and the number of vertices or facets of P. Generally speaking, the bounds involving the number of vertices are satisfactory, while those involving the number of facets are not. This is unfortunate, for the latter bounds are more directly related to linear programming. In any case, we shall report what is known and hope that interested readers will be able to fill some of the many gaps.

Most of the results reported in the previous sections can be modified so as to apply to pointed polyhedra as well as to polytopes.[21] Nevertheless, the discussion has been restricted to polytopes because that case is geometrically the most appealing. The same restriction applies in much of the present section, though it should be emphasized that not only polytopes but in fact all pointed polyhedra are of natural interest in connection with linear programming, where there is, in general, no guarantee that

---

[21] For an example, see footnote 4.

the feasible region is bounded. The restriction is made here for the sake of brevity and because the situation for polytopes is often a good indication of that for pointed polyhedra, even though quantitative details may be different in the two cases. In several of the geometric extremum problems which come from linear programming and which are initially formulated for a class of pointed polyhedra, there is an immediate reduction to a class of polytopes.[22]

Since we intend to present a large number of facts which are somewhat similar in nature, it will be worthwhile to employ a systematic notation. Let $\mathcal{P}_d$ denote the class of all d-polytopes, and for each $P \,\varepsilon\, \mathcal{P}_d$ let $v(P) = f_0(P)$ and $f(P) = f_{d-1}(P)$, the respective numbers of vertices and of facets of P. For each real-valued function g defined on $\mathcal{P}_d$ and for each $n > d$, let

$$m_v(g, d, n) = \inf \{g(P): P \,\varepsilon\, \mathcal{P}_d \ \text{with} \ v(P) = n\}$$

and

$$M_v(g, d, n) = \sup \{g(P): P \,\varepsilon\, \mathcal{P}_d \ \text{with} \ v(P) = n\}.$$

The numbers $m_f(g, d, n)$ and $M_f(g, d, n)$ are similarly defined. Thus, m stands for "minimum" and M for "maximum," and the subscripts v or f tell whether the polytopes under consideration are restricted to having n vertices or n facets. When they are used as superscripts, v and f indicate that attention is restricted to polytopes whose vertices or facets are of the simplest sort. Thus, $\mathcal{P}_d^v$ and $\mathcal{P}_d^f$ are the subclasses of $\mathcal{P}_d$ consisting, respectively, of the d-polytopes which are simple and those which are simplicial. Further, we define

$$m_v^v(g, d, n) = \inf \{g(P): P \,\varepsilon\, \mathcal{P}_d^v \ \text{with} \ v(P) = n\},$$

$$M_f^v(g, d, n) = \sup \{g(P): P \,\varepsilon\, \mathcal{P}_d^v \ \text{with} \ f(P) = n\},$$

etc.[23] The notation is complicated, but that seems inevitable, for in connection with each triple (g, d, n) we are concerned with twelve possibly different numbers. Note the obvious relations

$$m_v \leq \begin{matrix} m_v^v \leq M_v^v \\ m_v^f \leq M_v^f \end{matrix} \leq M_v,$$

and similarly with the subscript f.[24]

---

[22] As an example, we mention the problem of determining the maximum number $\mu'(d, n)$ of vertices of pointed d-polyhedra having n facets. A theorem of Klee (1964c) asserts that if P is an unbounded pointed d-polyhedron with n facets, then $n \geq d$, and if $n > d$, there exists a d-polytope which also has n facets but which has more vertices than P. Hence, $\mu'(d, d) = 1$ and $\mu'(d, n) = \mu(d, n)$ for $n > d$.

[23] Here some fussiness is necessary because of the fact that some of the classes may be empty. For example, there is no simple 3-polytope having an odd number of vertices. All statements about the numbers m_v^v, M_f^v, etc., are made under the tacit assumption that the relevant classes are nonempty.

[24] As above, it is assumed that the relevant classes are nonempty.

Of special interest for linear programming are the numbers which have f as subscript and which have either no superscript or v as superscript. The point is that in a general linear programming problem, we have the most direct information about the number of facets of the feasible region. Also, if the feasible region is bounded, then a slight perturbation of the constraints will produce a closely related problem in which the feasible region is a simple polytope. On the other hand, the twelve numbers are interrelated in various ways and are all of immediate geometric significance, so we feel that they are all worth studying, at least for the choices of g considered here.

Recall that a *path of length l* in a polyhedron P is a sequence $(x_0, x_1, \cdots, x_l)$ of consecutively adjacent vertices of P. A path is called a *simple path* provided that no vertex is repeated, and it is a *simple circuit* provided that $l \geq 3$ and $x_l = x_0$ but that there is no other repetition among the x_i's. A *Hamiltonian path* or *Hamiltonian circuit* in P is a simple path or simple circuit which runs through all the vertices of P. The Hamiltonian circuits were the first paths on polytopes to be considered seriously in the literature, first in connection with the so-called *Hamiltonian game* of finding such circuits for the regular dodecahedron (see Ball, 1944) and later in connection with the conjecture of Tait (1884) that every simple 3-polytope admits a Hamiltonian circuit. Tait's conjecture implies the four-color conjecture,[25] but a counterexample to the former was finally given by Tutte (1946 and 1960*a*). Balinski (1961*a*) asked whether every simple 3-polytope admits a Hamiltonian path, and the example of Tutte (1946) was employed independently by Grünbaum & Motzkin (1962) and T. A. Brown (1960) to provide a negative answer.

A difficult problem, of interest in connection with a classification scheme for organic compounds (see Lederberg, 1965), is that of determining the

[25] If all the vertices of a simple 3-polytope are arranged in a simple circuit, then the facets which contact the circuit on one side may be colored alternately 1 and 2 while those which contact the circuit on the other side may be colored alternately 3 and 4. This results in coloring all the facets in such a way that two facets which share an edge never have the same color.

Chuard (1932*a* and 1932*b*) claimed to prove Tait's conjecture, but his claim was disputed by Pannwitz (1932), and, of course, the matter was settled by Tutte (1946).

In order to describe another interesting connection between 3-polytopes and the four-color problem, we introduce some definitions. The *valence of a vertex* in a polytope (or of a node in a graph) is the number of edges incident to it; dually, the *valence of a facet* in a polytope is the number of subfacets incident to it. By *truncation* of a 3-polytope P we mean the operation of intersecting P with a closed halfspace Q such that Q omits a single vertex x of P but that all other vertices of P are interior to Q. The resulting intersection is a 3-polytope in which the vertex x has been replaced by a facet whose valence is equal to the valence of x in P. Hadwiger (1957) noted that the following assertion is equivalent to the four-color conjecture: For each 3-polytope P, there exists a finite sequence of truncations leading to a 3-polytope in which each facet has a valence divisible by 3.

smallest possible number n of vertices for a 3-polytope not admitting a Hamiltonian circuit. The example of Tutte (1946), showing that $n \leq 46$, has been modified by D. Barnette and S. Lederberg to show $n \leq 38$.

For each polytope P, let $\lambda(P)$ denote the length of the longest simple path in P. Then the following results are known:

$$(19) \qquad\qquad c_d \log n < m_v^v(\lambda, d, n) < 2n^a$$

for some constant $c_d > 0$ (depending only on d) and some constant $a < 1$ (independent of d and n—in particular, for $a = 1 - 2^{-19}$);

$$(20) \qquad\qquad m_v^f(\lambda, d, n) < 3dn^{\log 2/\log d};$$

$$(21) \qquad\qquad m_v(\lambda, 3, n) < (2n + 13)/3;$$

$$(22) \qquad M_v(\lambda, d, n) = M_v^f(\lambda, d, n) = n - 1;$$

$$(23) \qquad (d - 1)\left[\frac{n - 2}{d - 1}\right] + 1 \leq M_v^v(\lambda, d, n) \leq n - 1,$$

with equality throughout if $d \leq 3$ or $n \equiv 2 \bmod (d - 1)$;

$$(24) \qquad \left[\frac{n - \left[\frac{d+1}{2}\right]}{n - d}\right] + \left[\frac{n - \left[\frac{d+2}{2}\right]}{n - d}\right] - 1 \leq M_f^v(\lambda, d, n)$$

$$\leq M_f(\lambda, d, n) \leq \mu(d, n) - 1,$$

with equality throughout if $d \leq 8$, or $n \leq d + 3$, or $n \geq (d/2)^2 - 1$, or the MJSG conjecture is true;

$$(25) \qquad\qquad \left[\frac{n - 2}{d - 1}\right] + d - 1 \leq M_f^f(\lambda, d, n),$$

with equality if $d \leq 3$.

The two inequalities of (19) are due to Dirac (1952) and to Grünbaum & Motzkin (1962), respectively; (20) is due to Moon & Moser (1963), and (21) to T. A. Brown (1960). Grünbaum & Motzkin (1962) contains a number of conjectures and unsolved problems in this general area, some of which were settled by T. A. Brown (1960) and Klee (1964b). The results (22) through (25), due to Klee (1966a), are based on the observation that both the cyclic d-polytopes and their polars admit Hamiltonian circuits. The proof for the polars employs the combinatorial description by Gale (1963) of the facets of cyclic polytopes. The literature apparently contains no direct information on the numbers m_f, m_f^v, and m_f^f, though weak bounds may be obtained from (19) through (21) in conjunction with (9).

It would be interesting to have a practical criterion for determining when a d-polytope admits a Hamiltonian path, or at least to widen the class of polytopes known to admit such paths. For $d = 3$, the corresponding problem for Hamiltonian circuits was considered by Whitney (1931) and Tutte (1956). Whitney proved that if a simplicial 3-polytope P is such that every triangle in its 1-skeleton comes from a facet of P, then P admits a Hamiltonian circuit. Tutte's improvement of this result implies, in particular, that every 4-connected planar graph admits a Hamiltonian circuit. For abstract graphs, the literature contains a number of papers on longest simple paths or circuits and on the existence of Hamiltonian paths or circuits; however, polytopal graphs form such a special subclass that application of general theorems to them usually does not yield satisfactory results.

The simplex method of linear programming is designed primarily to find a particular vertex of a polyhedron—one which optimizes the linear objective function. However, the basic iterative step of the simplex method has been used by Balinski (1961*a*) in an algorithm for finding *all* the vertices of a polyhedron. In connection with this and with the problem of designing other algorithms for the same purpose (and also with measuring the relative efficiency of such algorithms), it would be of interest to study the following two functions of a polytope P:

(a) The length of the shortest path which includes all the vertices of P;

(b) The smallest number of simple paths which suffice to cover all the vertices of P.

For partial results, conjectures, and additional unsolved problems, see T. A. Brown (1961), Grünbaum & Motzkin (1962), and Barnette (1966*a*). Barnette's main tool is his theorem asserting that on every 3-polytope P there is a tree of maximum valence three which is formed from all of the vertices and some of the edges of P.

The *distance* between two vertices of a polyhedron P is defined as the length of the shortest path joining them, and the *diameter* $\delta(P)$ as the maximum of the distances between vertices of P. These notions are of interest in connection with linear programming, especially for the problem of determining lower bounds for the number of iterations which may be required in variants of the simplex method.[26] The following results are known:

$$(26) \qquad M_v(\delta, d, n) = M'_v(\delta, d, n) = \left[\frac{n - 2}{d}\right] + 1;$$

---

[26] If P is the feasible region of a linear programming problem, then (at least for the "worst" choice of the objective function and the initial vertex) *no* variant of the simplex method can guarantee a solution in fewer than $\delta(P)$ iterations. In connection with good choices of the initial vertex, it might be worthwhile to study the *radius* $\rho(P)$ of P, where $\rho(P) = \min_x \max_y \text{dist}(x, y)$, x and y ranging independently over the vertices of P. Note that $2\rho(P) \geq \delta(P)$. A conjecture on radii has been formulated by Jucovič & Moon (1965).

$$(27) \qquad M_v^v(\delta, d, n) \geq (d-1)\left[\frac{n-2}{2^d-2}\right] + 1 \quad \text{for} \quad n \geq 2^d;$$

$$(28) \qquad M_v^v(\delta, d, n) = M_v(\delta, d, n) \quad \text{for} \quad d \leq 3;$$

$$(29) \qquad M_f(\delta, d, n) = M_f^v(\delta, d, n) \geq (d-1)\left[\frac{n}{d}\right] - d + 2;$$

$$(30) \qquad M_f(\delta, d, n) = \left[\frac{(d-1)n}{d}\right] - d + 2 \quad \text{if} \quad d \leq 3 \quad \text{or} \quad n \leq d+4;$$

$$(31) \qquad M_f^f(\delta, d, n) \geq \left[\frac{n-2d}{2^d-2}\right] + 2.$$

One of the equalities of (26) was noted by Grünbaum & Motzkin (1962), who used the fact that the d-polytopal graphs are d-connected. The other results are due to Klee (1964b). The literature is apparently silent concerning the numbers $m_f^v(\delta, d, n)$ and $m_v^v(\delta, d, n)$. Note, however, that the cyclic d-polytopes are simplicial and (being neighborly) are of diameter 1 when $d \geq 4$. Hence, the following are true:

$$(32) \qquad m_v(\delta, d, n) = m_v^f(\delta, d, n) = 1 \quad \text{if} \quad d \geq 4;$$

$$(33) \qquad m_f(\delta, d, n) = m_f^f(\delta, d, n) = 1$$

for infinitely many values of n if $d \geq 4$.

Theorems (29) and (30) are related to a well-known conjecture of W. M. Hirsch and to a recent paper of Klee & Walkup (1965). In order to discuss these, we introduce a shorter notation, denoting $M_f(\delta, d, n)$ by $\Delta_b(d, n)$ and the corresponding maximum for polyhedra by $\Delta(d, n)$. That is, $\Delta(d, n)$ [resp. $\Delta_b(d, n)$] is the maximum diameter of d-polyhedra [resp. d-polytopes] having n facets. As stated by Dantzig (1963, pp. 160 and 168), the *Hirsch conjecture* asserts that $\Delta(d, n) \leq n - d$, while the *bounded Hirsch conjecture* asserts that $\Delta_b(d, n) \leq n - d$. (It is known that $\Delta(d, n) \geq n - d$ and $\Delta_b(d, n) \geq n - d$ for $n \leq 2d$.) Klee and Walkup show that $\Delta(d, 2d) = \Delta(d+k, 2d+k)$ and $\Delta_b(d, 2d) = \Delta_b(d+k, 2d+k)$ for all nonnegative k, and this justifies a special interest in the numbers $\Delta(d, 2d)$ and $\Delta_b(d, 2d)$ (see also Dantzig, 1962 and 1964). The assertions that $\Delta(d, 2d) = d$ and $\Delta_b(d, 2d) = d$ are known, respectively, as the *d-step conjecture* and the *bounded d-step conjecture*.

Klee and Walkup show that $\Delta_b(4, 9) = \Delta_b(5, 10) = 5$. Thus, the bounded d-step conjecture is correct for $d \leq 5$, and the exact value of $\Delta_b(d, n)$ is known when $d \leq 3$ and also when $n \leq d + 5$. No other exact values of $\Delta_b(d, n)$ are known, and little is known about the asymptotic behavior of $\Delta_b(4, n)$ or $\Delta_b(n, 2n)$ as $n \to \infty$.

Also proved by Klee & Walkup (1965) is the fact that $\Delta(4, 8) = 5$, and in fact $\Delta(d, 2d) \geq d + [d/4]$, so not only does the d-step conjecture fail for $d = 4$ but also the excess of the true value over the conjectured value tends to infinity with d. On the other hand, the Hirsch conjecture is correct for $d \leq 3$, as was proved by Klee (1965c and 1966a) with the aid of W_v paths.

A path $(x_0, \cdots, x_l)$ on a polyhedron P is called a W_v *path* provided that whenever F is a facet of P, $0 \leq i < j < k \leq l$, and x_i, $x_k \, \varepsilon \, F$, then also $x_j \, \varepsilon \, F$. It is easily seen that in a d-polyhedron having n facets, each W_v path is of length at most $n - d$. Hence, the fact that $\Delta(3, n) = n - 3$ is implied by the theorem of Klee (1966a), asserting that any two vertices of a 3-polyhedron can be joined by a W_v path. Refinements of this result appear in Klee (1965c) and Barnette (1966b). Klee & Walkup (1965) prove the equivalence, though not on a dimension-for-dimension basis, of the bounded Hirsch conjecture, the bounded d-step conjecture, and the conjecture of Wolfe and Klee to the effect that any two vertices of a polytope can be joined by a W_v path.

Finally, let us consider the three variants of the simplex method which correspond to the following rules for progressing from one vertex of the feasible region to the next in an attempt to maximize a linear objective function φ:

Rule 1. From the vertex v, survey the adjacent vertices until a vertex w is found for which $\varphi(v) < \varphi(w)$; then move to w and continue the process;

Rule 2. From the vertex v, survey all of the adjacent vertices in order to find one, say w, at which φ has the greatest value; then move to w and continue the process;

Rule 3. From the vertex v, survey all of the adjacent vertices in order to find one, say w, for which the slope $(\varphi(w) - \varphi(v))/||w - v||$ has the greatest value; then move to w and continue the process.[27]

For each pointed polyhedron P, let $\eta(P)$, $\sigma(P)$, and $\zeta(P)$ denote the maximum number of iterations required to solve a linear programming problem with P as feasible region by use of rules 1, 2, and 3, respectively.[28] The numbers $\eta(P)$, $\sigma(P)$, and $\zeta(P)$ are called, respectively, the *height*, the *strict height*, and the *steep height* of P.

The following results were obtained by Klee (1965a), where each of the assertions involving η remains valid when η is replaced by ζ:

$$(34) \qquad M_v(\eta, d, n) = M_v^f(\eta, d, n) = n - 1;$$

$$(35) \qquad M_v^v(\eta, d, n) \geq (d - 1)\left[\frac{n - 2}{d - 1}\right] + 1,$$

---

[27] Rule 3 depends on the choice of a norm for the containing space, but the results reported here are independent of that choice.

[28] The maximum is taken over all possible choices of the linear objective function φ.

with equality if $d \leq 3$ or $n \equiv 2 \bmod (d - 1)$;

(36) $\qquad M_f(\eta, d, n) \geq M_f^v(\eta, d, n) \geq (d - 1)(n - d) + 1,$

with equality if $d \leq 3$;

(37) $\qquad M_f^f(\eta, d, n) \geq \left[\dfrac{n - 2}{d - 1}\right] + d - 1,$

with equality if $d \leq 3$;

(38) $\qquad M_v(\sigma, d, n) = M_v^f(\sigma, d, n) = n - d;$

(39) $\qquad 2\left[\dfrac{n - 2}{d - 1}\right] \leq M_v^v(\sigma, d, n) \quad \text{if} \quad d \geq 4;$

(40) $\qquad M_v^v(\sigma, d, n) \leq \left[\dfrac{d(n - 2)}{2(d - 1)}\right],$

with equality if $d \leq 3$;

(41) $\qquad M_f(\sigma, d, n) = M_f^v(\sigma, d, n) \geq 2(n - d) - 1$

if $d \geq 4$;

(42) $\qquad M_f(\sigma, 3, n) = M_f^v(\sigma, 3, n) = \left[\dfrac{3n - 1}{2}\right] - 4;$

(43) $\qquad M_f^f(\sigma, d, n) \geq \left[\dfrac{n - 2}{d - 1}\right],$

with equality if $d \leq 3$.

The corresponding numbers $m_v, \cdots, m_f^f$ have not been studied.

We have now reported a number of facts concerning paths in polytopes and have raised, both explicitly and implicitly, a number of unsolved problems. Although these facts and problems are all of geometric interest, they vary widely in the extent of their connections with linear programming. For some readers, the connections themselves may have been obscured by our geometric language. Thus, we shall add a few words as an aid to perspective.

Although a linear programming problem in its most immediate form may have many constraints which are inequalities, it is customary, by the use of slack variables, to transform the problem into a standard form in which all of the constraints are equalities, except, of course, for the requirement that the variables shall all be nonnegative.[29] If the standard form has n variables, the feasible region is the intersection of a flat in $\mathbf{R}^n$ (defined by the equality constraints) with the positive orthant $\mathbf{O}^n$ (defined

---

[29] See, for example, Dantzig (1963). Note, however, that we have spoken in terms of maximizing the objective function, whereas in Dantzig's standard form it is to be minimized. This difference is immaterial.

by the nonnegativity constraints). Then, obviously, the feasible region is a pointed polyhedron. It is important to characterize the pointed polyhedra which can be realized in this way and thus to show how our geometric results can be interpreted for linear programming.

The following theorem of Klee (1964c) extends an earlier result of Davis (1952 and 1953):

Theorem (44). Suppose that d, j, and n are integers with $1 \leq d \leq n$ and $0 \leq j$. Then, for each pointed d-polyhedron P, the following two assertions are equivalent:

(a) P is affinely equivalent to the intersection of the n-dimensional positive orthant O^n with some $(d + j)$-flat in R^n;

(b) P has at most $n - j - 1$ facets or at most n facets when $j = 0$.

With the aid of (44), the results (36), (41), and (42) can easily be translated into linear programming terms. They correspond to pivot rules which are sometimes used in practice but not to Dantzig's original pivot rule, which is the one most commonly employed. Dantzig's rule is algebraically the most expedient and has a simple geometric interpretation as a maximum gradient method (Dantzig, 1963, chap. 7, and Klee, 1965b). However, the gradient is maximized with respect to the space of nonbasic variables, and since this space changes from one iteration to the next, the method is geometrically too complex for easy visualization. Klee (1965b) has given a coordinate-free treatment of Dantzig's pivot rule for the simplex algorithm and has introduced the notion of a *simplex* φ-*path* analogous to the types of φ-paths[30] considered above. That is, a simplex φ-path on a polyhedron is one which is produced by the application of Dantzig's pivot rule in a linear programming problem which has the polyhedron as its feasible region. He has constructed simple d-polytopes with n facets in which there are simplex φ-paths of length $(d-1)(n-d)+1$ passing through *all* the vertices of the polytope. As interpreted for some of the more standard forms of linear programming problems, this disproves various conjectures concerning the maximum number of iterations which may be required by the usual pivot rule (see Saaty, 1963). However, the true maximum has not been determined. In connection with this problem, see also Dantzig (1962, 1963, and 1964), Goldman & Kleinman (1964), and Quandt & Kuhn (1964). Another relevant paper is Fillipovich & Kozlov (1963), which I have not seen.

The relative advantages of various forms of the simplex method have been studied experimentally by Kuhn & Quandt (1963), Quandt & Kuhn (1962 and 1964), and Wolfe & Cutler (1963). In this report we have described the beginnings of a geometric study of the same question. It seems

---

[30] A path $(x_0, x_1, \cdots, x_l)$ is called a φ-*path* provided that $\varphi(x_0) < \varphi(x_1) < \cdots < \varphi(x_l)$. A *strict* φ-*path* $(x_0, \cdots, x_l)$ is one which is formed according to rule 2, that is, $\varphi(x_i) = \max \{\varphi(y) : y$ a vertex of P adjacent to $x_{i-1}\}$ for $1 \leq i \leq l$.

clear that much more effort will be required on both fronts before any definite conclusions can be reached. I would like to recommend rule 2 of the present section[31] for special attention because of its good behavior, both in my studies and in those of Kuhn and Quandt, and because of its affine invariance, which makes for easier theoretical investigation.

In closing this section, we shall compare certain of the numbers which were encountered earlier. Suppose that P is a d-polytope which has n facets and that φ is a linear form on the containing space. We have seen that if P and φ are not restricted in any other way, then one or more (but not all) of the following statements may be true:

$$P \text{ has } \left[\begin{array}{c} n - \left[\dfrac{d+1}{2}\right] \\ n - d \end{array} \right] + \left[\begin{array}{c} n - \left[\dfrac{d+2}{2}\right] \\ n - d \end{array} \right] \text{ vertices;}$$

P admits a simple path of length

$$\left[\begin{array}{c} n - \left[\dfrac{d+1}{2}\right] \\ n - d \end{array} \right] + \left[\begin{array}{c} n - \left[\dfrac{d+2}{2}\right] \\ n - d \end{array} \right] - 1;$$

P admits a φ-path of length $(d-1)(n-d)+1$;
P admits a simplex φ-path of length $(d-1)(n-d)+1$;
P admits a strict φ-path of length $2(n-d)-1$ if $d \geq 4$ and of length $\left[\dfrac{3n-1}{2}\right] - 4$ if $d = 3$.

In each case, it is conjectured that no larger number can be attained. In each case, this has been proved for $d = 3$, and perhaps under other restrictions on d or n, but it has not been completely settled. These are surely some of the most interesting and most important of the many unsolved problems which have been mentioned in this report.

ADDITIONAL RESULTS AND PROBLEMS

The topics to be treated in this section are all related to our general subject, but they have little in common with each other. We mention first the problem of degeneracy and cycling in linear programming, the geometric aspects of which have not yet been fully explored. As the simplex method is carried out in practice, a vertex x of the d-polyhedral feasible region is specified in terms of d hyperplanes whose intersection is x, each

---

[31] At each iteration, this rule calls for maximum absolute improvement in the objective function.

hyperplane corresponding to one of the linear constraints which define the feasible region. Progressing to the next vertex corresponds to replacing one of these hyperplanes by a different one. This replacement leads to a new vertex if x lies on only d of the constraint hyperplanes, but otherwise it may lead merely to a new presentation of the same vertex x. Problems in which this occurs are said to be *degenerate*. They may entail *cycling*, meaning that pivot rules which are adequate when each vertex lies on exactly d constraint hyperplanes may otherwise lead to a self-repeating sequence of d-tuples of hyperplanes which never arrives at the desired vertex. Of course, the constraints may be perturbed slightly so as to avoid degeneracy, but this is unnecessary in view of various refined pivot rules which have been shown to avoid cycling. Each of these rules must correspond to some fact in the affine geometry or metric geometry of polyhedra. This is especially evident for the recent rule of Azpeitia & Dickinson (1964); in other cases, it has not been made so explicit. Other references are Beale (1955), Dantzig (1963), Hoffman (1953), and Wolfe (1962 and 1963). See also the recent thesis of Ollmert at the University of the Saar.

Among the many practical problems which have been attacked by means of linear programming, we mention the *transportation problem* and the *traveling salesman problem*.

The first is especially simple in structure and has been studied in great detail. In particular, sharp upper bounds have been obtained for the number of vertices of the feasible region and for the number of iterations required to reach an optimal solution. See Demuth (1961), Doig (1963), Simmonard & Hadley (1959), and Zhu (1963).

The traveling salesman problem is especially complicated in structure and offers many challenges, including some on the facial structure of certain polytopes. The polytopes associated with this problem have been studied by Heller (1955a, 1955b, and 1956), Kuhn (1955), Motzkin (1956), and Norman (1955). See Dantzig (1962 and 1964) for a statement of some unsolved problems in this area.[32]

Gale (1963) proved that if d is even and $d < n < d + 4$, then every $[d/2]$-neighborly d-polytope is combinatorially equivalent to a cyclic d-polytope. On the other hand, Grünbaum (1966b) shows that among the 4-polytopes with eight vertices which are polar to the polytopes studied by Brückner (1909), there are some which are 2-neighborly but which are not combinatorially equivalent to cyclic polytopes. The classification problem for 2-neighborly 4-polytopes is described by Grünbaum as "hopelessly difficult."

---

[32] For a general survey of the traveling salesman problem, see paper 8.

The following is established by Grünbaum (1966b):

Theorem (45). If $m = [d/2]$ and P is an m-neighborly simplicial d-polytope which has n vertices, then

$$f_s(P) = \frac{n - (d - 2m)(n - s - 2)}{n - s - 1} \sum_{i=0}^{m} \begin{bmatrix} n - 1 - i \\ s + 1 - i \end{bmatrix} \begin{pmatrix} n - s - 1 \\ d - 2m - 1 - s + 2i \end{pmatrix}$$

for $0 \le s \le d - 1$.

The inductive proof of the existence of neighborly polytopes given by Gale (1956) is longer than the proofs of Carathéodory (1911) and Gale (1963) by means of cyclic polytopes, but it is of independent interest. Let S^k denote the unit sphere $\{x : \|x\| = 1\}$ in Euclidean $(k + 1)$-space. A family of subsets of S^k is said to be a j-*fold covering* provided that each point of S^k lies in at least j of the sets. Gale (1956) proved the following:

Theorem (46). Every j-fold covering of S^k by $k + 2j$ open hemispheres can be extended to a $(j + 1)$-fold covering of S^k by $k + 2j + 2$ open hemispheres;

Corollary (46a). For each pair of positive integers j and k, S^k admits a j-fold covering by $k + 2j$ open hemispheres;

Corollary (46b). For each pair of positive integers j and k, there is a set of $k + 2j$ points in S^k such that each open hemisphere contains at least j of the points.

The result (46b) is equivalent to (46a) by means of polarity, and (46b) is used to show that, for each $n > 2m$, there are m-neighborly $(2m)$-polytopes having n vertices. For a reason related to this construction, Gale conjectures that "... the likelihood of getting polyhedra every m of whose vertices are neighbors increases rapidly with the dimension of the space .... Thus we might expect that finding every pair of points of P neighbors would be the expected rather than the exceptional case [Gale, 1956, p. 262]." A relevant calculation is that of Wendel (1962), who showed that if n points are randomly distributed in S^{d-1}, the n distributions being uniform and independent, and if $p_{d,n}$ denotes the probability that all n of the points lie in a hemisphere, then

$$p_{d,n} = 2^{1-n} \sum_{i=0}^{d-1} \binom{n - 1}{i}.$$

Let I^d denote the set of all points of $\mathbf{R}^d$ which have exclusively integral coordinates. A polytope in $\mathbf{R}^d$ will be called an *integral polytope* provided that all of its vertices lie in I^d. When X is a bounded subset of $\mathbf{R}^d$, the *associated integral polytope* is defined as the convex hull of the intersection $X \cap I^d$. As was noted by Grünbaum, the proof of (2) shows that every

3-polytope is combinatorially equivalent to an integral 3-polytope. However, we do not know of a simple direct proof of this fact, and we do not know whether the statement is true for d-polytopes with $d > 3$.[33] A study of this question would be of interest in connection with integer programming,[34] as would the following problem: Which d-polytopes are combinatorially equivalent to integral d-polytopes associated with d-polytopes of given combinatorial type? Equivalently, what can be said about the combinatorial type of a d-polytope P if it is known only that P is the integral polytope associated with a d-polytope of given combinatorial type? Nothing can be said if $d = 2$, for whenever $m \geq 3 \leq n$ there exists a convex m-gon in R^2 whose associated integral polytope is a convex n-gon. (This was pointed out to me by P. Renz.)

---

[33] Added in proof. In a private communication, M. Perles has described an 8-polytope with 12 vertices which is not combinatorially equivalent to any integral polytope.

[34] For a general survey of integer programming, see paper 14 and also Balinski (1965).

ACKNOWLEDGMENTS

I am indebted to George Dantzig, Theodore Motzkin, and Philip Wolfe for some helpful comments and to Branko Grünbaum for many long and stimulating conversations on the subjects treated in this report.

REFERENCES

ALEXANDROFF, P., and H. HOPF. 1935. Topologie, vol. I. Berlin: Springer.

AZPEITIA, A. G., and D. J. DICKINSON. 1964. A decision rule in the simplex method that avoids cycling. Numer. Math., 6:329–31.

BALINSKI, M. L. 1961a. An algorithm for finding all vertices of convex polyhedral sets. J. Soc. Indust. Appl. Math., 9:72–88.

———. 1961b. On the graph structure of convex polyhedra in n-space. Pacific J. Math., 11:431–34.

———. 1965. Integer programming: methods, uses, computation. Management Sci., 12:253–313.

BALL, W. W. R. 1944. Mathematical recreations and essays, rev. H. S. M. COXETER. New York: Macmillan.

BARNETTE, D. 1966a. Trees in polyhedral graphs. Canad. J. Math. (in press).

———. 1966b. W_v paths in 3-polytopes. J. Combinatorial Theory (in press).

BEALE, E. M. L. 1955. Cycling in the dual simplex algorithm. Naval Res. Logist. Quart., 2:269–76.

BERGE, C. 1958. Théorie des graphes et ses applications. Paris: Dunod. (English translation, 1962. London: Methuen.)

BOUWKAMP, C. J., A. J. W. DUIJVESTIJN, and P. MEDEMA. 1960. Table of c-nets of orders 8 to 19 inclusive. Eindhoven, Neth.: Philips Research Laboratories.

BROWN, T. A. 1960. Hamiltonian paths on convex polyhedra. Unpublished note P-2069. Santa Monica, Calif.: The RAND Corp.

———. 1961. Simple paths on convex polyhedra. Pacific J. Math., 11:1211–14.

BROWN, W. G. 1963. Enumeration of non-separable planar maps. Canad. J. Math., 15:526–45.

BROWN, W. G., and W. T. TUTTE. 1964. On the enumeration of non-separable planar maps. Canad. J. Math., 16:572–77.

BRÜCKNER, M. 1893. Die Elemente der vierdimensionalen Geometrie mit besonderer Berücksichtigung der Polytope. Jber. Verein. Natuurk. Zwickau, 61 pages.

———. 1900. Vielecke und Vielfläche: Theorie und Geschichte. Leipzig: Teubner.

———. 1909. Über die Ableitung der allgemeinen Polytope und die nach Isomorphismus verschiedenen Typen der allgemeinen Achtzelle (Oktatope). Verh. Nederl. Akad. Wetensch. Afd. Natuurk. Sect. I, part 10:3–27.

BUCK, R. C., and E. P. STARKE. 1951. Possible number of edges for a polyhedron. Amer. Math. Monthly, 58:190.

CAIRNS, S. S. 1951. Peculiarities of polyhedra. Amer. Math. Monthly, 58:684–89.

CARATHÉODORY, C. 1911. Über den Variabilitätsbereich der Fourierschen Konstanten von positiven harmonischen Funktionen. Rend. Circ. Mat. Palermo, 32:193–217. (Also in Gesammelte mathematischen Schriften, vol. III, 1955. Munich: C. H. Beck'sche, 78–110.)

CHABAUTY, C. 1952a. Empilement de sphères égales dans R^n et valeur asymptotique de la constante γ_n d'Hermite. C. R. Acad. Sci. Paris, 235:529–32.

———. 1952b. Nouveaux résultats de geometrie des nombres. C. R. Acad. Sci. Paris, 235:567–69.

———. 1953. Results sur l'empilement de calottes égales sur une périsphère de R^n et correction à un travail antérieur. C. R. Acad. Sci. Paris, 236:1462–64.

CHARNES, A., W. W. COOPER, and A. HENDERSON. 1953. An introduction to linear programming. New York: Wiley.

CHUARD, J. 1932a. Une solution du problème des quatres couleurs. Verh. Internat. Mat. Kongr. Zürich, 2:199–200.

———. 1932b. Les réseaux cubiques et le problème des quatres couleurs. Mém. Soc. Vaudoise Sci. Nat., 4:41–101.

COXETER, H. S. M. 1948. Regular polytopes. London: Methuen.

DANTZIG, G. B. 1951. Maximization of a linear function of variables subject to linear inequalities *in* Activity analysis of production and allocation (Cowles Commission monograph no. 13), ed. T. C. KOOPMANS. New York: Wiley, 339–47.

———. 1960. Inductive proof of the simplex method. IBM J. Res. Develop., 4:505–6.

———. 1962. Ten unsolved problems. Hectographed notes. Berkeley: Univ. of California.

———. 1963. Linear programming and extensions. Princeton, N. J.: Princeton Univ. Press.

———. 1964. Eight unsolved problems from mathematical programming. Bull. Amer. Math. Soc., 70:499–500.

DANTZIG, G. B., A. ORDEN, and P. WOLFE. 1955. The generalized simplex method for minimizing a linear form under linear inequality constraints. Pacific J. Math., 5:183–95.

DAVIS, C. 1952. The intersection of a linear subspace with the positive orthant. Michigan Math. J., 1:163–68.

———. 1953. Remarks on a previous paper. Michigan Math. J., 2:23–25.

DEHN, M. 1905. Die Eulersche Formel im Zusammenhang mit dem Inhalt in der nichteuklidischen Geometrie. Math. Ann., 61:561–86.

DEMUTH, O. 1961. A remark on the transportation problem (in Czech, with German and Russian summaries). Časopis Pěst. Mat., 86:103–10.

DERRY, D. 1956. Convex hulls of simple space curves. Canad. J. Math., 8:383–88.

DIRAC, G. A. 1952. Some theorems on abstract graphs. Proc. London Math. Soc., 2:69–81.

———. 1961. A contraction theorem for abstract graphs. Math. Ann., 144:93–96.

———. 1963. Some results concerning the structure of graphs. Canad. Math. Bull., 6:183–210.

DOIG, A. G. 1963. The minimum number of basic feasible solutions to a transport problem. Operational Res. Quart., 14:387–91.

EBERHARD, V. 1891. Zur Morphologie der Polyeder. Leipzig: Teubner.

EGGLESTON, H. G., B. GRÜNBAUM, and V. KLEE. 1965. Some semicontinuity theorems for convex polytopes and cell-complexes. Comment. Math. Helv., 39:165–88.

EULER, L. 1752. Elementa doctrinae solidorum. Novi Comment. Acad. Sci. Imp. Petropol., 4:109–60.

FABRICIUS-BJERRE, F. 1962. On polygons of order n in projective n-space, with an application to strictly convex curves. Math. Scand., 10:221–29.

FICKEN, F. A. 1961. The simplex method of linear programming. New York: Holt Rinehart & Winston.

FIELDHOUSE, M. 1961. Linear programming. Unpublished Ph.D. dissertation, Cambridge Univ., Eng. (Reviewed in Operations Res., 1962, 10:740.)

——. 1962. Some properties of simplex polytopes. Dittoed notes. Cambridge, Mass.: Harvard Univ.

FILLIPOVICH, E. I., and O. M. KOZLOV. 1963. The number of steps in the solution of linear programming problems by the simplex method (in Russian). Tekhnologicheskaya Kivernetika, Kïïv (USSR), 140–44. (Reviewed in Internat. Abstracts Operations Res., 1964, 4:336.)

FLORES, A. 1933–1934. Über n-dimensionale Komplexe die im R_{2n+1} absolut selbstverschlungen sind. Ergeb. Math. Kolloq., 6:4–7.

GALE, D. 1951. Convex polyhedral cones and linear inequalities *in* Activity analysis of production and allocation (Cowles Commission monograph no. 13), ed. T. C. KOOPMANS. New York: Wiley, 287–97.

——. 1956. Neighboring vertices on a convex polyhedron *in* Linear inequalities and related systems (Ann. of Math. study no. 38), ed. H. W. KUHN and A. W. TUCKER. Princeton, N. J.: Princeton Univ. Press, 255–63.

——. 1963. Neighborly and cyclic polytopes *in* Convexity (Proceedings of symposia in pure mathematics, vol. VII), ed. V. L. KLEE. Providence, R. I.: Amer. Math. Soc., 225–32.

——. 1964. On the number of faces of a convex polytope. Canad. J. Math., 16:12–17.

GERSTENHABER, M. 1951. Theory of convex polyhedral cones *in* Activity analysis of production and allocation (Cowles Commission monograph no. 13), ed. T. C. KOOPMANS. New York: Wiley, 298–316.

GOLDMAN, A. J. 1956. Resolution and separation theorems for polyhedral convex sets *in* Linear inequalities and related systems (Ann. of Math. study no. 38), ed. H. W. KUHN and A. W. TUCKER. Princeton, N. J.: Princeton Univ. Press, 41–51.

GOLDMAN, A. J., and D. KLEINMAN. 1964. Examples relating to the simplex method. Operations Res., 12:159–61.

GOLDMAN, A. J., and A. W. TUCKER. 1956. Polyhedral convex cones *in* Linear inequalities and related systems (Ann. of Math. study no. 38), ed. H. W. KUHN and A. W. TUCKER. Princeton, N. J.: Princeton Univ. Press, 19–40.

GOLDSTEIN, A. J. 1963. A procedure for determining the convex hull of a set of points or hyperplanes. Abstract in program for 1963 national conference in Denver. New York: Assoc. Comput. Mach., 12.

GRACE, D. W. 1965. Computer search for non-isomorphic convex polyhedra. Technical report CS15. Stanford, Calif.: Stanford Univ., Computer Science Dept.

GRÜNBAUM, B. 1964a. Unambiguous polyhedral graphs. Israel J. Math., 2:235–38.

——. 1964b. A simple proof of a theorem of Motzkin. Nederl. Akad. Wetensch. Indag. Math., 26:382–84.

——. 1965. On the facial structure of convex polytopes. Bull. Amer. Math. Soc., 71:559–60.

——. 1966a. The number of faces of convex polytopes *in* Proceedings of a colloquium on convexity held in Copenhagen in 1965 (in press).

——. 1966b. Convex polytopes. New York: Wiley.

GRÜNBAUM, B., and T. S. MOTZKIN. 1962. Longest simple paths in polyhedral graphs. J. London Math. Soc., 37:152–60.

——. 1963a. On polyhedral graphs *in* Convexity (Proceedings of symposia in pure mathematics, vol. VII), ed. V. L. KLEE. Providence, R. I.: Amer. Math. Soc., 285–90, 498.

——. 1963b. The number of hexagons and the simplicity of geodesics on certain polyhedra. Canad. J. Math., 15:744–51.

HADWIGER, H. 1955. Eulers Charakteristik und kombinatorische Geometrie. J. Reine Angew. Math., 194:101–10.

———. 1957. Ungelöste Probleme, Nr. 17. Elem. Math., 12:61–62.

HELLER, I. 1955a. On the traveling salesman's problem *in* Proceedings of the second symposium in linear programming, vol. II. Washington, D. C.: Nat. Bur. Standards, 643–65.

———. 1955b. Geometric characterization of cyclic permutations. Abstract 427t. Bull. Amer. Math. Soc., 61:227.

———. 1956. Neighbor relations on the convex of cyclic permutations. Pacific J. Math., 6:467–77.

HOFFMAN, A. J. 1953. Cycles in the simplex algorithm. Nat. Bur. Standards report no. 2974. Washington, D. C.: Govt. Printing Office.

JACOBS, W. W., and E. D. SCHELL. 1959. The number of vertices of a convex polytope. Abstract. Amer. Math. Monthly, 66:643.

JUCOVIČ, E., and J. W. MOON. 1965. The maximum diameter of a convex polyhedron. Math. Mag., 38:31–32.

KARLIN, S., and L. S. SHAPLEY. 1953. Geometry of moment spaces. Mem. Amer. Math. Soc., no. 12.

KENDALL, M. G. 1955. Rank correlation methods. London: Griffin.

KENDALL, M. G., and B. BABINGTON SMITH. 1940. On the method of paired comparisons. Biometrika, 31:324–45.

KIRKMAN, T. P. 1857. On autopolar polyhedra. Philos. Trans. Roy. Soc. London Ser. A, 147:183–215.

KLEE, V. 1959. Some characterizations of convex polyhedra. Acta Math., 102:79–107.

———. 1963. The Euler characteristic in combinatorial geometry. Amer. Math. Monthly, 70:119–27.

———. 1964a. A combinatorial analogue of Poincaré's duality theorem. Canad. J. Math., 16:517–31.

———. 1964b. Diameters of polyhedral graphs. Canad. J. Math., 16:602–14.

———. 1964c. On the number of vertices of a convex polytope. Canad. J. Math., 16:701–20.

———. 1964d. A property of d-polyhedral graphs. J. Math. Mech., 13:1039–42.

———. 1965a. Heights of convex polytopes. J. Math. Anal. Appl., 11:176–90.

———. 1965b. A class of linear programming problems requiring a large number of iterations. Numer. Math., 7:313–21.

———. 1965c. Paths on polyhedra, I. J. Soc. Indust. Appl. Math., 13:946–56.

———. 1966a. Paths on polyhedra, II. Pacific J. Math., 16:(in press).

———. 1966b. Problem size in linear programming *in* Proceedings of a colloquium on convexity held in Copenhagen in 1965 (in press).

———. 1966c. A comparison of primal and dual methods for linear programming. Unpublished manuscript.

KLEE, V., and D. WALKUP. 1965. The d-step conjecture for polyhedra of dimension $d < 6$. Document D1-82-0495. Seattle: Boeing Scientific Research Laboratories.

KOTZIG, A. 1965. Colouring of trivalent polyhedra. Canad. J. Math., 17:659–64.

KRUSKAL, J. B. 1963. The number of simplices in a complex *in* Mathematical optimization techniques. Berkeley: Univ. of California Press, 251–78.

KUHN, H. 1955. On certain convex polyhedra. Abstract 799t. Bull. Amer. Math. Soc., 16:557–58.

KUHN, H., and R. E. QUANDT. 1963. An experimental study of the simplex method *in* Experimental arithmetic, high-speed computing and mathematics (Proceedings of symposia in applied mathematics, vol. XV), ed. N. C. METROPOLIS *et al.* Providence, R. I.: Amer. Math. Soc., 107–24.

KURATOWSKI, K. 1930. Sur le problème des courbes gauches en topologie. Fund. Math., 15:271–83.

LEBESGUE, H. 1940. Quelques conséquences simples de la formule d'Euler. J. Math. Pures Appl., 19:27–43.

LEDERBERG, J. 1965. Topological mapping of organic molecules. Proc. Nat. Acad. Sci. U. S., 53:134–39.

LYUSTERNIK, L. A. 1963. Convex figures and polyhedra, tr. T. J. SMITH. New York: Dover. (Original Russian edition, 1956. Moscow: Gosudarstv. Izdat. Tekh.-Teoret. Lit.)

MAGHOUT, K. 1963. Applications de l'algèbre de Boole a la théorie des graphs et aux programmes linéaires et quadratiques. Cahiers Centre Études Rech. Opér., 5:21–99.

MINKOWSKI, H. 1897. Allgemeine Lehrsätze über die konvexen Polyeder. Nachr. Ges. Wiss. Göttingen Math.-Phys. Kl., 198–219. (Also in Gesammelte Abhandlungen, vol. II, 1911. Leipzig: Teubner, 103–21.)

MOON, J. W., and L. MOSER. 1963. Simple paths on polyhedra. Pacific J. Math., 13: 629–31.

MOTZKIN, T. S. 1936. Beiträge zur Theorie der linearen Ungleichungen. Ph.D. dissertation, Univ. of Basel, Switz.

———. 1956. The assignment problem *in* Numerical analysis (Proceedings of symposia in applied mathematics, vol. VI), ed. J. H. CURTISS. New York: McGraw-Hill, 109–25.

———. 1957. Comonotone curves and polyhedra. Abstract 111. Bull. Amer. Math. Soc., 63:35.

———. 1964. The evenness of the number of edges of a convex polyhedron. Proc. Nat. Acad. Sci. U. S., 52:44–45.

MOTZKIN, T. S., H. RAIFFA, G. L. THOMPSON, and R. M. THRALL. 1953. The double description method *in* Contributions to the theory of games, vol. II (Ann. of Math. study no. 28), ed. H. W. KUHN and A. W. TUCKER. Princeton, N. J.: Princeton Univ. Press, 51–73.

MULLIN, R. C. 1964. Enumeration of rooted triangular maps. Amer. Math. Monthly, 71:1007–10.

———. 1965. On counting rooted triangular maps. Canad. J. Math., 17:373–82.

NORMAN, R. Z. 1955. On the convex polyhedra of the symmetric traveling salesman problem. Abstract 804t. Bull. Amer. Math. Soc., 61:559.

PANNWITZ, E. 1932. Review of Chuard (1932b). Jbuch. Fortschr. Math., 58:1204.

PERLES, M. 1966. *f*-vectors of a polytope with a given group of symmetries. Unpublished manuscript.

POINCARÉ, H. 1893. Sur la généralisation d'un théorème d'Euler relatif aux polyèdres. C. R. Acad. Sci. Paris, 117:144 45.

———. 1899. Complément à l'Analysis Situs. Rend. Circ. Mat. Palermo, 13:285–343.

QUANDT, R. E., and H. KUHN. 1962. On some computer experiments in linear programming. Bull. Inst. Internat. Statist., 363–72.

———. 1964. On upper bounds for the number of iterations in solving linear programs. Operations Res., 12:161–65.

RADEMACHER, H. 1965. On the number of certain types of polyhedra. Illinois J. Math., 9:361–80.

SAATY, T. L. 1955. The number of vertices of a polyhedron. Amer. Math. Monthly, 62:326–31.

———. 1963. A conjecture concerning the smallest bound on the iterations in linear programming. Operations Res., 11:151–53.

SALLEE, G. T. 1966. Incidence graphs of polytopes. Unpublished manuscript.

SCHLÄFLI, L. 1901. Theorie der vielfachen Kontinuität (published posthumously, written in 1850–1852). Nachr. Denkschr. Schweiz. Ges. Naturwiss., 38:1–237. (Also in Gesammelte mathematische Abhandlungen, vol. I, 1950. Basel, Switz.: Birkhäuser. English translation, in part, by A. CAYLEY, 1858 and 1860. Quart. J. Math., 2:269–301 and 3:54–68, 97–108.)

SCHLEGEL, V. 1883. Theorie der homogen zusammengesetzen Raumgebilde. Nova Acta Acad. Leop. Carol, 44:343–459.

SCHOUTE, P. H. 1905. Mehrdimensionale Geometrie. Teil II: Die Polytope. Leipzig.

SHASHKIN, YU. A. 1963. A remark on neighboring vertices of convex polyhedra (in Russian). Uspehi Mat. Nauk, 18:209–12.

SIMMONARD, M. A., and G. F. HADLEY. 1959. Maximum number of iterations in the transportation problem. Naval Res. Logist. Quart., 6:125–29.

SOMMERVILLE, D. M. Y. 1927. The relations connecting the angle-sums and volume of a polytope in space of n dimensions. Proc. Roy. Soc. London Ser. A, 115:103–19.

158   *Victor Klee*

————. 1929. An introduction to the geometry of N dimensions. London: Methuen.
Steinitz, E. 1906. Über die Eulersche Polyederrelationen. Arch. Math. Phys., 11:86–88.
————. 1922. Polyeder und Raumeinteilungen *in* Enzyklopädie der mathematischen Wissenschaften, vol. III, part 1, second half. Leipzig: Teubner, 1–139.
Steinitz, E., and H. Rademacher. 1934. Vorlesungen über die Theorie der Polyeder. Berlin: Springer.
Sz.–Nagy, B. 1941. Sur un problème pour les polyedres convexes dans l'espace n-dimensionnel. Bull. Soc. Math. France, 69:3–4.
Tait, P. G. 1884. On Listing's "Topologie." Philos. Mag., 17:30–46.
Tucker, A. W. 1955. Linear inequalities and convex polyhedral sets *in* Proceedings of the second symposium in linear programming, vol. II. Washington, D. C.: Nat. Bur. Standards, 569–602.
————. 1962. Simplex method and theory. Memorandum RM-3199-PR. Santa Monica, Calif.: The RAND Corp.
Tutte, W. T. 1946. On Hamiltonian circuits. J. London Math. Soc., 21:98–101.
————. 1956. A theorem on planar graphs. Trans. Amer. Math. Soc., 82:99–116.
————. 1960a. A non-Hamiltonian planar graph (Russian summary). Acta Math. Acad. Sci. Hungar., 11:371–75.
————. 1960b. Convex representations of graphs. Proc. London Math. Soc., 10:304–20.
————. 1961. A theory of 3-connected graphs. Nederl. Akad. Wetensch. Indag. Math., 23:441–55.
————. 1962a. A census of planar triangulations. Canad. J. Math., 14:21–38.
————. 1962b. A census of Hamiltonian polygons. Canad. J. Math., 14:402–17.
————. 1962c. A new branch of enumerative graph theory. Bull. Amer. Math. Soc., 68:500–4.
————. 1963a. A census of planar maps. Canad. J. Math., 15:249–71.
————. 1963b. How to draw a graph. Proc. London Math. Soc., 13:743–67.
Ungar, P. 1963. On diagrams representing maps. J. London Math. Soc., 28:336–42.
van Kampen, E. R. 1932. Komplexe in Euklidische Räumen. Abh. Math. Sem. Univ. Hamburg, 9:72–78, 152–53.
Wendel, J. G. 1962. A problem in geometrical probability. Math. Scand., 11:109–11.
Weyl, H. 1935. Elementare Theorie der konvexen Polyeder. Comment. Math. Helv., 7:290–306. [English translation by H. W. Kuhn, 1950. *in* Contributions to the theory of games (Ann. of Math. study no. 24), ed. H. W. Kuhn and A. W. Tucker. Princeton, N. J.: Princeton Univ. Press, 3–18.]
Whitney, H. 1931. A theorem on graphs. Ann. of Math., 32:378–90.
————. 1932. Congruent graphs and the connectivity of graphs. Amer. J. Math., 54:150–68.
Wolfe, P. 1962. The composite simplex algorithm. Memorandum RM-3579-PR. Santa Monica, Calif.: The RAND Corp.
————. 1963. A technique for resolving degeneracy in linear programming. J. Soc. Indust. Appl. Math., 11:205–11.
Wolfe, P., and L. Cutler. 1963. Experiments in linear programming *in* Recent advances in mathematical programming, ed. R. L. Graves and P. Wolfe. New York: McGraw-Hill, 177–200.
Zhu, Y.-J. 1963. Maximum number of iterations in the dual algorithm of the Kantorovič-Hitchcock problem in linear programming. Chinese Math., 3:307–13.

Statistical Mechanics

10
Statistical Mechanics of Biological Macromolecules

JULIAN H. GIBBS
Brown University

In reviewing some of our calculations before an audience of mathematicians, I fear I may have cause to sympathize with the fellow chemist who rode through the State of Wisconsin by train in the company of a physicist and a mathematician. Looking out at the fields, this chemist spotted a white cow and remarked, "There are white cows in the State of Wisconsin." The physicist immediately corrected his statement: "There is at least one white cow in the State of Wisconsin." Then the mathematician corrected both of them: "There is in the State of Wisconsin at least one cow that is white on at least one side."

Chemists these days are very interested in what cows represent. Economically, cows are important to us as sources of proteins. A living organism can virtually be defined as one which can take the proteins of another organism, break them down into their monomer units (defined later), and then reassemble them into new proteins according to patterns which are characteristic of the organism's own species.

The proteins are what chemists call polymers. Professor Speyer has discussed biological polymers (paper 5), and Professor Wall has discussed synthetic polymers (paper 4). Therefore, I may observe the dictum presented earlier and glide nimbly over the essentials; however, not knowing what is obvious to this group, I can hardly stress it!

Polymer molecules are long, chain-like affairs with molecular weights of millions. If the links, or monomers as they are called, are all identical, we call the polymer a homopolymer; otherwise we call it a copolymer.

In passing, I note that the polymer molecules which chemists can make synthetically are the basis of the rubber industry, the plastics industry, the fiber industry, the film industry, the paint industry, etc. More than three quarters of our chemical industry today is involved in one important way or another with polymers.

In the area of naturally occurring polymers there are three classes of outstanding importance: the nucleic acids, the proteins, and the carbohydrates. I shall be concerned exclusively with nucleic acids and proteins.

In the case of proteins, there are 20 different types of monomers (the amino acids). This means, for example, that there are 20^{100} distinguishable copolymers among the set of 100-mers alone. Thus it is clear that there is no difficulty in accounting for the complexity and variety of life, at least in principle.

This variety of proteins is translated into variety and complexity of life largely through the agency of chemical catalysis; virtually every chemical reaction that occurs in a living cell is catalyzed by an enzyme, which is a protein. The term "enzyme" merely means a protein whose function it is to catalyze a reaction. Unfortunately, we do not yet understand clearly how enzymes catalyze chemical reactions.

There are also structural proteins. The dry weight of animal cells is largely attributable to proteins. Physiological functions, such as sense reception, contraction, ion transport, secretion, etc., all involve proteins in fundamentally important but ill-understood ways.

It is clear, however, that the multiplicity of roles for proteins is a direct manifestation of the multiplicity of possible amino acid (link) sequences available in the construction of protein molecules.

Our use of the same generic name for all amino acids implies that they have common features in their structures. In the usual two-dimensional representation, the chemical formula for each amino acid is

$$
\begin{array}{c}
\mathrm{H} \quad \mathrm{R} \\
\diagdown \diagup \\
\mathrm{C} \quad \mathrm{O} \\
\diagup \diagdown \diagup\diagup \\
\mathrm{R'-N} \quad \mathrm{C} \\
\mid \diagdown \\
\mathrm{H} \qquad \mathrm{OH}
\end{array}
$$

the $\mathrm{H-N}$ (with H below, and a bond going up) group on the left (R′ is usually H) and the $-\mathrm{C}$ (with O double bonded above and OH below) group on the right being the amino group and the (carboxylic) acid group (respectively) from which these amino acids get their generic name. In 18 of the 20 amino acids, the symbol R′ represents a hydrogen atom, but we use here the noncommittal symbol R′ rather than H to include the two cases (proline and hydroxy proline) where it does not. The symbol R refers to any one of 20 different groups of atoms. In only one case (glycine) is this group a single hydrogen atom. It is thus the variations in this

R group alone that distinguish 18 of the amino acids from each other. In the two unusual cases (proline and hydroxy proline) the groups R and R′ are actually bonded together; thus, these two molecules contain closed rings of atoms.

Now, although the synthesis of a protein from its constituent amino acids involves a complicated mechanism, the net change as far as the amino acids are concerned is a simple one. Amino groups condense with carboxylic acid groups intermolecularly (not intramolecularly) in the formation of "peptide" linkages with loss of water to form polymers called polypeptides:

$$
\begin{array}{c}
\text{H} \quad \text{R} \quad \text{O} \text{H} \quad \text{R} \quad \text{O} \text{H} \quad \text{R} \quad \text{O} \\
-\text{N}-\text{C}-\text{C}-\text{N}-\text{C}-\text{C}-\text{N}-\text{C}-\text{C}- \\
\text{R}' \text{R}' \text{R}'
\end{array}
$$

Here the vertical dashed partitions have been drawn only as an aid to the recognition of those parts (amino acid "residues") of the polymer molecule which were derived from individual amino acid molecules (monomers). As always, such a two-dimensional formulation of the molecule is not intended to represent the actual arrangement of the atoms in three-dimensional space.

The bio-synthetic mechanism which carries out these "polymerizations," as they are called, has the remarkable property of controlling the sequence, as well as the number, of the various amino acids incorporated into any given polypeptide molecule; accordingly, we refer to the latter as a particular protein (e.g., trypsinogen).

This control is effected by a section of a giant "blueprint" molecule, deoxyribonucleic acid or DNA for short, the section or "cistron," as it is called, corresponding roughly to the classical "gene." These blueprint molecules, the nucleic acids, are also copolymers of definite monomer sequence, but the monomers in this case are not the 20 amino acids but rather the 4 "nucleotides." We shall have more to say about these later. For the moment it will suffice to note that the set of cistrons, distinguishable from one another by their nucleotide sequences, that an organism contains determines the set of proteins that the organism can make and therefore all the chemistry and physics that it can display—which defines the organism.

The actual three-dimensional structure of any particular protein depends upon its own particular amino acid sequence. However, there is one feature that seems to be a common theme in the structure of most proteins. This is the tendency of the hydrogen atom, which in 18 of the 20 amino acid residues constitutes the group R', to interact strongly, through the formation of what the chemist calls a "hydrogen bond," with the oxygen atom of the fourth nearest residue (to its left in our representation). To form such a bond, the relevant hydrogen and oxygen atoms must obviously lie next to one another in three-dimensional space. This proximity is achieved by a helical coiling of the molecular chain in such a way that 4 amino acid residues constitute slightly more than one turn of the helix (actually 18 residues make five turns in this "α-helix"; see Pauling and Corey, 1951). Thus the oxygen atom, which in "chemical space" is actually the fourth one removed from a given R' hydrogen, is in physical space actually the closest one, lying nearby on the next turn of the helix.

Such helical sections will, of course, be likely to terminate at any proline or hydroxy-proline residue, since these residues lack the hydrogen atom that might otherwise form the helix-stabilizing hydrogen bond. Other factors, in particular interactions of various types between side groups R, also may limit the number and length of helical sections in a protein. Some of these interactions are salt bridges, some are of the type called hydrophobic (water is the normal solvent), others are side-group hydrogen bonds, still others are actual chemical cross-links (disulfide bonds). Since the disruptions in helical structure introduce bonds between the rod-like helical sections, the over-all shape of a protein may actually be more or less globular (e.g., the "globulins").

Now the helix-stabilizing hydrogen bonds and various side-group interactions that determine the apparently almost rigid three-dimensional structure of a protein are not nearly as strong as ordinary chemical bonds, and our experience with similar physical forces in other systems leads us to expect that these "bonds" can be broken by various rather mild treatments (e.g., moderate heating). Indeed, this proves to be the case.

However, an, at first sight, surprising feature emerges concerning this bond-breaking process in the case of proteins. It proves to be associated with what the physical chemist calls a cooperative process. That is, in the case, for example, of thermal breakage of these bonds, virtually all the bonds rupture in the same, very narrow, temperature range; once the process begins, it tends to go all the way without the need of (much) further encouragement (heating). Such processes are certainly not otherwise unknown in physical chemistry. Phase transitions in macroscopic systems, such as the melting of a crystal, are extreme examples of just such cooperative processes, since they occur at essentially one temperature. Nevertheless the cooperative character of this protein "denaturation" is remarkable in that, in this case, the cooperative "transition" is one that occurs within each individual protein molecule.

As we shall see, nucleic acid molecules also display such transitions.

At this point it will be advantageous to focus our attention not on the denaturations of naturally occurring proteins, which are complicated by the interactions between side groups, but rather on the at least partly related transition that we can observe in a synthetic polypeptide of simpler structure, in particular a homopolypeptide formed from an amino acid (not necessarily a naturally occurring one) with an uncharged and non-hydrogen-bond-forming side group R. An example of one such polypeptide that has been widely studied, by Doty and Yang (1956), is poly-γ-benzyl L glutamate, which is soluble only in non-aqueous solvents. This polypeptide exhibits, under appropriate conditions, a molecular structure which is simply one long uninterrupted α-helix. Upon alteration of the temperature or solvent composition, this molecule, originally a rigid helical rod, is observed to collapse (as demonstrated by light-scattering studies by Doty and Yang, 1956) to a mobile (as demonstrated by nuclear magnetic resonance studies by Mandel, 1964[1]), randomly coiled structure.

The mobility and randomness of the latter (physical) structure of the polypeptide molecule is a consequence of the fact that, in the absence of intra-chain (as opposed to chain-to-solvent) helix-stabilizing hydrogen bonds, intramolecular rotation can occur around chemical bonds in the molecular backbone.

The transition is often called the "helix-coil transition." It is a cooperative process, though not as highly cooperative as the "denaturation" of a typical protein.

The transition exhibited by poly-γ-benzyl L glutamate in non-aqueous solvent is inverted relative to that of other polypeptides, and proteins, in water; that is, in this case the helix exists at the higher temperatures, whereas the random coil is more stable in the lower temperature region. The reason for this apparently involves the hydrogen bonding of solvent molecules to the NH and CO groups of the random coil. If, as seems to be the case in the non-aqueous systems, the trading of the NH-to-CO hydrogen bonds of the helix (and possible solvent-to-solvent bonds) for the NH-to-solvent and CO-to-solvent bonds associated with the random coil represents a decrease in energy, as contrasted with the increase that is apparently associated with the corresponding process in aqueous systems, the helix would not exist in either the higher or lower temperature ranges unless the entropy change should also be of sign opposite to that in the aqueous case. However, the latter circumstance is to be expected, in spite of the fact that the change in entropy associated with the polymer chains alone must certainly be positive in both non-aqueous and aqueous

---

[1] Similar studies of polynucleotides have been made by McTague, Ross, and Gibbs (1964) and by McDonald, Phillips, and Penman (1964).

helix-to-coil transitions, because the loss in entropy suffered by solvent molecules in binding to the random coil should be large in the case of non-aqueous solvent molecules whose capabilities of bonding to each other are not as extensive as those of water molecules.

Allowance, in a statistical mechanical theory, for the influence of solvent binding is not difficult but will not be discussed explicitly here, as it introduces no unfamiliar combinatorial questions. In fact, the principal effect of solvent binding in a statistical mechanical theory is merely to alter the values of certain quantities appearing in the theory.

Let us now set about to formulate a theory[2] for this helix-coil transition. We have noted that in the α-helix the R′ hydrogen of each amino acid residue is hydrogen-bonded to the oxygen of its fourth nearest-neighbor residue (in "chemical space"). Thus each amino acid residue is bridged by three hydrogen bonds. All three of these must be broken before rotation around any chemical bonds in the residue is possible.

The physical basis of the cooperative character of this transition is clear already. To break a hydrogen bond involves the expenditure of energy, and no entropy is gained in return if the break is an isolated one (intact hydrogen bonds on each side of the break). To break one of the hydrogen bonds neighboring the first one broken costs about the same amount of energy, and still no significant entropy is gained in return, as there is still at least one hydrogen bond holding each amino acid residue in the helical posture. Thus the process of breaking hydrogen bonds begins only with difficulty. Once two adjacent hydrogen bonds have been broken anywhere, however, the rupture of a third hydrogen bond adjacent to either of the first two is a much easier matter, for although this third rupture costs no more energy than either of the others, now the full entropy associated with the internal rotation around (certain) chemical bonds of one amino acid residue is to be gained upon this third rupture. The process of breaking hydrogen bonds tends to go to completion under conditions barely more than sufficient to get it started.

Mathematically, our task is to formulate the partition function for a canonical ensemble of such polypeptide chains, since temperature and number of residues (essentially equal to the number of possible hydrogen bonds for sufficiently long chains) in each polypeptide chain are the appropriate independent variables, and knowledge of the canonical ensemble partition function in terms of these variables will permit evaluation of any equilibrium-thermodynamic property. In our case the partition func-

---

[2] For this polypeptide case we follow the treatment of Gibbs and DiMarzio (1959), but see also Zimm and Bragg (1959).

tion may be written as

$$Q = \sum_{\{n_i\}} W(\{n_i\}) \, \exp\,[-E(\{n_i\})/kT], \tag{10.1}$$

where the sum is over all sets of numbers $\{n_i\}$ that satisfy the auxiliary condition

$$\sum_{j=1}^{N} jn_j \leq n. \tag{10.2}$$

In these equations n is the total number of hydrogen bonds (of the α-helix type, the only type considered here) that it is possible to form (or break), n_j is the number of uninterrupted sequences containing j and only j adjacent broken hydrogen bonds in a particular chain configuration, $W(\{n_i\})$ is the number of chain configurations characterized by the set of numbers $\{n_i\}$, where $1 \leq j \leq n$, and $E(\{n_i\})$ is the energy of each configuration characterized by $\{n_i\}$.

In writing the partition function this way, we have made use of the reasonable assumption that configurations with the same $\{n_i\}$ have essentially the same energy. In fact, we assume

$$E(\{n_i\}) = \sum_j jn_j E_H, \tag{10.3}$$

E_H being the energy required to break a hydrogen bond.

If we also assume that the chains are sufficiently long that the special conditions at either end may be neglected, $W(\{n_i\})$ may be decomposed into two factors:

$$W(\{n_i\}) = g(\{n_i\})h(\{n_i\}), \tag{10.4}$$

where $h(\{n_i\})$ describes the number of ways the various sequences of broken hydrogen bonds may be located along the chain for each $\{n_i\}$ and where $g(\{n_i\})$ introduces the total rotational "degeneracy" arising from the totality of sequences for which $j \geq 3$ in a given $\{n_i\}$, in accordance with our previous discussion.

To evaluate $h\{n_i\}$ it is convenient to represent the arrangement of intact and broken hydrogen bonds in each chain configuration as a linear array of 1's and 0's, with 1's standing for intact hydrogen bonds and 0's for broken ones, and to imagine a partition placed to the right of every 1:

```
  | |      | |        |   | | | |       | | |         | | | | |          |
0 1|1|0 0 1|1|0 0 0 0 1|0 1|1|1|1|0 0 0 1|1|1|0 0 0 0 1|1|1|1|1|0 0 0 1|
  | |      | |        |   | | | |       | | |         | | | | |          |
1 |0|  2  |0|    4    | 1 |0|0|0|   3   |0|0|    5     |0|0|0|0|    3    |
  | |      | |        |   | | | |       | | |         | | | | |          |
```

This partitioning divides each chain configuration into "j-let" sequences of total length $j + 1$ (including as part of each j-let the intact bond at its right end) and gives meaning to the value 0 for j (the appropriate j-values are shown below the j-let sequences in the diagram).

We note, in passing, that, with the value 0 for j thus introduced, we may replace the inequality (10.2) with the equality

$$\sum_{j=0}^{N} (j + 1)n_j = n. \tag{10.5}$$

The factor $h(\{n_i\})$ is now readily seen as

$$h(\{n_i\}) = \frac{\left(\sum_i n_j\right)!}{\prod_i n_i!}, \tag{10.6}$$

an observation that requires no further comment.

We evaluate the factor $g(\{n_i\})$ by recalling that a rotational degeneracy, now designated as Z, is introduced wherever there exists a triplet break. A quadruplet break clearly counts as two triplets, a quintuplet as three, $\cdots$ a j-let as $(j - 2) \cdots$. Thus the rotational degeneracy associated with a j-let is Z^{i-2} for $j \geq 3$ and is 0 otherwise. We may, therefore, write

$$g(\{n_i\}) = \prod_{j=2}^{N} Z^{(j-2)n_j}$$

$$= \prod_{j=0}^{N} Z^{(j-2)n_j(1-\delta_{0j})(1-\delta_{1j})}, \tag{10.7}$$

where

$$\delta_{ij} = \begin{cases} 1, & i = j \\ 0, & i \neq j \end{cases}.$$

Substitution of the relations (10.6) and (10.7) into (10.4), and (10.3) and (10.4) into (10.1), yields an equation for Q which, subject to (10.5), constitutes the formulation of our problem.

The evaluation of Q thus arrived at may be effected by either the method of steepest descent or the method of the maximum term. The latter relies on two observations, familiar in statistical mechanics. The first is that for a sufficiently large system (sufficiently long molecular chain in this case) the logarithm of the maximum term in the partition function for the system is only negligibly different from the logarithm of the whole partition function. The second is that it is the logarithm of the partition function, rather than the partition function itself, which is the significant quantity. In particular, the Helmholtz free energy, from which all other thermodynamic properties may be obtained, in this case wherein T and n are the independent variables, is given as

$$F = -kT \log Q$$

and, therefore,

$$F = -kT \log Q_{max},$$

where by Q_{max} is meant the largest term in Q. This largest term, which, like all others, must satisfy the auxiliary condition (10.5), is easily found by the method of undetermined, or Lagrangian, multipliers.

Since the principal object of this conference is to illustrate the various contexts in which combinatorial problems may arise, rather than to review standard methods for their solution, I will leave this problem at this point with the observation that the solution (Gibbs and DiMarzio, 1959; Zimm and Bragg, 1959) in this case proves to agree (Zimm, Doty, and Iso, 1959) perfectly with the available relevant experimental observations. In particular, the optical rotatory power of a solution of such polypeptide chains, which has been measured at various temperatures (Doty and Yang, 1956; Zimm, Doty, and Iso, 1959), proves to be linear in the helical content of the chains, calculated, from the partition function, through its proportionality to the average number of hydrogen bonds, which in turn is proportional to the thermodynamic energy given by the standard relation

$$U = \frac{\partial(F/T)}{\partial(1/T)} = kT^2 \frac{\partial \log Q}{\partial T}. \tag{10.8}$$

A plot of, for example, the calculated U versus T yields a sharp sigmoid curve, the sharpness being a manifestation of the cooperative character we have discussed.

The other class of polymer molecules on which all life is based, the nucleic acids, also exhibit a cooperative structural transition.

Unlike the proteins, nucleic acid molecules are often double-stranded, the two strands being twisted around one another in a helix (Watson and Crick, 1953), which is therefore akin to a two-stranded rope.

The individual strands, however, are more nearly analogous to chains than rope fibers, since, like the proteins, they are composed of monomeric "links." As mentioned earlier, the number of different types of links in this case is four, rather than twenty as in the case of the proteins. There exists, again in this case, the feature that the structures of the various types of links contain parts which are similar (ribose ring and phosphate group) for all members of the set of four and also parts which distinguish the members of the set from one another, the so-called "bases." We shall denote the four types of monomers by the first letters, A, G, C, and T, of the chemical names, adenine, guanine, cytosine, and thymine, of the bases they contain. Actually we are speaking here of the types of monomers in the genetic substance, deoxyribonucleic acid, i.e. DNA. The other type of nucleic acid, ribonucleic acid, i.e. RNA, has a set of monomer units which is closely similar to, but not identical with, that of DNA considered here.

Though we shall not need to concern ourselves with the details of the structures of these monomer units of DNA, we must note one of their properties, which is of supreme importance. This, called Watson-Crick base-pairing after the discoverers of both it and the DNA double-helix based on it, is the ability of an A unit to form a strong hydrogen bond with a T unit and that of a G unit to form one with a C unit. Furthermore, in the native double-helical structure of a DNA molecule, this type of hydrogen-bonding can and does exist only between adjacent bases on opposite strands of the double-helix, not between bases on the same strand. It is, in fact, this hydrogen-bonding of apposite bases of different strands that holds the duplex structure together.

It is an important corollary of this proposition that every A unit on one strand must be apposed (nearest-neighbored) by a T unit on the other, and similarly for G and C, so that a specific sequence of units in one strand implies a definite, complementary as it is called, sequence in the other. Thus, the genetic information, stored in the sequence of bases in the molecule, is actually carried twice over, a vastly important feature which permits replication of the "genes" (special sequences in one or more DNA molecules).

This replication amounts, in essence, to an unravelling of the DNA double-helix, adsorption of complementary monomers onto each of the parental strands as they separate, and polymerization of the newly adsorbed monomers, the end result being two double-helical DNA molecules identical with each other and with the parental duplex and each containing one of the strands originally belonging to the parental duplex and one newly synthesized one ("semi-conservative" replication).

The unravelling process can be carried out alone, either by the application of heat or by the alteration of pH, or both. When this is done, the temperature or pH range over which the process occurs is found to be very narrow, indicating that this transition from helix to (two) random coil(s) is cooperative, as was the protein helix-coil transition. In this case the cooperative character is attributable to two effects. First, the total degeneracy, associated with rotation around bonds, available to a "loop," created by the breakage of adjacent helix-stabilizing hydrogen bonds, increases faster than linearly with the size of the loop. Second, there are, in the double-helix, strong interactions, which we shall call "stacking" interactions, between (chemically and physically) adjacent bases attached to the same strand, in addition to the Watson-Crick hydrogen bonds between bases on opposite strands. The first breakage of a hydrogen bond, wholly within a helical sequence of units, obviously involves, in addition, the breakage of two pairs of these stacking interactions, whereas the successive further breakage of hydrogen bonds, adjacent to already broken ones, clearly involves the associated breakage of only one pair of stacking interactions for each hydrogen bond broken. Both of these effects tend to make the transition process more difficult to start, on heating for example, than to continue; that is, they make it cooperative.

The first of these effects is difficult to evaluate and, as we shall see, will be circumvented by choice, for study, of a system in which the second is much the larger effect.

This second effect, that of the stacking interactions, is analogous to the role of hydrogen bonds in the polypeptide case, though the "interlacing" feature is missing in this polynucleotide case. It will be recalled that three polypeptide hydrogen-bonding interactions had to be broken in order to effect an initial disruption in the interior of the α-helix, whereas this disruption, once formed, could grow with the further breakage of but one hydrogen-bonding interaction per amino acid residue. In the polynucleotide case two pairs of stacking interactions must be broken to initiate a disruption in the helix interior, but the further breakage of but one pair of interactions per Watson-Crick residue-pair suffices for growth of the disruption (random coil region).

In both cases, however, the situation is different at the ends of the polymer chains. At each polymer chain end, clearly, only one interaction, or one pair, need be broken for initiation as well as for growth of the randomly coiled configuration. Thus, unravelling from the ends is the predominant mechanism of helix disruption in those cases in which the polymer chains are not sufficiently long for end effects to be diluted by the numerical superiority of interior loci.

There is no difficulty associated with including, in our analysis, this special effect at chain ends. We have ignored it in our brief discussion here of the polypeptide case[3] and thereby restricted our discussion of polypeptides to long chains, because it introduces no combinatorial features appropriate to this symposium. In fact, for sufficiently short chains, unravelling from the ends would dominate the helix disruption process, and the combinatorial features associated with disruption of helix interiors would lose their physical significance.

Similarly, in the polynucleotide case we could restrict our attention to cases in which at least one of the two chains of the Watson-Crick

---

[3] This end effect has been included in the analyses of the polypeptide problem given by Gibbs and DiMarzio (1959) and Zimm and Bragg (1959).

duplex is long, but the method that we shall use in this case is not altered by so doing.

In this polynucleotide case, however, there is a distinct advantage associated with treating situations in which one, but not necessarily both, of the strands of the Watson-Crick duplex is composed of a series of short molecules. If the other chain is long, combinatorial features are not suppressed by end effects, and yet the difficulty, mentioned previously, associated with evaluation of the configurational degeneracy available to a "loop" is avoided, as the dominant helix-disrupting mechanism will be one in which each small molecule initiates its dissociation from the long one at one of its (the small molecule's) ends without the formation of "loops."

We treat (Magee, Gibbs, and Zimm, 1963; Magee, Gibbs, and Newell, 1965), then, the case of conversion to random coil (or the reverse) of a polynucleotide double-helix in which one strand is a homopolymer, which may be very long, and the other is comprised of a series of identical small molecules ("oligomers"), the monomeric residues (nucleotides) of which are each the complement of the nucleotide of which the long homopolymer strand is composed. For example, one strand might be poly-C, in which case the other would surely be an oligo-G and might be tri-G or tetra-G, say.

It may seem that we are removing all physical significance from the problem being discussed here by choosing this somewhat artificial, idealized case rather than a naturally occurring DNA. However, polymers of the type we are to treat can be synthesized, and their helix-coil transitions can be studied experimentally. Furthermore, comparison of such experimental results with those of the theoretical calculations should permit fairly reliable evaluation of such important parameters as the helix-stabilizing energies associated with both the stacking interactions between bases and the Watson-Crick hydrogen bonds of the allowed base-pair types. Thus, the mathematical convenience of both the restriction to short molecules for one strand, to suppress the complications of loops, and the restriction to homopolymer and (complementary) homo-oligomer, to isolate the various pairwise interactions of each type, may be translated into some physical utility. The experimental data requisite to this program have not yet been obtained, however. Ultimately, one will want to use the parameters evaluated by such a procedure in a (necessarily approximate) theory for the naturally occurring nucleic acids.

We let the number of nucleotide residues in the long-chain polymer be n and that in each of the short oligomers be p. We consider one n-mer and whatever number of p-mers are bound to it as the individual system in our statistical ensemble of systems, the ensemble being, therefore, canonical with respect to n-mers but grand canonical with respect to

p-mers. In the language of thermodynamics, rather than statistical mechanics, we should say that our system is closed with respect to n-mers but open with respect to p-mers.

For pedagogical reasons only, we now assume (Magee, Gibbs, and Zimm, 1963) that whenever at least one nucleotide of a p-mer is bound to the n-mer, all p nucleotides of the p-mer are bound.[4] That is, a p-mer is either completely bound (to p adjacent nucleotides of the n-mer), or it is not bound at all, states of partial binding ("dangling") being prohibited. This assumption does not remove any interesting features from the calculation but does reduce the number of parameters, the size of the matrix that we shall invoke, and the tedium of the calculation. It is not a bad approximation if p is small.

We now number the segments of the n-mer, from 1 to n, and those of each p-mer, from 1 to p. There is no ambiguity with regard to the direction of this numbering, and symmetry number considerations do not arise, since each polynucleotide has a directionality or sense associated with its chemical structure.

Next we classify the possible states of the ith segment of an n-mer according to the following scheme. This segment is in state 0 if no segment of a p-mer is bound to it and in state J, where $1 \leq J \leq p$, if the jth segment of a p-mer is bound to it.

In accordance with a procedure developed and used for the evaluation of partition functions by Kramers and Wannier (1941), Montroll (1941), Onsager (1944), and Zimm and Bragg (1959), we define a statistical-weight row matrix $\mathbf{a}^{(i)}$ each component $a_J^{(i)}$ of which is the aggregate statistical weight (unnormalized probability) associated with the totality of configurations of the first i segments of the n-mer which are compatible with the restriction that segment i is in state J. That is, the element $a_J^{(i)}$ is a sum of terms, one for each configuration of the first $i - 1$ segments which is compatible with state J for segment i. Each term in this sum is a product of suitable Boltzmann and degeneracy factors, for the first i n-mer segments, and, since the ensemble is grand canonical with respect to p-mers, of p-mer absolute activity factors, one for each oligonucleotide bound in the configuration represented by the term in question. $a_J^{(i)}$ may be viewed as the (semi-grand) partition function for a chain containing only these first i segments and subject to the constraint that its last segment must be in state J. The sum of all the elements of $\mathbf{a}^{(n)}$ is clearly the desired partition function for the n-mer.

The utility of this introduction of the statistical-weight row matrix $\mathbf{a}^{(i)}$ lies in the following circumstances. First, $\mathbf{a}^{(1)}$ is easy to write. Second,

---

[4] This assumption has been removed in Magee, Gibbs, and Newell (1965).

the matrix, designated as $\mathbf{G}^{i-1,i}$, which converts $\mathbf{a}^{(i-1)}$ into $\mathbf{a}^{(i)}$ is identical with $\mathbf{G}^{i,i+1}$ for all i. (This is not true for $\mathbf{G}^{n-1,n}$ unless we relax the "no-dangling" condition at the end of the chain or accommodate this condition by taking our partition function to be the sum not over all elements of $\mathbf{a}^{(n)}$ but only over certain elements; it would not be true in general for copolymeric chains.) We therefore write this matrix simply as $\mathbf{G}$. Third, the dimensionality of $\mathbf{G}$ is not greater than the number of states available to a residue of the n-mer ($P + 1$ in our case) if, as in the present case, only nearest-neighbor "stacking" interactions are considered.

The element of G_{JK} of $\mathbf{G}$ is clearly the unnormalized probability that state K of segment $(i + 1)$ can follow state J of segment i. If we take the unbonded (except perhaps to solvent) state as the zero point for both hydrogen bond energy and stacking energy, write ΔE_H for the hydrogen bond energy and ΔE_S for the stacking energy thus defined, "normalize" our partition function in such a way that the term in it corresponding to the completely unbonded random coil is unity (Magee, Gibbs, and Zimm, 1963; Magee, Gibbs, and Newell, 1965), write λ for the absolute activity ($\lambda = e^{\mu/kT}$, where μ is the corresponding chemical potential), and write Z_1, Z_2, and Z_3 for various internal (rotational and vibrational) partition function ratios (or degeneracies in the simplest view), then we may write the various types of elements of $\mathbf{G}$ as follows:

$$G_{0,1} = \lambda Z_1 \exp\left[-\Delta E_H/kT\right] = \lambda Z_1 M^{-1},$$

$$G_{p,1} = \lambda Z_2 \exp\left[-\Delta E_H/kT\right] \exp\left[-\Delta E_S/kT\right] = \lambda Z_2 M^{-(a+1)},$$

$$G_{J,J+1} = Z_3 \exp\left[-\Delta E_H/kT\right] \exp\left[-\Delta E_S/kT\right]$$
$$= Z_3 M^{-(a+1)} \quad \text{for} \quad 1 \le j \le p - 1,$$

$$G_{p,0} = G_{0,0} = 1,$$

$$G_{JK} = 0 \text{ for all other cases (no "dangling" or "looping" allowed).}$$

The new variables M and a have been introduced solely to simplify the expressions.

The matrix $\mathbf{G}$ may now be written as

$$\mathbf{G} = (G_{JK}) = \begin{bmatrix} 1 & \lambda Z_1 M^{-1} & 0 & 0 & \cdots & 0 \\ 0 & 0 & Z_3 M^{-(a+1)} & 0 & \cdots & 0 \\ 0 & 0 & 0 & Z_3 M^{-(a+1)} & \cdots & 0 \\ \vdots & \vdots & \vdots & \vdots & \vdots & \vdots \\ 0 & 0 & 0 & 0 & \cdots & Z_3 M^{-(a+1)} \\ 1 & \lambda Z_2 M^{-(a+1)} & 0 & 0 & \cdots & 0 \end{bmatrix}.$$

$$(10.9)$$

The row matrix $\mathbf{a}^{(1)}$ for the first n-mer segment is identical with the first row of $\mathbf{G}$. A column matrix which is identical with the first column of $\mathbf{G}$ and which we designate as $\mathbf{e}^{\dagger}$ will also have a special significance in that post-multiplication of $\mathbf{a}^{(n)}$ by it will effect the sum over just those terms of $\mathbf{a}^{(n)}$ that obey the no-dangling condition at the end of the chain.

The general procedure for evaluation of a partition function by this matrix method is straightforward and, of course, independent of many of the detailed properties of $\mathbf{G}$. It is clear from what has been said that $\mathbf{a}^{(n)}$ can be generated from $\mathbf{a}^{(1)}$ by $n-1$ applications of $\mathbf{G}$ and that the (semi-grand) partition function γ can then be obtained from $\mathbf{a}^{(n)}$ by post-multiplication by $\mathbf{e}^{\dagger}$:

$$\gamma = \mathbf{a}^{(n)}\mathbf{e}^{\dagger} = \mathbf{a}^{(1)}\mathbf{G}^{n-1}\mathbf{e}^{\dagger}. \tag{10.10}$$

If $\mathbf{G}$ can be diagonalized by a transformation,

$$\mathbf{\Lambda} = \mathbf{T}^{-1}\mathbf{G}\mathbf{T}, \tag{10.11}$$

$\mathbf{G}^{n-1}$ may be written as

$$\mathbf{G}^{n-1} = (\mathbf{T}\mathbf{\Lambda}\mathbf{T}^{-1})^{n-1} = \mathbf{T}\mathbf{\Lambda}^{n-1}\mathbf{T}^{-1}, \tag{10.12}$$

and calculations are simplified, the elements of $\mathbf{\Lambda}^{n-1}$ being just the $(n-1)$th powers of the corresponding elements of $\mathbf{\Lambda}$. Substituting equation (10.12) into equation (10.10) and letting $n \to \infty$, one can easily show that, in this case,

$$\log \gamma \cong n \log X_{(max)}, \tag{10.13}$$

where $X_{(max)}$ is the largest element of $\mathbf{\Lambda}$. Since the eigenvalues of $\mathbf{G}$ are invariant under the similarity transformation, the problem is reduced to the solution of the characteristic equation of $\mathbf{G}$ for its maximum root.

The thermodynamic energy U can now be obtained from the standard statistico-mechanical formula

$$U = -k[\partial \log \gamma/\partial(1/T)]_{\lambda,n},$$

or

$$U = -\Delta E_H(\partial \log \gamma/\partial \log m)_{\lambda,n}, \tag{10.14}$$

the subscripts, λ, n, indicating the variables being held constant under the partial differentiation, in accordance with the usual custom peculiar to thermodynamics.

This procedure applied to the present problem yields results which, as exemplified by the energy-temperature curve, must be described as highly cooperative, just as in the polypeptide case. Two particular features of the results obtained from an approximation to the characteristic equation of **G** should be noted. First, the reciprocal of a "transition temperature" (roughly the mid-point or inflection point of the sharp transition in the U versus T curve) is a linear function of the reciprocal of the degree of polymerization, p, of the oligonucleotides. Second, the reciprocal of this "transition temperature" is a linear function of the negative logarithm of the absolute activity, λ, of the oligonucleotides. The former of these results has also been observed experimentally (Steiner and Beers, 1961, p. 224); the latter has not been investigated but is in accordance with approximate expectations from more elementary considerations (law of mass action).

In summary, we should note that the treatment of the cooperative transitions in both of these classes of macromolecular systems has involved the use of only very simple mathematics, primarily because it has been possible to represent the relevant combinatorial features by a one-dimensional physical model. When, however, one progresses to related "Ising problems" in two dimensions, the situation is very different indeed, the solution, by Onsager, of even the simplest of these having involved the use of mathematical devices well beyond the ken of most chemists.

It is particularly unfortunate that no experimentally attainable system corresponds closely to this two-dimensional problem that Onsager was able to solve, since three-dimensional cooperative problems, that would correspond to phase transitions (e.g., melting and boiling), have proved completely intractable. Interaction between theory and experiment is, of course, required for the evaluation of unknown parameters and hence for the development of that appreciation of the relative significances of various effects which the chemist often calls "physical intuition." Therefore, the discovery of cooperative transitions in simple synthetic homopolypeptides and homopolynucleotides, reasonably good one-dimensional theoretical models for which could be given exact treatments, as we have seen, is of considerable interest to the physical chemist, who nevertheless continues to await theoretical developments in three dimensions with primary interest.

The biochemist, on the other hand, will want to know, in the case of the polypeptides, the extent to which the particular cooperative effects that we have been able to elucidate in the synthetic homopolymers are important in the reversible "denaturations" of the corresponding naturally occurring copolymers, the proteins, the latter transitions being complicated and perhaps dominated by varieties of interactions between side groups that we have not discussed.

In the case of polynucleotides, the biochemist will want to know how the polymerization of new strands of DNA, in gene "replication," and of RNA, in gene "transcription," is coupled to the requisite unravelling of the two parental DNA strands. That the unravelling will not occur without the free energy decrease associated with some process (probably the polymerization reaction but perhaps involving a protein) other than the mere adsorption of monomers can be seen from the following argument. One can, in a thermodynamic discussion, decompose the process into two steps, whether or not the overall process occurs this way:

1. The unravelling of the parental strands into two randomly coiled polymer molecules;
2. The subsequent adsorption of monomers onto each.

With reasonable conditions of pH, salt concentration, etc., Step 1 only occurs at temperatures well above ordinary physiological temperatures (high transition temperature, T_0, when both n and p are large); that is, the helix is more stable than the random coils at ordinary temperatures, and the transition will not occur by itself (positive free energy change). Step 2 only occurs at temperatures well below ordinary physiological temperatures (low transition temperature, T_0, when $p = 1$ and λ is not very large); that is, at moderate monomer concentrations (small λ) the separated random coils and monomers are more stable than the complexes that might be formed by Watson-Crick bonding of monomers to the randomly coiled polymers, and this process will not occur (positive free energy change). The free energy change for the overall process is thus the sum of two positive free energy changes, and the overall process cannot occur by itself. That monomers are poor competitors of polymers in the matter of bonding to polymers is clear from the obvious proposition that n monomers gain more entropy on release from binding than does an n-mer.

Our discussion of polynucleotides has thus brought us very close to the important question of biological control of gene "replication" (synthesis of DNA) and "transcription" (synthesis of RNA and, subsequently, protein). Our discussion of polypeptides raises not only the question of their suitability as models for proteins but also the question of a possible role for cooperative reversible protein "denaturations," or related conformational changes, in physiological processes. We have, at the moment, no definite answers to these questions, but important information is being gathered in a great many laboratories at a remarkable rate. Not being a biochemist, I am free to say it; biochemistry is the science of our time.

REFERENCES

DOTY, P., and J. T. YANG. 1956. J. Amer. Chem. Soc., 78:498.
GIBBS, J. H., and E. A. DiMARZIO. 1959. J. Chem. Phys., 30:271.
KRAMERS, H. A., and G. H. WANNIER. 1941. Phys. Rev., 60:252, 263.
MAGEE, W. S., Jr., J. H. GIBBS, and G. F. NEWELL. 1965. J. Chem. Phys., 43:2115.

MAGEE, W. S., JR., J. H. GIBBS, and B. H. ZIMM. 1963. Biopolymers, 1:133.
MANDEL, M. 1964. Proc. Nat. Acad. Sci., U. S., 52:736.
McDONALD, C. C., W. D. PHILLIPS, and S. PENMAN. 1964. Science, 144:1234.
McTAGUE, J. P., V. ROSS, and J. H. GIBBS. 1964. Biopolymers, 2:163.
MONTROLL, E. W. 1941. J. Chem. Phys., 9:706.
ONSAGER, L. 1944. Phys. Rev., 65:117.
PAULING, L., and R. B. COREY. 1951. Proc. Nat. Acad. Sci. U. S., 37:241.
STEINER, R. F., and R. F. BEERS, JR. 1961. Polynucleotides. Amsterdam: Elsevier.
WATSON, J. D., and F. H. C. CRICK. 1953. Nature, 171:737.
ZIMM, B. H., and J. K. BRAGG. 1959. J. Chem. Phys., 31:526.
ZIMM, B. H., P. DOTY, and K. ISO. 1959. Proc. Nat. Acad. Sci. U. S., 45:1601.

DISCUSSION

C. N. YANG: It seems to me that the statistical mechanics for a one-dimensional problem like this is mathematically very simple. Is the application, to which you are using it, giving a realistic description of the biological phenomenon? For example, in the case of the polypeptide chain, is it true that the hydrogen bonds in order of magnitude of energy are reasonable in quantitative terms?

J. H. GIBBS: Yes, you are right; it is a very simple problem. The importance of the treatments of the cases I discussed is that they do check out very nicely with the experimental results *in vitro* on the synthetic polypeptides and polynucleotides respectively, by which I mean two things: first, that the thermal profiles of the transitions, as studied by optical rotation, for example, fit the experimental data for various chain lengths, and, second, that the values of the relevant parameters, the hydrogen bond energies and the internal partition functions for rotation, etc., that are needed to fit the data are well within our experimental knowledge of what they ought to be.

C. N. YANG: Including the geometrical factor?

J. H. GIBBS: About the Z factor, or internal partition function ratio, we, of course, know very little. This is the price we pay for the internal averaging, disguised in this factor, that lends rigor to the calculation. In the polypeptide case, I think the number we needed was something like 20; Pauling has argued that a closely related number might be as high as 72, and others have argued that it should be as small as 3, so this does not really provide much of a check. The hydrogen bond energy, which is actually a difference between such energies when the hydrogen bonding to and among solvent molecules is allowed for, comes out about right, and the stacking energy, which, in the case of nucleic acid transition, governs the cooperative character, also proves to be reasonable. The biologically occurring polymers, and their environments *in vivo*, require much more intensive study.

11
Cluster Size and Percolation Theory[1]

MICHAEL E. FISHER

King's College, University of London,
visiting at *The Rockefeller Institute**

STATEMENT OF THE PROBLEM

Consider a lattice L defined as a connected linear graph of N sites (or vertices) and M bonds (or lines). In most cases of practical interest, L will be a regular two- or three-dimensional space lattice (or network) of finite or infinite extent. Of particular interest are the plane square (S), triangular (T), and honeycomb (H) lattices and the three-dimensional simple cubic, body-centered cubic, and face-centered cubic lattices.

In the *bond problem*, each bond of L is *occupied* (or *active*, or *colored black*, or *open*, etc.) with probability p or *vacant* with probability $q = 1 - p$. (Different probabilities might be contemplated for different bonds, but we shall neglect this complication.) Occupied bonds are *connected* if they meet at a common site, and a connected set of s bonds forms a *bond cluster* of size s. In the *site problem*, each site is occupied with probability p and vacant with probability q. Occupied sites are connected to form *site clusters* if they are adjacent through the bonds of L.

The task is to calculate such quantities as $K(p)$, the expected number of bond (or site) clusters per site of L, the probability $F(p)$ that a randomly chosen bond (or site) belongs to a cluster (of size $s = 1, 2, 3, \cdots$), the mean cluster size $S(p)$, and so on.

Instances of this problem, which was first introduced by Broadbent and Hammersley (1957) for bonds and by Domb (1959) for sites, arise in many contexts. Two examples will suffice. Consider an orchard of regularly arrayed fruit trees. An infection is introduced on a few trees and spreads from one tree to an adjacent one with probability p. How many trees will be infected? Will the infection assume epidemic proportions and run through the whole orchard, leaving only isolated pockets of

---

* At Cornell University from July 1966.

healthy trees? How far apart should the trees be spaced to ensure that p is so small that any outbreak is confined locally? This is a bond or "percolation" problem, the infection being thought of as percolating through the orchard via the "open" bonds linking adjacent trees.

An example of the site problem is a random crystalline alloy of magnetic and nonmagnetic ions in proportions p to q (see, for example, Sato, Arrott, and Kikuchi, 1959, and Elliott, Heap, Morgan, and Rushbrooke, 1960). Adjacent magnetic ions interact, and so clusters of different sizes have different magnetic susceptibilities. If the magnetic ions are sufficiently concentrated, infinite clusters can form, and at a low enough temperature long-range ferromagnetic order can spread through the whole crystal. Below a certain density of magnetic ions, no such ordering can take place.

CRITICAL PROBABILITIES

The above examples show heuristically that for an infinite lattice L there will be a critical probability $p_c = p_c(b, L)$ or $p_c(s, L)$ for the bond or site problems such that for $p < p_c$ all clusters will be finite while for $p > p_c$ there will, with positive probability, be an infinite cluster in L. More formally, if

$$F(p) = F_1(p) + F_2(p) + F_3(p) + \cdots \tag{11.1}$$

is the probability that a bond (or site) belongs to a *finite* cluster of size 1, 2, 3, $\cdots$, then, since the probability of belonging to any cluster is just p, the probability of belonging to an *infinite* cluster is

$$R(p) = p - F(p). \tag{11.2}$$

The critical probability is now defined by

$$p_c = \limsup_{R(p)=0} p. \tag{11.3}$$

It is clearly of great interest to calculate p_c and, if possible, $R(p)$ itself.

The complete analytic solution of the cluster size and percolation problem has been obtained only for special and somewhat artificial lattices (Fisher and Essam, 1961). In particular, for a *Bethe lattice* B, (or an infinite Cayley tree) of constant coordination number ν, one finds that $p_c = 1/(\nu - 1)$. Futhermore, one discovers that the onset of the formation of an infinite cluster is signaled by the divergence of the mean cluster size $S(p)$, which behaves like $1/|p_c - p|$ as $p \to p_c$. The density $R(p)$ of the infinite cluster in the lattice increases linearly with $(p - p_c)$ as p rises above the critical probability. Correspondingly, $F(p)$ and the mean number of clusters $K(p)$ are both nonanalytic functions at $p = p_c$.

One anticipates that nonanalyticity at $p = p_c$ should be a general feature of the problem for any infinite lattice, whereas the particular type of singularity [for example, $S(p)$ diverging as a simple pole] probably depends on the nature of the lattice and especially on its dimensionality.

FORMULATION AS A GRAPH-EMBEDDING PROBLEM

To indicate how the problem is solved on the Bethe lattices and how it may be studied numerically on a more general lattice, we shall show that it is equivalent to a certain combinatorial graph-embedding problem. Indeed, many problems in statistical mechanics reduce to this same general type of embedding problem (see, for example, Fisher and Sykes, 1959).

For concreteness, let us consider the bond problem on a plane square lattice of N sites (wrapped on a torus to avoid "edge effects"), and let us ask for the mean number of bond clusters of one bond. Now there are $2N$ bonds on the lattice. The probability that one of them is occupied is p, but in order for it to be an isolated cluster, the six adjacent *perimeter* bonds must be vacant. The mean density (expected number per site) of "one-clusters" is thus $2pq^6$. Similarly, two-clusters have a perimeter of eight bonds, so their density is $6p^2q^8$. There are various shapes and types of three-cluster, one of which has a different perimeter and must therefore be considered separately. Continuing, we thus have in total

$$K(p) = 2pq^6 + 6p^2q^8 + \cdots , \tag{11.4}$$

or for small p, putting $q = 1 - p$,

$$K(p) = 2p - 6p^2 + \cdots , \tag{11.5}$$

while for p near unity, that is, small q, we have

$$K(p) = 2q^6 - 2q^7 + \cdots . \tag{11.6}$$

In general, we may introduce the basic two-variable generating function

$$H(x, y) = \sum_{s,t} h_{s,t} x^s y^t, \tag{11.7}$$

where $Nh_{s,t}$ is the number of distinct clusters of size s and perimeter t that can be constructed on L. We then have

$$K(p) = H(p, q), \tag{11.8}$$

$$R(p) = p - [(x \, \partial/\partial x)H(x, y)]_{x=p, y=q}, \tag{11.9}$$

and, for $p < p_c$,

$$S(p) = [(x \, \partial/\partial x)^2 H(x, y)]_{x=p, y=q}, \tag{11.10}$$

with similar formulas for other moments of the distribution of cluster size.

The simplicity of a Bethe lattice B_ν follows from the observation that although there are many possible types of bond clusters, the size and perimeter are uniquely related by

$$t = (\nu - 2)s + \nu. \tag{11.11}$$

The generating function $H(x, y)$ thus depends on a function of only a single variable. By using the fact that $R(p) \equiv 0$ for $p < p_c$, we can then show that

$$H(x, y) = y^\nu \beta_\nu(xy^{\nu-2}), \tag{11.12}$$

where

$$\beta_\nu(z) = (1/\nu)[2 - \nu X(z)][1 - X(z)]^{-\nu}, \tag{11.13}$$

in which $X(z)$ is the root of

$$X(1 - X)^{\nu-2} = z, \tag{11.14}$$

which vanishes with z (Fisher and Essam, 1961). From these formulas follow the results for $K(p)$, $R(p)$, and $S(p)$ mentioned above. In particular, $K(p)$ is analytic for all real $0 \le p \le 1$ except at $p = p_c = 1/(\nu - 1)$. These results may be extended to certain more general lattices such as a *cactus* (Husimi tree of triangles) and decorated Bethe lattices (Fisher and Essam, 1961).

From its definition, we see that the coefficients $h_{s,t}$ may be calculated by considering all possible ways of embedding finite linear graphs of s lines in the lattice L. Formally, let G_l^v be a connected linear graph of v vertices and l lines. We define a *weak embedding* of G in L by the condition:

Each vertex of G must lie on a distinct site of L and each line of G on a distinct bond of L (that is, G is a subgraph of L).

The number of distinct weak embeddings $(G_l^v)^L$ is a basic property of the relation of G to L. Domb and Sykes have termed this number the *lattice constant* of G in L (in the "high-temperature" sense; see Domb, 1960).

If we further specify that the embedding must have a *definite number t of perimeter bonds*, and if we denote this more specialized lattice constant by $(G_l^v)_t^L$, we can express the basic generating function for the bond problem as

$$H(x, y; b, L) = \sum_G (G_s^v)_t^L x^s y^t, \tag{11.15}$$

where the sum runs over all connected linear graphs.

For the site problem, we need to define *strong embedding* by the additional condition:

If two vertices of G lie on two sites of L which are directly connected by a bond of L, then a line of G must lie on this bond (that is, the neighboring site connectivity of L must be retained in G).

The corresponding number of *strong embeddings*[2] $[G_i^s]_L$ may be further restricted by specifying a *definite number t of perimeter sites* (these being the sites that must be vacant if G is to correspond to an isolated cluster of v sites). If we denote this restricted lattice constant by $[G_i^s]_L^t$, we can express the generating function for the site problem as

$$H(x, y; s, L) = \sum_G [G_i^s]_L^t x^s y^t, \qquad (11.16)$$

the sum again running over all connected graphs.

It is interesting to note that the exact solution (11.12), (11.13), and (11.14) for the Bethe lattice is equivalent to the combinatorial result

$$t_n(B_\nu) = \nu(\nu - 1)[(\nu-1)n+\nu-2]!/n\,![(\nu-2)n+\nu]!, \qquad (11.17)$$

where

$$t_n(B_\nu) = \sum_{\text{trees}} (T_n^{m+1})^{B_\nu} \qquad (11.18)$$

is the number per site of trees of n lines that can be embedded in a Bethe lattice.

NUMERICAL METHODS

By calculating the appropriate lattice constants, we may derive $H(x, y)$ and thence series for $K(p)$, $R(p)$, and $S(p)$. Numerical estimation of the radius of convergence of the series for $S(p)$ yields an estimate of the critical point p_c. This method has been used to study the principal two- and three-dimensional lattices (Domb and Sykes, 1961, and Sykes and Essam, 1964a). For example, from nine or ten terms of the series, the estimates for the bond problem on the square, triangular, and honeycomb lattices are

$$p_c(b, S) \simeq 0.500, \qquad (11.19)$$

$$p_c(b, T) \simeq 0.344, \qquad (11.20)$$

and

$$p_c(b, H) \simeq 0.656, \qquad (11.21)$$

with "uncertainties" of ± 0.004. These limits are, of course, in no sense strict bounds, and it is very desirable to have rigorous checks on the

---

[2] These numbers have been termed lattice constants in the "low-temperature" sense (see Domb, 1960). There is a general linear relation between $(G_i^s)^L$ and $[G_i^s]_L$.

accuracy of the extrapolation procedures used. As we shall see, some such checks are now available.

With the aid of electronic digital computers, Monte Carlo methods have also been used to study the problem on large finite lattices (Frisch, Gordon, Vyssotsky, and Hammersley, 1962; Frisch, Hammersley, and Welsh, 1962; Frisch, Sonnenblick, Vyssotsky, and Hammersley, 1961; Frisch, Vyssotsky, Gordon, and Hammersley, 1961; Dean, 1963). These calculations lead to estimates of the critical probabilities for infinite lattices. Typical results are

$$p_c(b, S) \simeq 0.493 \pm 0.013, \qquad 0.492 \pm 0.011, \qquad (11.22)$$

$$p_c(b, T) \simeq 0.341 \pm 0.011, \qquad 0.329 \pm 0.021, \qquad (11.23)$$

and

$$p_c(b, H) \simeq 0.640 \pm 0.18, \qquad 0.635 \pm 0.020, \qquad (11.24)$$

where the uncertainties represent standard deviations but do not allow for possible bias effects (which, in the absence of an exact solution, are difficult, if not impossible, to rule out).

To see how checks on the approximate numerical calculations may be provided, we turn now to the mathematical theory that has been developed.

CONNECTIVITY RELATIONS

Certain relations between the critical probabilities for different lattices follow from simple topological considerations (Fisher, 1961). Thus, suppose that a lattice L *contains* a lattice L' in the sense that L' can be derived from L by the removal of certain bonds and sites. Since such removal could only reduce the size of any finite or infinite cluster, we have the inequality

$$p_c(L) \leq p_c(L') \qquad (11.25)$$

for both the site and bond problems. This yields the chain of inequalities

$$p_c(T) \leq p_c(S) \leq p_c(H) \qquad (11.26)$$

and similar inequalities for the three cubic lattices.

A useful concept is that of the *covering lattice* L^c of a lattice L (see Fisher, 1961). This is constructed by replacing each bond of L by a site and connecting these sites so that if two bonds of L meet at a vertex of L, the corresponding sites of L^c are joined by a direct bond of L^c (see Figure 1). We discover, for example, that the covering lattice of the honeycomb net is the kagomé lattice. Similarly, the covering lattice of the square net is found to be a checkerboard of alternate squares and complete graphs of four vertices (see Figure 2).

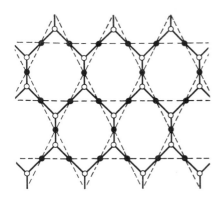

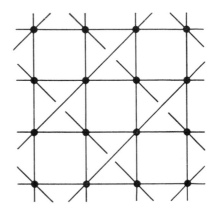

FIGURE 1. The honeycomb lattice (open circles and solid lines) and its covering lattice, the kagomé lattice (solid circles and broken lines)

FIGURE 2. Covering lattice of the square net. This is a semiplanar lattice based on the square net.

From the definition of L^C, it is clear that the site problem on L^C is completely isomorphic to the bond problem on L so that, in particular, we have

$$p_c(b, L) \equiv p_c(s, L^C). \tag{11.27}$$

Since every lattice has a covering lattice, although the converse is false, the site problem includes the bond problem and is of greater generality. It is convenient, nonetheless, to retain the distinction since L^C is usually a more complicated lattice than L. Combining (11.27) and (11.25), we have

$$p_c(b, S) = p_c(s, S^C) \leq p_c(s, S) \tag{11.28}$$

and, similarly,

$$p_c(b, T) \leq p_c(s, T), \tag{11.29}$$

so that the critical probabilities for the bond problems on the square and triangular lattices are lower than those for the corresponding site problems (Fisher, 1961). In fact, Hammersley (1961) has shown that these are instances of the general theorem

$$p_c(b, L) \leq p_c(s, L). \tag{11.30}$$

RIGOROUS BOUNDS FOR CRITICAL PROBABILITIES

A lower bound for p_c on a general lattice may be obtained in terms of the *excluded volume problem*, which is concerned with self-avoiding random walks on a lattice (see, for example, Fisher and Sykes, 1959). This question is also a graph-embedding problem since the number of n-step, *self-avoiding walks* from the origin is simply

$$c_n(L) = 2(C_n^{m+1})^L, \qquad (11.31)$$

where C denotes an open chain of lines. It is known that the limit

$$\mu(L) = \lim_{n \to \infty} |c_n|^{1/n} \qquad (11.32)$$

exists (Hammersley and Morton, 1954); in addition, Broadbent and Hammersley (1957) have shown generally that

$$p_c(b, L) \geq 1/\mu(L). \qquad (11.33)$$

This result is easily extended to the site problem (Fisher, 1961), or we may use (11.30).

For a Bethe lattice, $c_n = \nu(\nu - 1)^{n-1}$, and this bound is best possible. For the square, triangular, and honeycomb lattices, known bounds on $\mu(L)$ (Fisher and Sykes, 1959) yield the rigorous bounds

$$p_c(b, S) \geq 0.369, \qquad (11.34)$$

$$p_c(b, T) \geq 0.222, \qquad (11.35)$$

and

$$p_c(b, H) \geq 0.519, \qquad (11.36)$$

but comparison with the numerical estimates (11.19) through (11.24) shows that these are rather weak.

Hammersley (1959) has shown how to compute certain upper bounds for p_c, but these also prove to be rather weak. The strongest bounds obtained so far are lower bounds for certain two-dimensional lattices derived by Harris (1960) and Fisher (1961).

PLANAR LATTICES

Harris considered the bond problem on the plane square lattice and proved that

$$p_c(b, S) \geq \tfrac{1}{2}. \qquad (11.37)$$

Comparison with the numerical estimates suggests quite strongly that this result is best possible, so that $p_c(b, S) = \tfrac{1}{2}$. It will also be noticed that the Monte Carlo estimates (11.22) seem to have a bias at least as large as the observed standard deviations. The reason for this is not understood.

Although Harris' proof is intricate and rather lengthy, the underlying ideas are quite simple. To introduce them, consider a particular configuration (or realization) Γ of occupied and vacant bonds on L appropriate to the probability p. This can be associated with a *complementary configuration* Γ' in which occupied and vacant bonds are exchanged and which hence corresponds to a *complementary probability* $p' = 1 - p$. Clearly, there is complete symmetry between the two situations; in particular, if the density of infinite clusters of *occupied* bonds is $R(p)$, then the density of infinite clusters of *vacant* bonds is $R(1 - p)$. Consequently, if $p_c < \frac{1}{2}$, there is a range of values of p (from p_c to $1 - p_c$) for which an infinite cluster of occupied bonds *coexists* with an infinite cluster of vacant bonds. Picturesquely, we may say that the lattice configuration then represents a "random sponge."

Any *planar lattice* L_2 (that is, a lattice that can be embedded in the plane without crossing bonds) has a (unique) *dual lattice* L_2^D which is constructed by placing a site in each *face* of L (including the infinite or *exterior face*) and joining sites in adjacent faces by bonds which may be drawn to cross the bonds of L_2 separating the faces (Figure 3). Thus,

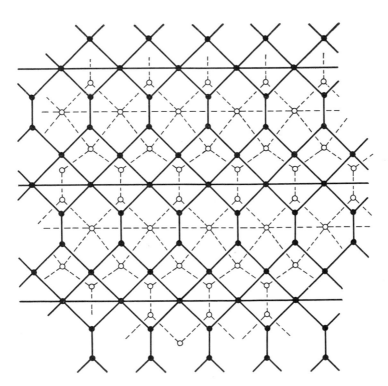

FIGURE 3. A planar lattice L_2 (solid circles and solid lines) and its dual L_2^D (open circles and broken lines). This particular lattice is self-dual.

the bonds in L_2 and L_2^D are in a one-one correspondence, and we may associate a configuration Γ on L_2 with the *complementary dual configuration* Γ^D on L_2^D (and corresponding probability $p^D = 1 - p$).

Now an infinite square lattice is planar and furthermore is *self-dual* ($S \equiv S^D$). Consequently, if we choose $p = \frac{1}{2}$, the situations on the lattice and its complementary dual are identical. Suppose now that $R(S; p = \frac{1}{2}) > 0$, so that with positive probability there is an infinite cluster of *occupied* bonds in S when $p = \frac{1}{2}$ (and hence an infinite cluster of *occupied* bonds on S^D). With this hypothesis Harris proves that:

A. *With probability one there is a closed (connected) chain of occupied bonds on the lattice which encloses the origin site O (and any specified finite region surrounding O).*

It follows that a similar chain exists on the complementary dual lattice S^D. But such a chain on S^D corresponds to a set of *vacant* bonds on S (not necessarily connected) which will *encircle the origin in the form of the perimeter of some finite cluster.* Consequently, with probability one the origin of L_2 belongs only to a *finite* cluster. But this implies that $R(S; \frac{1}{2}) = 0$, which contradicts the hypothesis. Thus, $R(S; \frac{1}{2}) = 0$, and it is clear that the critical probability cannot be less than $\frac{1}{2}$. This establishes the theorem (11.37). We might say that we have shown the impossibility of a "random sponge" based on the square lattice.

The mathematical complexity of Harris' proof arises in the difficulty of establishing assertion A rigorously. In particular, it is found necessary to prove similar intermediate results for infinite clusters lying first in a quarter-plane and then in a half-plane. These results are finally assembled with the aid of the reflection symmetry of the square lattice.

The proof of assertion A may be generalized for any dual pair of spatially uniform lattices[3] (see Fisher, 1961) to establish the assertion:

B. *The hypothesis $R(L_2; p) > 0$ implies $R(L_2^D; 1 - p) = 0$.*

In other words, one cannot simultaneously have infinite bond clusters on a lattice and on its complementary dual. Since $R(p)$ is an increasing function of p, this implies the inequality

$$p_c(b, L_2) + p_c(b, L_2^D) \geq 1, \qquad (11.38)$$

which relates the critical point of a planar lattice to that of its dual. The square lattice result (11.37) is a special case of (11.38), since for any self-dual lattice we will have

---

[3] One needs to assume that L_2 has two symmetry axes (which may then be chosen orthogonally) and that it is translationally invariant with a unit cell containing only finitely many sites and bonds.

$$p_c(b, L_2) \geq \tfrac{1}{2} \qquad (L_2 \equiv L_2^D). \tag{11.39}$$

Another example of a self-dual lattice is the lattice shown in Figure 3.

The honeycomb and triangular lattices are a dual pair, and an ingenious further argument due to Sykes and Essam (1963) enables us to obtain similarly strong lower bounds for them. Consider the *star-triangle transformation* which replaces alternate triangles of T by *stars* of three lines, thus converting T into H, as shown in Figure 4. The probabilities that one vertex of a transformed triangle is connected via its bonds (a) to neither of the other two vertices, (b) to only one other vertex, and (c) to both remaining vertices are:

$$P_a^T = 1 - 2p + p^2,$$

$$P_b^T = 2p(1 - p)^2, \qquad P_c^T = 3p^2 - 2p^3. \tag{11.40}$$

Similarly, for the *complementary* star in H (for which the bond occupation probability is $p' = 1 - p$), the connective probabilities are easily seen to be:

$$P_a^H = p + p^2 - p^3,$$

$$P_b^H = 2p(1 - p)^2, \qquad P_c^H = (1 - p)^3. \tag{11.41}$$

By comparing these formulas, we see that the two sets of connective probabilities will be identical when

$$1 - 3p + p^3 = 0, \tag{11.42}$$

which equation has the solution

$$p = p_0 = 2 \sin(\pi/18). \tag{11.43}$$

It follows that if, with positive probability, there is an infinite cluster on T when $p = p_0$, then there will be one on H when $p = 1 - p_0$. But

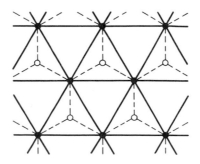

FIGURE 4. The star-triangle transformation of the triangular lattice into the honey-comb lattice

since H and T are dual lattices, assertion B shows that this is impossible. Consequently, we may deduce the lower bounds

$$p_c(b, T) \geq p_0 = 2\sin(\pi/18) = 0.347\ 296 \tag{11.44}$$

and

$$p_c(b, H) \geq 1 - p_0 = 0.652\ 701. \tag{11.45}$$

Comparison with the numerical estimates (11.19) through (11.24) suggests that these bounds may also be best possible and shows that the Monte Carlo estimates again seem to be biased low.

For the *site* problem on a planar lattice, it is sufficient to consider a *fully triangulated lattice* L_2^T, since any infinite planar lattice L_2 is contained in some suitable L_2^T. [Any face of L_2 which is not a triangle may be triangulated by drawing sufficiently many (noncrossing) diagonals to yield an L_2^T.] By (11.25), a lower bound for $p_c(s, L_2^T)$ will also be a lower bound for $p_c(s, L_2)$. In this case, we do not need to introduce the dual lattice, since if we can prove assertion A for L_2^T on the hypothesis $R(L_2^T; \frac{1}{2}) > 0$, then the equivalence with the complementary site problem $(p' = \frac{1}{2})$ shows that there will be a connected chain of *vacant* sites surrounding the origin.[4] Since the lattice is planar, such a chain of vacancies represents the perimeter of some *finite* cluster of occupied sites so that, as before, the origin belongs to a finite cluster with probability one; but this contradicts the hypothesis. We thus prove for the site problem on a planar lattice that

$$p_c(s, L_2) \geq \tfrac{1}{2}. \tag{11.46}$$

The numerical results for the plane triangular lattice suggest that (11.46) may be best possible for a triangulated lattice (although it will not be so for the square or honeycomb site problems). The Monte Carlo estimates

$$p_c(s, T) \simeq 0.493 \pm 0.018 \quad \text{and} \quad 0.486 \pm 0.017 \tag{11.47}$$

are once again systematically low.

DUALITY THEOREMS FOR THE BOND PROBLEM

The inequalities (11.38), (11.44), and (11.45) and the indications that they are best possible suggest that further relations might be found between the bond problems on a planar lattice and on its dual. Such a theorem has been discovered recently by Sykes and Essam (1963 and 1964b). They actually prove a more general theorem for the site problem (which, as explained, includes the bond problem), but we shall outline the proof for the bond problem in a form due to Kasteleyn (1963).

---

[4] The proof has been given by Fisher (1961) under the conditions stated in footnote 3.

We consider, in the first instance, a finite planar lattice and associate with each configuration Γ a *configuration graph* $G(\Gamma)$ formed of the N sites of L_2 and those bonds of L_2 which are occupied in the configuration Γ. In general, $G(\Gamma)$ will not be connected but will be made up of N_c connected parts. These will correspond either to bond clusters or to isolated points (see Figure 5), and so the expected number of connected parts will be

$$\langle N_c \rangle = N K_0(p) = N K(p) + N P(p). \tag{11.48}$$

Here $P(p)$ is the expected number of isolated points (per site), which is easily calculated: for example, if the lattice has a constant coordination number ν, we have

$$P(p) = q^\nu. \tag{11.49}$$

More generally, if $\nu(i)$ is the number of bonds leaving the ith site, the result is

$$NP(p) = \sum_{i=1}^{N} q^{\nu(i)}. \tag{11.50}$$

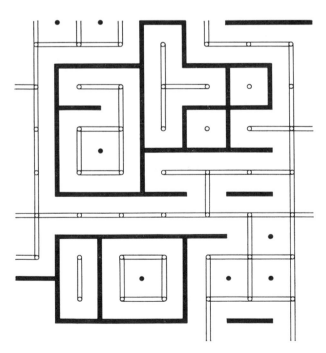

Figure 5. A configuration graph G on the square lattice (solid lines and solid circles) and its complementary dual graph G^D (open lines and open circles)

Knowledge of $K_0(p)$ is thus equivalent to knowledge of $K(p)$, but the former function is more convenient here.

Now for a connected planar graph of n_0 vertices, n_1 lines, and n_2' *interior* faces, we have Euler's famous theorem which may be stated as

$$n_0 - n_1 + n_2' = 1 \qquad (11.51)$$

(see, for example, Berge, 1962, chap. 21). By summing over the connected parts of an arbitrary planar graph of N_0 vertices, N_1 lines, N_2 faces (including now the single exterior face), and N_c connected parts, we prove the generalization

$$N_0 - N_1 + N_2 = N_c + 1, \qquad (11.52)$$

where the 1 represents the contribution of the infinite face.

Let us apply this theorem to each configuration graph $G(\Gamma)$ and average over all Γ. Then, since $N_0 = N$ and $\langle N_1 \rangle = Mp$, where M is the number of bonds of L_2, we have

$$N - Mp + \langle N_2 \rangle = \langle N_c \rangle + 1$$
$$= NK_0(p) + 1. \qquad (11.53)$$

To evaluate $\langle N_2 \rangle$, the expected number of faces of $G(\Gamma)$, consider the graph G^D of the complementary dual configuration Γ^D in which occupied bonds on L_2 correspond to vacant bonds on L_2^D, and vice versa. Now:

C. *Each face of G encloses a connected part of the dual graph G^D and hence encloses either a bond cluster on L_2^D or an isolated site. Conversely, each connected part of G^D is enclosed in a face of G.*[5]

This situation is illustrated in Figure 5 for a section of the square lattice. Thus, we have

$$\langle N_2 \rangle = \langle N_c^D \rangle = N^D K_0^D(1 - p), \qquad (11.54)$$

where N^D is the number of sites of L_2^D (and hence the number of faces of L_2) and where $K_0^D(p^n)$ is the corresponding mean cluster number (including isolated sites).

Substituting this result into the relation (11.53) yields

$$N - Mp + N^D K_0^D(1 - p) = NK_0(p) + 1. \qquad (11.55)$$

On applying Euler's theorem to the lattice L_2, we see that

$$N - M + N^D = 2. \qquad (11.56)$$

[5] These statements embody a lemma on planar graphs and their duals which is easily verified by inspection of examples. A formal proof, however, is available (Sykes and Essam, 1964b, and Kasteleyn, 1963).

Eliminating M yields the more symmetrical result

$$NK_0(p) + (N^D - 1)p = N^D K_0^D(1 - p) + (N - 1)(1 - p), \qquad (11.57)$$

which relates the expected number of clusters on a finite planar lattice L_2 at probability p to the expected number on the dual lattice at the complementary probability $1 - p$.

For a sufficiently regular sequence of finite lattices which approach an *infinite* planar lattice L_2 with mean coordination number

$$\bar{v} = \lim_{M \to \infty} 2M/N \qquad (11.58)$$

and a dual lattice L_2^D with mean coordination $\bar{v}^D$, we obtain the duality relation

$$\bar{v}^D[K_0(p) - (1 - p)] = \bar{v}[K_0^D(1 - p) - p], \qquad (11.59)$$

which for a *self-dual lattice* reduces to

$$K_0(p) = 1 - 2p + K_0(1 - p). \qquad (11.60)$$

From this remarkable theorem, we see that if the mean cluster number $K_0(p)$ [or $K(p)$] has a singularity of some sort at $p = p_1$, then on the dual lattice $K_0^D(p)$ has a similar singularity at $p_1^D = 1 - p_1$, so that for each singularity we have

$$p_1 + p_1^D = 1. \qquad (11.61)$$

The exact results for the Bethe lattices (Fisher and Essam, 1961) suggest strongly the truth of the following hypothesis:

D. *For real p $(0 < p < 1)$ the function $K_0(p)$ has only one singularity which occurs at the critical point $p = p_c$.*

Granted this hypothesis, we may write (11.61) as

$$p_c(b, L_2) + p_c(b, L_2^D) = 1. \qquad (11.62)$$

This would indeed show that the (rigorous) inequality (11.38) is best possible. Hypothesis D is very plausible, although so far a proof is lacking. Thus, we expect the mean number of (finite) clusters [and the derivatives of $K(p)$] to vary smoothly until the sudden appearance of an infinite cluster causes a nonanalytic change in behavior. Thereafter, the variation should once again be smooth. Our confidence is further increased by the somewhat analogous situation in the Ising problem for planar lattices, where there is a single singularity at the critical point which was correctly located by a similar duality argument (Onsager, 1944, and Wannier, 1945). Indeed, for any self-dual lattice, (11.62) yields

$$p_c(b, L_2) = \tfrac{1}{2} \qquad (L_2 \equiv L_2^D), \tag{11.63}$$

which confirms the conjecture that $p_c = \tfrac{1}{2}$ for the square net bond problem but also applies to the lattice of Figure 3. From (11.60) we see that $K_0(p)$ is continuous at the critical point (as it is for the Bethe lattices).

The rigorous lower bounds (11.44) and (11.45) for the triangular and honeycomb lattices are consistent with (11.62) only if they are actually attained (since they sum to unity). On the basis of the duality theorem and hypothesis D, we thus conclude that

$$p_c(b, T) = 2 \sin(\pi/18) \tag{11.64}$$

and

$$p_c(b, H) = 1 - 2 \sin(\pi/18). \tag{11.65}$$

Although these results cannot be regarded as established with complete rigor, they are undoubtedly correct.

By straightforward generalization of the duality theorem to the case where the bond probabilities are not all the same, and by a similar extension of the star-triangle transformation argument, we see that the critical equation for a triangular lattice with three different probabilities p_x, p_y, p_z along the hexagonal axes is simply

$$1 - p_x - p_y - p_z + p_x p_y p_z = 0 \tag{11.66}$$

(Sykes and Essam, 1963). [This result should be compared with equation (11.42).] Putting $p_z = 0$ yields the result for an asymmetric square lattice, namely,

$$p_x + p_y = 1. \tag{11.67}$$

MATCHING THEOREMS FOR THE SITE PROBLEM

As demonstrated by the construction of the covering lattice, the duality theorems for the bond problem imply similar theorems for corresponding site problems. In general, the covering lattice L_2^C of a planar lattice L_2 will not be planar since crossing bonds are necessarily introduced (consider S^C, see Figure 2). However, Sykes and Essam discovered that L_2^C always belongs to a more general class of lattices for which we may introduce the term *semiplanar*.

A semiplanar lattice L_σ is defined as a lattice which can be constructed from an *underlying planar lattice* L_2 by converting any of the faces of L_2 into *multifaces* which are made by drawing (internally) all possible diagonals of the chosen faces. A multiface of v vertices is thus a complete graph of $\frac{1}{2}v(v-1)$ lines. The covering lattice of the square net is clearly a semiplanar lattice obtained from the square net by the completion of alternate faces (see Figure 2).

Sykes and Essam (1964b) have further shown that each semiplanar lattice L_σ has a *matching lattice* $L_\sigma^\dagger$ which is the analog of a dual lattice for a planar lattice. The matching lattice is constructed by replacing all multifaces of L_σ by ordinary faces and completing all ordinary faces to multifaces. Clearly, the matching lattice is a semiplanar lattice based on the same underlying planar lattice (and hence having the same number of sites). We also have

$$(L_\sigma^\dagger)^\dagger = L_\sigma. \tag{11.68}$$

From the definition, we may verify that the matching lattice of a covering lattice is the covering lattice of the dual lattice, that is,

$$(L_2^C)^\dagger = (L_2^D)^C. \tag{11.69}$$

Thus, the covering lattice of a self-dual lattice is *self-matching* (as can be checked from Figure 2). Since a triangular face is already complete, it is evident that *any fully triangulated lattice is self-matching*.

Now Euler's theorem may be extended to semiplanar lattices by defining the weight of a multiface of v vertices as

$$w_v = 1 + \tfrac{1}{2}v(v-3). \tag{11.70}$$

In analogy with our previous definition of the graph of a bond configuration in L_2, we may define the graph G_σ of a *site configuration* in L_σ (by selecting the occupied sites) and apply the extended Euler's theorem to it. We have to prove that the faces of G_σ enclose the connected parts of the *complementary graph* $G_\sigma^\dagger$ on the *matching lattice*, and vice versa (Sykes and Essam, 1964b). Averaging over all configurations, we finally establish a matching theorem which may be written in the symmetric form

$$\boxed{K(p) - g(p) = K^\dagger(1-p) - g^\dagger(1-p),} \tag{11.71}$$

where $K(p)$ and $K^\dagger(p)$ are the expected number of *site* clusters (per site) of L_σ and $L_\sigma^\dagger$. The matching function $g(p)$ may be defined by

$$g(p) = \tfrac{1}{2}p + \tfrac{1}{2}\sum_{v=3} \pi_v[2p^v - v(p^2 - \tfrac{1}{2}) - 1], \tag{11.72}$$

where π_v is the number of *ordinary* faces of v vertices (per site) of L_σ [and similarly for $g^\dagger(p)$].

For any infinite, fully triangulated (and hence self-matching) lattice, the matching relation reduces to

$$K(p) = p(1 - p)(1 - 2p) + K(1 - p) \qquad (11.73)$$

(Sykes and Essam, 1964b).

If, as before, we accept hypothesis D concerning the singularities of $K(p)$, we conclude from (11.71) that

$$p_c(s, L_\sigma) + p_c(s, L_\sigma^\dagger) = 1. \qquad (11.74)$$

By (11.69), this includes the bond duality relation (11.62). Finally, for a fully triangulated lattice, we obtain

$$p_c(s, L_2^T) = \tfrac{1}{2}. \qquad (11.75)$$

This result confirms that the bound (11.46) is best possible. As for the square net bond problem, we see from (11.73) that $K(p)$ will be continuous at p_c.

CONCLUSIONS

It is tempting to speculate, in the light of the history of the Ising problem (Onsager, 1944, and Wannier, 1945), that these duality and matching relations foreshadow the complete analytic calculation of the mean size functions $K(p)$ for a range of lattices. More pessimistically, however, we should perhaps recall the duality relations for the generalized Ising model with r equally probable species of atom (Ashkin and Teller, 1943, and Potts, 1952). These relations, discovered over ten years ago, locate the critical point for the square lattice [at $\tanh (J/kT_c) = 1/(1 + \sqrt{r})$], but they have not yet been followed by a complete solution.

ACKNOWLEDGMENTS

I am most grateful to Dr. M. F. Sykes and to Professor P. W. Kasteleyn for fruitful discussions and correspondence. I am also indebted to them and to Dr. J. W. Essam for informing me of their unpublished work on which much of this lecture has been based.

REFERENCES

ASHKIN, J., and E. TELLER. 1943. Statistics of two-dimensional lattices with four components. Phys. Rev., 64:178.

BERGE, C. 1962. The theory of graphs. New York: Wiley.

BROADBENT, S. R., and J. M. HAMMERSLEY. 1957. Percolation processes. I: Crystals and mazes. Proc. Cambridge Philos. Soc., 53:629.

DEAN, P. 1963. A new Monte Carlo method for percolation problems on a lattice. Proc. Cambridge Philos. Soc., 59:397.

DOMB, C. 1959. Conference on "Fluctuation phenomena and stochastic processes" at Birkbeck College, London, March 1959. Nature, 184:509.

———. 1960. On the theory of cooperative phenomena in crystals. Advances in Phys., 9:sect. 5.1.

DOMB, C., and M. F. SYKES. 1961. Cluster size in random mixtures and percolation processes. Phys. Rev., 122:77.

ELLIOTT, R. J., B. R. HEAP, D. J. MORGAN, and G. S. RUSHBROOKE. 1960. Equivalence of the critical concentrations in the Ising and Heisenberg models of ferromagnetism. Phys. Rev. Letters, 5:366.

FISHER, M. E. 1961. Critical probabilities for cluster size and percolation problems. J. Math. Phys., 2:620.

FISHER, M. E., and J. W. ESSAM. 1961. Some cluster size and percolation problems. J. Math. Phys., 2:609.

FISHER, M. E., and M. F. SYKES. 1959. Excluded volume problem and the Ising model of ferromagnetism. Phys. Rev., 114:45.

FRISCH, H. L., S. B. GORDON, V. A. VYSSOTSKY, and J. M. HAMMERSLEY. 1962. Monte Carlo solution of bond percolation processes in various crystal lattices. Bell System Tech. J., 41:909.

FRISCH, H. L., J. M. HAMMERSLEY, and D. J. A. WELSH. 1962. Monte Carlo estimates of percolation probabilities for various lattices. Phys. Rev., 126:949.

FRISCH, H. L., E. SONNENBLICK, V. A. VYSSOTSKY, and J. M. HAMMERSLEY. 1961. Critical percolation probabilities (site problem). Phys. Rev., 124:1021.

FRISCH, H. L., V. A. VYSSOTSKY, S. B. GORDON, and J. M. HAMMERSLEY. 1961. Critical percolation probabilities (bond problem). Phys. Rev., 123:1566.

HAMMERSLEY, J. M. 1959. Bornes supérieures de la probabilité critique dans un processus de filtration *in* Le calcul des probabilités et ses applications (Colloques internationaux du centre national de la recherche scientifique, LXXXVII). Paris: Centre National de la Recherche Scientifique, 17–37.

———. 1961. Comparison of atom and bond percolation processes. J. Math. Phys., 2:728.

HAMMERSLEY, J. M., and K. W. MORTON. 1954. Poor man's Monte Carlo. J. Roy. Statist. Soc. Ser. B, 16:23.

HARRIS, T. E. 1960. A lower bound for the critical probability in a certain percolation process. Proc. Cambridge Philos. Soc., 56:13.

KASTELEYN, P. W. 1963. Personal communication.

ONSAGER, L. 1944. Crystal statistics. I: A two-dimensional model with an order-disorder transition. Phys. Rev., 65:117.

POTTS, R. B. 1952. Some generalized order-disorder transformations. Proc. Cambridge Philos. Soc., 48:106.

SATO, H., A. ARROTT, and R. KIKUCHI. 1959. Remarks on magnetically dilute systems. J. Phys. Chem. Solids, 10:19.

SYKES, M. F., and J. W. ESSAM. 1963. Some exact critical percolation probabilities for bond and site problems in two dimensions. Phys. Rev. Letters, 10:3.

———. 1964a. Critical percolation probabilities by series methods. Phys. Rev., 133:A310.

———. 1964b. Exact critical percolation probabilities for site and bond problems in two dimensions. J. Math. Phys., 5:1117.

WANNIER, G. H. 1945. Statistical problem in cooperative phenomena. Rev. Modern Phys., 17:50.

DISCUSSION

QUESTION: Is there any way of relating these critical probabilities to the transition points of the Ising problem?

M. E. FISHER: It seems to be very difficult. For the Ising problem, there is a very well-known method whereby you convert it into a matrix problem. One then needs to know the largest eigenvalue of the matrix which is of the order $2^N \times 2^N$. There *is* a matrix formulation of the percolation problem, but the order of the matrix is much larger; because you have to remember all the connectivity, it is something like $2^{N1} \times 2^{N1}$.

QUESTION: Is there any possibility that the error in the Monte Carlo methods came about from the numeral 1 which occurs on the right of equation (11.55) in the finite case but disappears in the infinite case? Would that be of the right magnitude? Presumably the lattice used was confined to the memory of the machine.

M. E. FISHER: That might be so. However, I think the general point with any Monte Carlo method is that you only know you are looking at an unbiased statistic if you have an analytical solution to the problem. That may be fine in population sampling, where you know what is an unbiased statistic. The trouble here is that you are not sure what is an unbiased statistic until you have solved the problem—which is what you are trying to do! So I do not think that is the answer.

QUESTION: What method of generating pseudorandom numbers were they using, or were they even using pseudorandom numbers?

M. E. FISHER: Various methods have been used, and I would guess that they were reasonably harmless.

12

Some Combinatorial Aspects of the Theory of Toeplitz Matrices

Mark Kac

The Rockefeller Institute

My topic is peripheral both to the subject of this symposium (combinatorial problems) and to the specific concern of this session (statistical mechanics). It is nevertheless a fact that in recent years many connections between the theory of Toeplitz matrices and various problems of statistical mechanics have been uncovered, and there is little doubt that many more will emerge. The reader interested in some of the physical background is referred to Montroll, Potts, and Ward (1963) and Lenard (1964); I shall confine myself here to a purely mathematical presentation.

Let $\{c_n\}$ be a sequence of complex numbers, with n ranging from $-\infty$ to $+\infty$.

An $m \times m$ Toeplitz matrix C_m is simply the matrix whose (i, j) element is c_{i-j}, $0 \leq i, j \leq m - 1$, that is,

$$C_m = [(c_{i-j})], \qquad 0 \leq i, j \leq m - 1. \tag{12.1}$$

It is convenient, though by no means necessary, to assume that

$$c_{-n} = c_n{}^*, \tag{12.2}$$

in which case C_m is Hermitian.

It is also assumed that

$$\sum_{-\infty}^{+\infty} c_n e^{in\theta}$$

is a Fourier series of a function $f(\theta)$, where

$$f(\theta) \sim \sum_{-\infty}^{+\infty} c_n e^{in\theta}.$$

For the purposes of our discussion, I shall further assume that

$$\sum_{-\infty}^{+\infty} |n| \, |c_n| < \infty, \tag{12.3}$$

which ensures that $f'(\theta)$ is continuous.[1]

One of the principal results is the following remarkable theorem of Szegö:

For sufficiently small $|\xi|$,

$$\lim_{m \to \infty} \frac{\det (I - \xi C_m)}{\exp \left\{ \dfrac{m}{2\pi} \displaystyle\int_{-\pi}^{\pi} \log [1 - \xi f(\theta)] \, d\theta \right\}} = \exp \left\{ \sum_{n=1}^{\infty} n \, |\gamma_n(\xi)|^2 \right\}, \qquad (12.4)$$

where

$$\gamma_n(\xi) = \frac{1}{2\pi} \int_{-\pi}^{\pi} \log [1 - \xi f(\theta)] e^{-in\theta} \, d\theta, \qquad (12.5)$$

and it is understood that the series

$$\sum_{n=1}^{\infty} n \, |\gamma_n(\xi)|^2 \qquad (12.6)$$

converges. If (12.6) diverges, the limit (12.4) is infinite.

If (12.2) does not hold, the series (12.6) should be replaced by

$$\sum_{n=1}^{\infty} n \gamma_n(\xi) \gamma_{-n}(\xi). \qquad (12.7)$$

What I consider most remarkable is that such a purely analytic result is implied by a simple combinatorial identity. Indeed, as I have shown elsewhere (see Kac, 1959), formula (12.4) is implied by the following lemma (first stated and proved by G. A. Hunt):

Let $a_1, \cdots, a_n$ be real numbers, and let

$$\sigma = \begin{pmatrix} 1, & 2, & \cdots, & n \\ \sigma_1, & \sigma_2, & \cdots, & \sigma_n \end{pmatrix} \qquad (12.8)$$

be a permutation.

Consider the numbers

$$a_{\sigma_1}, \; a_{\sigma_1} + a_{\sigma_2}, \; \cdots, \; a_{\sigma_1} + a_{\sigma_2} + \cdots + a_{\sigma_n},$$

and denote by $N(\sigma)$ the number of positive ones among them. Then

$$\sum_{\sigma} \max (0, a_{\sigma_1}, a_{\sigma_1} + a_{\sigma_2}, \cdots, a_{\sigma_1} + \cdots + a_{\sigma_n}) = \sum_{\sigma} N(\sigma) a_{\sigma_1}, \qquad (12.9)$$

where the summation is over *all* permutations σ.

---

[1] Much less will suffice, as shown by Baxter and Hirschman. See Hirschman (1965), where references to the work of Baxter can be found.

Let me sketch briefly how (12.9) is related to (12.4). First, it is easily proved that

$$\text{tr}\,\{C_m^n\} = \sum_{j=0}^{m} \lambda_j^n(m)$$

$$= \frac{m}{2\pi} \int_{-\pi}^{\pi} f^n(\theta)\, d\theta - \sum_{l_1 + \cdots + l_n = 0} [\max (0, l_1, l_1 + l_2, \cdots, l_1 + \cdots + l_{n-1})$$

$$- \min (0, l_1, l_1 + l_2, \cdots, l_1 + \cdots + l_{n-1})]_m\, c_{l_1} c_{l_2} \cdots c_{l_n}, \qquad (12.10)$$

where

$$[y]_m = y \quad \text{if} \quad y \le m, \quad \text{and} \quad m \quad \text{if} \quad y > m. \qquad (12.11)$$

Next, as $m \to \infty$, one proves, using (12.3) (or weaker conditions of Baxter and Hirschman), that

$$\lim_{m \to \infty} \left\{ \sum_{j=0}^{m} \lambda_j^n(m) - \frac{m}{2\pi} \int_{-\pi}^{\pi} f^n(\theta)\, d\theta \right\}$$

$$= -2 \sum_{l_1 + \cdots + l_n = 0} \max (0, l_1, \cdots, l_1 + \cdots + l_{n-1}) c_{l_1} c_{l_2} \cdots c_{l_n}. \qquad (12.12)$$

Since $c_{l_1} c_{l_2} \cdots c_{l_n}$ is invariant under *all* permutations, we have

$$\sum_{l_1 + \cdots + l_n = 0} \max (0, l_1, \cdots, l_1 + \cdots + l_{n-1}) c_{l_1} c_{l_2} \cdots c_{l_n}$$

$$= \sum_{l_1 + \cdots + l_n = 0} \max (0, l_1, \cdots, l_1 + \cdots + l_n) c_{l_1} c_{l_2} \cdots c_{l_n}$$

$$= \frac{1}{n!} \sum_{l_1 + \cdots + l_n = 0} c_{l_1} c_{l_n} \sum_{\sigma} \max (0, l_{\sigma_1}, \cdots, l_{\sigma_1} + \cdots + l_{\sigma_n})$$

$$= \frac{1}{n!} \sum_{l_1 + \cdots + l_n = 0} c_{l_1} \cdots c_{l_n} \sum_{\sigma} N(\sigma) l_{\sigma_1}$$

$$= \frac{1}{n!} \sum_{l_1 + \cdots + l_n = 0} \sum_{\sigma} N(\sigma) l_{\sigma_1} c_{l_{\sigma_1}} c_{l_{\sigma_n}}$$

$$= \sum_{l_1 + \cdots + l_n = 0} N(e) l_1 c_{l_1} \cdots c_{l_n}, \qquad (12.13)$$

where e is the identity permutation, and hence $N(e)$ is the number of positive numbers among

$$l_1, l_1 + l_2, \cdots, l_1 + \cdots + l_{n-1}.$$

Let

$$\theta(x) = \begin{cases} 1, & x > 0, \\ 0, & x \le 0, \end{cases}$$

and note that

$$N(e) = \sum_{k=1}^{n} \theta(l_1 + \cdots + l_k). \qquad (12.14)$$

Now,

$$\sum_{l_1 + \cdots + l_n = 0} N(e) l_1 c_{l_1} \cdots c_{l_n} = \sum_{l_1 + \cdots + l_n = 0} \sum_{k=1}^{n} l_1 \theta(l_1 + \cdots + l_k) c_{l_1} \cdots c_{l_n}$$

$$= \sum_{k=1}^{n} \sum_{l_1 + \cdots + l_n = 0} l_1 \theta(l_1 + \cdots + l_k) c_{l_1} \cdots c_{l_n}$$

$$= \sum_{k=1}^{n} \frac{1}{k} \sum_{l_1 + \cdots + l_n = 0} (l_1 + \cdots + l_k) \theta(l_1 + \cdots + l_k) c_{l_1} \cdots c_{l_n}.$$

In the last step I again make use of the commutativity of multiplication. Observe now that

$$\sum_{l_1 + \cdots + l_n = 0} (l_1 + l_2 + \cdots l_k) \theta(l_1 + \cdots + l_k) c_{l_1} \cdots c_{l_k} c_{l_{k+1}} \cdots c_{l_n}$$

$$= \sum_{l>0} l \Big(\sum_{l_1 + \cdots + l_k = l} c_{l_1} \cdots c_{l_k} \Big) \Big(\sum_{l_{k+1} + \cdots + l_n = -l} c_{l_{k+1}} \cdots c_{l_n} \Big) \qquad (12.15)$$

$$= \sum_{l=0} l \frac{1}{2\pi} \int_{-\pi}^{\pi} f^k(\theta) e^{-il\theta} \, d\theta \frac{1}{2\pi} \int_{-\pi}^{\pi} f^{n-k}(\theta) e^{il\theta} \, d\theta.$$

Combining (12.13), (12.14), and (12.15), we have

$$\sum_{l_1 + \cdots + l_n = 0} \max(0, l_1, \cdots, l_1 + \cdots + l_{n-1}) c_{l_1} c_{l_2} \cdots c_{l_n}$$

$$= \sum_{k=1}^{n-1} \frac{1}{k} \sum_{l=1}^{\infty} l \frac{1}{2\pi} \int_{-\pi}^{\pi} f^k(\theta) e^{-il\theta} \, d\theta \frac{1}{2\pi} \int_{-\pi}^{\pi} f^{n-k}(\theta) e^{il\theta} \, d\theta. \qquad (12.16)$$

It is now a matter of routine to derive (12.4) from (12.12) and (12.16).

I have reviewed in such detail a derivation which has been published previously because I want to introduce an unsolved problem which, in my opinion, is of great interest and importance. In particular, it is related to unsolved problems pertaining to the two-dimensional Ising model.

The problem I have in mind is: What becomes of Szegö's result if the c_n's are matrices?

Let us, for the sake of definiteness, assume that each c_n is a 2 × 2 matrix so that C_m is now a $2m \times 2m$ matrix, still of the Toeplitz form,

$$C_m = \begin{bmatrix} c_0 & c_1 & \cdots & c_{m-1} \\ c_{-1} & c_0 & \cdots & c_{m-2} \\ c_{-2} & c_{-1} & \cdots & c_{m-3} \\ \vdots & \vdots & & \vdots \\ c_{-m+1} & c_{-m+2} & \cdots & c_0 \end{bmatrix}.$$ (12.17)

Let us again assume that

$$c_{-n} = c_n{}^*$$ (12.18)

and introduce the function

$$f(\theta) \sim \sum_{-\infty}^{\infty} c_n e^{in\theta},$$ (12.19)

which now is a 2×2 matrix.

The analog of (12.12) is now

$$\lim_{m\to\infty} \left\{ \sum_{j=i}^{2m} \lambda_j^n(m) - \frac{(2m)}{2\pi} \int_{-\pi}^{\pi} \text{tr } [f^n(\theta)] \, d\theta \right\}$$
$$= -2 \sum_{l_1 + \cdots + l_n = 0} \max (0, l_1, \cdots, l_1 + \cdots + l_{n-1}) \text{ tr } \{c_{l_1} c_{l_2} \cdots c_{l_n}\},$$ (12.20)

and we run into an immediate obstacle to imitating the preceding procedure in that the trace of $c_{l_1} \cdots c_{l_n}$ is no longer invariant under *all* permutations of the indices.

In general,

$$\text{tr } \{c_{l_1} c_{l_2} \cdots c_{l_n}\}$$

is invariant only under a cyclic subgroup of the permutation group, and there seems to be no useful lemma analogous to (12.9) when σ runs through such a cyclic subgroup.

In one very special case, I have succeeded in obtaining an answer, and even though this seems as yet to throw no light on the general situation, it may be worthwhile to discuss it briefly.

I assume that $c_n = 0$ for $n \geq 2$ and, in addition, that

$$c_0^2 = \gamma_0 c_0, \qquad c_1^2 = \gamma_1 c_1 \qquad (c_1 = c_{-1}),$$ (12.21)

and I set

$$\text{tr } (c_0 c_1) = \gamma_{0_1} \neq \gamma_0 \gamma_1.$$ (12.22)

The assumption (12.21) is not as restrictive as it looks, since by the

Cayley-Hamilton theorem the matrices c_0 and c_1, being 2×2 matrices, would satisfy quadratic equations.

The ratio

$$a = \frac{\gamma_{0_1}}{\gamma_0 \gamma_1} \tag{12.23}$$

is a measure of noncommutativity. Without going into details (which are elementary but slightly tedious), let me state the result.

Let

$$I_p = \sum_{m_1 + \cdots + m_p = 0} \max(0, m_1, m_1 + m_2, \cdots, m_1 + \cdots + m_{p-1}), \tag{12.24}$$

where each m_s is either 1 or -1. Then

$$\sum_{l_1 + \cdots + l_n = 0} \max(0, l_1, l_1 + l_2, \cdots, l_1 + \cdots + l_{n-1}) \operatorname{tr}(c_{l_1} \cdots c_{l_n})$$

$$= \sum_{r=0}^{n} I_{n-r} \gamma_0^r \gamma_1^{n-r} \times \text{coeff of } z^r \text{ in tr } \{G^n\}, \tag{12.25}$$

where

$$G = \begin{bmatrix} 1 & \sqrt{az} \\ \sqrt{az} & z \end{bmatrix}. \tag{12.26}$$

It is interesting to observe that

$$\operatorname{tr}\{G^n\} = \left(\frac{1 + z + \sqrt{(1+z)^2 - 4(1-a)z}}{2}\right)^n$$

$$+ \left(\frac{1 + z - \sqrt{(1+z)^2 - 4(1-a)z}}{2}\right)^n \tag{12.27}$$

so that, for $a = 1$ (the commutative case),

$$\operatorname{tr}\{G^n\} = (1 + z)^n. \tag{12.28}$$

Thus, in the commutative case,

$$\sum_{l_1 + \cdots + l_n = 0} \max(0, l_1, \cdots, l_1 + \cdots + l_{n-1}) \operatorname{tr}(c_{l_1} \cdots c_{l_n})$$

$$= \sum_{r=0}^{n} I_{n-r} \binom{n}{r} \gamma_0^r \gamma_1^{n-r}. \tag{12.29}$$

This indeed can be verified if one keeps in mind that

$$\operatorname{tr}(c_{l_1} \cdots c_{l_n}) = \gamma_{l_1} \gamma_{l_2} \cdots \gamma_{l_n}$$

and that, by (12.16),

$$I_p = 2^p \sum_{k=1}^{p-1} \frac{1}{k} \sum_{l=1}^{\infty} l \frac{1}{2\pi} \int_{-\pi}^{\pi} \cos^k \theta e^{-il\theta} d\theta \frac{1}{2\pi} \int_{-\pi}^{\pi} \cos^{p-k} \theta e^{il\theta} d\theta. \qquad (12.30)$$

It is not clear whether formula (12.25) contains in itself the seeds of generality. In any case, it would be of great interest and value to study noncommutative situations in the search, perhaps, of a wholly new combinatorial background.

In conclusion, I should like to point out some advantages of the combinatorial approach to Szegö's theorem.

If the c_n's (in the scalar case) are nonnegative ($c_n \geq 0$) and such that

$$\sum_{-\infty}^{\infty} c_n = 1, \qquad (12.31)$$

the result (12.10) can be interpreted probabilistically.

In fact, let X_1, X_2, $\cdots$ be independent, identically distributed, random variables such that

$$\mathrm{pr}\ \{X_i = n\} = c_n, \qquad -\infty < n < \infty, \qquad (12.32)$$

and set, as usual,

$$s_k = X_1 + \cdots + X_k. \qquad (12.33)$$

Then (12.10) can be written in the form

$$\sum_{j=0}^{m} \lambda_j^n(m) = \frac{m}{2\pi} \int_{-\pi}^{\pi} f^n(\theta)\ d\theta - \mathrm{pr}\ \{s_n = 0\} E\{[\max\ (0, s_1, \cdots, s_{n-1})$$

$$- \min\ (0, s_1, \cdots, s_{n-1})]_m\ |\ s_n = 0\}, \qquad (12.34)$$

and therefore

$$\log \det \{I - C_m\} - \frac{m}{2\pi} \int_{-\pi}^{\pi} \log\ [1 - f(\theta)]\ d\theta$$

$$= \sum_{n=1}^{\infty} \frac{1}{n} \mathrm{pr}\ \{s_n = 0\} E\{[\max\ (0, s_1, \cdots, s_{n-1})$$

$$- \min\ (0, s_1, \cdots, s_{n-1})]_m\ |\ s_n = 0\}. \qquad (12.35)$$

Let us now assume that

$$\sigma^2 = \sum_{-\infty}^{\infty} n^2 c_n < \infty \qquad (12.36)$$

and break up the sum in (12.35) as follows:

$$\sum_{n \le \delta m^2} + \sum_{n > \delta m^2} \tag{12.37}$$

where $\delta > 0$.

As far as the second sum is concerned, we have

$$\sum_{n > \delta m^2} < m \sum_{n > \delta m^2} \frac{1}{n} \, \text{pr} \, \{s_n = 0\}.$$

Since the condition (12.36) implies that $\text{pr} \, \{s_n = 0\}$ is of the order of $n^{-1/2}$, the sum in question is less than $C/\sqrt{\delta}$, where C is a certain constant depending only on σ.

The first sum in (12.37) can be replaced by

$$2 \sum_{n \le \delta m^2} \frac{1}{\sqrt{n}} \, \text{pr} \, \{s_n = 0\} E \left\{ \max \left(0, \frac{s_1}{\sqrt{n}}, \cdots, \frac{s_{n-1}}{\sqrt{n}} \right) \mid s_n = 0 \right\},$$

since in n steps the random walk is unlikely to wander off farther than $\sqrt{n} = m \sqrt{\delta}$, and hence, for small δ, the truncation implied by the symbol $[\ \ ]_m$ can be neglected.

Finally, for all n except a few small ones, the expectation

$$E \left\{ \max \left(0, \frac{s_1}{\sqrt{n}}, \cdots, \frac{s_{n-1}}{\sqrt{n}} \right) \mid s_n = 0 \right\}$$

can be replaced by the Brownian-motion expectation

$$\sigma E \{ \max \, [0, x(\tau)], \, 0 \le \tau \le 1 \mid x(1) = 0 \} = \frac{\sigma \sqrt{2\pi}}{4}.$$

It thus appears that (12.35) becomes

$$\log \frac{\det \, \{I - C_m\}}{\exp \left\{ \dfrac{m}{2\pi} \displaystyle\int_{-\pi}^{\pi} \log \, [1 - f(\theta)] \, d\theta \right\}} = \frac{\sigma \sqrt{2\pi}}{2} \sum_{n \le \delta m^2} \frac{1}{\sqrt{n}} \, \text{pr} \, \{s_n = 0\}$$

+ terms which depend on δ but remain finite as $m \to \infty$. (12.38)

All this can be made entirely rigorous and many conditions weakened or even removed. One can also get more precise asymptotic results. To eliminate any doubts, let us check (12.38) by considering

$$f(\theta) = \cos \theta = \tfrac{1}{2} e^{-i\theta} + \tfrac{1}{2} e^{i\theta},$$

in which case

$$C_m = \begin{bmatrix} 0 & \frac{1}{2} & \cdots\cdots & 0 \\ \frac{1}{2} & 0 & \frac{1}{2} & \cdots & 0 \\ 0 & \frac{1}{2} & 0 & \frac{1}{2} & \cdots & 0 \\ \cdots\cdots\cdots \\ 0 & \cdots\cdots & \frac{1}{2} & 0 \end{bmatrix}$$

and

$$\det (I - C_m) = (\tfrac{1}{2})^m (m+1).$$

Furthermore,

$$\frac{1}{2\pi} \int_{-\pi}^{\pi} \log (1 - \cos \theta)\, d\theta = \log \tfrac{1}{2}$$

and consequently, by direct calculation,

$$\log \frac{\det \{I - C_m\}}{\exp \left\{ \dfrac{m}{2\pi} \displaystyle\int_{-\pi}^{\pi} \log (1 - \cos \theta)\, d\theta \right\}} \sim \log m. \tag{12.39}$$

To apply formula (12.38), we note that

$$\mathrm{pr}\,\{s_n = 0\} = \begin{cases} 0, & n \text{ odd} \\ \dbinom{2l}{l} \dfrac{1}{2^{2l}}, & n = 2l \end{cases}$$

and consequently

$$\sum_{n \le \delta m^2} \frac{1}{\sqrt{n}}\, \mathrm{pr}\,\{s_n = 0\} = \sum_{2l < \delta m^2} \frac{1}{\sqrt{2l}} \binom{2l}{l} \frac{1}{2^{2l}}.$$

Using Stirling's formula, we get

$$\frac{1}{2^{2l}} \binom{2l}{l} \sim \frac{1}{\sqrt{\pi l}},$$

and, since $\sigma = 1$ in the case under consideration, the righthand side of (12.38) becomes

$$\frac{\sqrt{2\pi}}{2} \sum_{2l < \delta m^2} \frac{1}{\sqrt{2l}} \frac{1}{\sqrt{\pi l}} + \text{terms remaining finite as } m \to \infty$$

$$= \log m + O(1),$$

in agreement with (12.39).

While this is not strictly speaking part of combinatorial background, how can one draw a line between probability theory and combinatorics?

The fact remains that the approach based on combinatorics and/or probability theory permits one to go beyond Szegö's theorem and get asymptotic results even when

$$\sum n \ |\gamma_n(\xi)|^2$$

diverges.

REFERENCES

HIRSCHMAN, I. I., JR. 1965. On a theorem of Szegö, Kac, and Baxter. J. Analyse Math., 14:225–34.

KAC, M. 1959. Probability and related topics in physical sciences. New York: Interscience.

LENARD, A. 1964. Momentum distribution in the ground state of the one-dimensional system of impenetrable bosons. J. Math. Phys., 5:930–43.

MONTROLL, E. W., R. B. POTTS, and J. C. WARD. 1963. Correlations and spontaneous magnetization of the two-dimensional Ising model. J. Math. Phys., 4:308–22.

Operations Research II

13
The Cutting Stock Problem

P. C. GILMORE

IBM *Corporation*

INTRODUCTION

In order to make this paper somewhat intelligible to those without a knowledge of linear programming, a brief introduction to that subject will be provided.

An m-equation linear programming problem is defined by: a finite set A of m-dimensional vectors α, called *activities*, to be thought of as column vectors; an m-dimensional (column) vector γ, called the *demand vector*; and a real-valued function $C(\alpha)$ defined for all $\alpha \in A$, called the *cost-coefficient function*.

A solution to an m-equation linear programming problem is a set of m activities $\alpha_1, \alpha_2, \cdots, \alpha_m$ satisfying:

(a) $\alpha_1, \cdots, \alpha_m$ are linearly independent;

(b) $[\alpha_1, \cdots, \alpha_m]^{-1} \cdot \gamma$ has nonnegative components;

(c) the value of the *objective function* $F(\alpha_1, \cdots, \alpha_m)$ defined to be $[C(\alpha_1), \cdots, C(\alpha_m)] \cdot [\alpha_1, \cdots, \alpha_m]^{-1} \cdot \gamma$ is minimum.

That (a) is true means that the inverse of the matrix $[\alpha_1, \cdots, \alpha_m]$ used in (b) and (c) is defined. The vector $[\alpha_1, \cdots, \alpha_m]^{-1} \cdot \gamma$ of (b) is the vector of levels at which the vectors $\alpha_1, \cdots, \alpha_m$ are to be used; that is, the jth component of the vector $[\alpha_1, \cdots, \alpha_m]^{-1} \cdot \gamma$ is the amount the activity α_j is to be used and is to be nonnegative. Since $C(\alpha_j)$ is the cost coefficient for the activity α_j, that is, the cost per unit usage of α_j, $F(\alpha_1, \cdots, \alpha_m)$ as defined in (c) is the cost of satisfying the demands by using the activities $\alpha_1, \cdots, \alpha_m$.

Another way of looking at $F(\alpha_1, \cdots, \alpha_m)$ is to regard the ith coefficient of γ as defining the demand for a commodity associated with the ith row.

Then the ith component of the vector π defined to be $[C(\alpha_1), \cdots, C(\alpha_m)] \cdot [\alpha_1, \cdots, \alpha_m]^{-1}$ can be regarded as the price per unit amount of the commodity associated with the ith row; in linear programming terminology, it is the vector of *shadow prices*.

The vector π is particularly significant for the primal simplex algorithm. This algorithm, once $\alpha_1, \cdots, \alpha_m$ have been found satisfying (a) and (b), will find a solution to the linear programming problem. The algorithm depends on the following fundamental theorem:

Given $\alpha_1, \cdots, \alpha_m$ satisfying (a) and (b), then:

(A) if α is an activity satisfying

$$\pi \cdot \alpha > C(\alpha), \tag{13.1}$$

then, for some i, $\alpha_1, \cdots, \alpha_{i-1}, \alpha, \alpha_{i+1}, \cdots, \alpha_m$ satisfy (a), (b), and

$$F(\alpha_1, \cdots, \alpha_{i-1}, \alpha, \alpha_{i+1}, \cdots, \alpha_m) \leq F(\alpha_1, \cdots, \alpha_m); \tag{13.2}$$

(B) if no activity α satisfies (13.1), then $\alpha_1, \cdots, \alpha_m$ satisfy (c).

Once $\alpha_1, \cdots, \alpha_m$ have been found satisfying (a) and (b), the primal simplex algorithm proceeds by determining if there is an activity α satisfying (13.1); if there is no such α, then $\alpha_1, \cdots, \alpha_m$ satisfy (c) also; if there is such an α, a set of activities $\alpha_1, \cdots, \alpha_{i-1}, \alpha, \alpha_{i+1}, \cdots, \alpha_m$, which at least does not decrease the value of the objective function, can be found.

Without the assurance of strict inequality in (13.2), this algorithm could cycle; however, methods exist for the prevention of cycling as well as for determining i in part (A) of the theorem. To completely specify the algorithm, therefore, it is sufficient to give a method for solving what we shall call the *pivot problem*:

Find $\alpha \in A$ for which $\pi \cdot \alpha - C(\alpha)$ is maximum.

For if the maximum value of $\pi \cdot \alpha - C(\alpha)$ is not positive, then part (B) of the theorem applies, while if it is positive, the maximizing α can be used as in part (A) of the theorem. Computational experience further suggests that the extra computation needed to find a maximizing α for $\pi \cdot \alpha - C(\alpha)$, rather than just one for which this function is positive, is worthwhile.

Since A is finite, the pivot problem is always solvable by the most obvious means: order the members of A in some fashion, and define V to be initially zero; then for each α calculate in turn the value of $\pi \cdot \alpha - C(\alpha)$, and determine whether this value exceeds V; if so, update V to this new value, record α, and proceed; if not, leave V unchanged. But this obvious method of solution is not practical for an important class of linear programming problems for which A is extremely large.

ONE-DIMENSIONAL NONINTEGER CUTTING STOCK PROBLEMS

The one-dimensional noninteger cutting stock problem occurs when a continuous sheet of material of fixed width W (for example, paper) has to be slit into sheets of smaller widths so as to satisfy demands for given lineal amounts $d_1, \cdots, d_m$ of given ordered widths $w_1, \cdots, w_m$. The problem is called noninteger because the demand for any given ordered width may be satisfied by supplying any number of pieces of any length of the given width, just so long as the total length supplied is the demanded length.

In Figure 1 a possible solution of a one-dimensional noninteger cutting stock problem is illustrated. The stock sheet width is 13.5, the ordered widths are 3, 5, and 7, while their demands for lengths are, respectively, 9, 12, and 12. The demand for width 3 is met by supplying two pieces of length 3.6 and one piece of length 1.8. The demand for width 5 is met by supplying two pieces of length 1.8 and one piece of length 8.4. The demand for width 7 is met by supplying one piece of length 8.4 and one piece of length 3.6. The total length of stock used is 13.8.

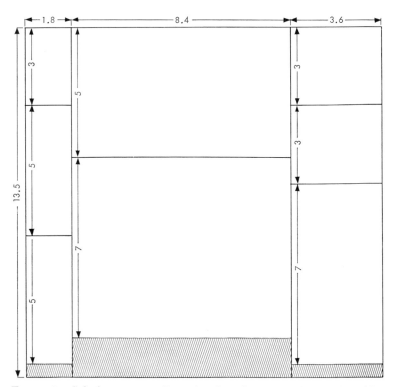

FIGURE 1.   Solution to a one-dimensional noninteger cutting stock problem

This cutting stock problem can be formulated as a linear programming problem as follows: the set A of activities consists of all vectors $(a_1, a_2, \cdots, a_m)$ of nonnegative integers such that

$$W \geq w_1 a_1 + w_2 a_2 + \cdots + w_m a_m; \qquad (13.3)$$

the demand vector γ is $(d_1, d_2, \cdots, d_m)$; and the cost-coefficient function is defined as $C(\alpha) = 1$ for all $\alpha \, \epsilon \, A$. If $\alpha_1, \cdots, \alpha_m$ is a solution to the problem, then the jth component of $[\alpha_1, \cdots, \alpha_m]^{-1} \cdot \gamma$ is the length of the stock material of width W which is to be slit as described by the vector α_j; that is, if $\alpha_j = (a_1, a_2, \cdots, a_m)$, then a_1 strips of width w_1, a_2 strips of width w_2, $\cdots$, and a_m strips of width w_m are to be slit from the sheet.

It has long been known that noninteger cutting stock problems can be formulated as linear programming problems; see, for example, Kantorovich (1962), Eisemann (1957), and Reith (n.d.). But until recently no method was known for solving the difficulty of the immense number of activities for the problem. Quite common cutting stock problems can have so many activities that it is impossible to store them all physically in a computer and to search through them each time the pivot problem must be solved. For example, when m is 40 and $\sum_{i=1}^{m} a_m$ for an activity is on the average 5, the number of activities is of the order of $40^5/5!$ or 10^6.

One method tried, for example, in Reith (n.d.) for dealing with such large problems was to select a relatively small number of "good" activities, according to some *ad hoc* concept of goodness, and to solve the resulting reduced linear programming problem; since an optimal solution to the reduced problem is not necessarily an optimal solution to the original problem, only approximate solutions for cutting stock problems were possible. But if one recognizes (as was done in Gilmore and Gomory, 1961) that the pivot problem for the cutting stock problem is a simple integer programming problem for which fast algorithms can be developed (one is described in Gilmore and Gomory, 1963), then the problem of the size of A vanishes. At any time, only m members of A need be recorded, namely, the members of the current solution, and the pivot problem of searching through A for an improving activity is solved by solving a simple integer programming problem. In the case of the one-dimensional cutting stock problem, the pivot problem is the generalized knapsack problem, a generalization of a problem first studied by Bellman (1954) and Dantzig (1957): maximize $\pi \cdot \alpha$ subject to $W \geq \omega \cdot \alpha$, where $\omega = (w_1, w_2, \cdots, w_m)$. Efficient methods for solving this problem have been developed and are described in Gilmore and Gomory (1963 and 1965). A further study of the theory and computation for this problem in both its one-dimensional and higher-dimensional forms can be found in Gilmore and Gomory (1966).

SOLVABLE VARIANTS OF THE

ONE-DIMENSIONAL NONINTEGER CUTTING STOCK PROBLEM

An immediate generalization to be made of the cutting stock problem described in the previous section occurs when more than one width of stock is available, say, W_1, W_2, $\cdots$, W_k. Associated with each stock width W_j will be a cost C_j, which is the cost of a unit length of the stock material of width W_j. The cutting stock problem is to satisfy demands by cutting any or all of the stock widths available and to do so at least cost with cost calculated from the amounts of each stock width used.

The only difference between a formulation of this generalized problem as a cutting stock problem and the formulation of the one-stock width problem is in the definition of the cost-coefficient function $C(\alpha)$ defined for all activities α. In the case of the one-stock width problem, $C(\alpha) = 1$ for all α, while for the multiple-stock width problem, $C(\alpha) = C_j$ if the activity α cuts the stock width W_j.

Computationally, the generalized problem is little more difficult than the original, while its range of application is considerably broader because of the ability to set the costs C_j. Three instances of the generalized problem will be discussed here.

One instance of the generalized problem occurs sometimes as a variant of the one-stock width problem. Sometimes the waste resulting from the slitting of the stock width W into ordered widths can have value when it is not too narrow. However, it is generally not as valuable as material cut to satisfy a customer's order. The problem is to satisfy the demands by slitting the stock width W but to satisfy the demands at least cost with "waste" of certain widths having certain values. For example, if $W = 200$ and waste of 20 has a value of 10% below that of a customer's width, then the cutting stock problem can be described by introducing two stock widths $W_1 = 200$ and $W_2 = 180$ with costs 200 and 182, respectively. The figure 182 is arrived at as follows: Since width 200 costs 200, the material is worth one unit of cost per unit of width, and any customer's width will be worth that much also. However, the width 20 is discounted at 10% and is therefore worth only 18, so the cost of the width 180 is the cost of the width 200 minus the width of the material of width 20, that is, $200 - 18 = 182$.

A second important instance of the generalized problem occurs in striking a balance between manufacturing costs and material costs, as, for example, in the manufacture of corrugated paper. In this case, a single machine produces the materials of widths W_1, W_2, $\cdots$, W_k, and the cost of a stock width W_j is the cost of the raw materials used in manufacturing the material plus the cost of operating the machine that manufactures the material. In many cases, for example, the cost C_j of the stock width W_j is $C + KW_j$, where C is the cost of operating the machine long enough to manufacture a unit length of stock material of any width and where K is the cost of the raw materials in one unit length of stock material of unit width. Consequently, the cost in this case per unit width of a stock width W_j, that is, (C_j/W_j), *increases* as W_j decreases, because the cost of manufacture is constant. But a smaller stock width may have less wastage than a wider one when used to meet certain demands, and its usage would therefore result in a smaller material cost. Thus, the problem of balancing machine costs against material costs is solved in this cutting stock problem.

As soon as multiple stock widths are introduced, one is led to consider limitations on the supply of the widths or possibly a balancing of the usage of the widths. For each limitation or balancing equation introduced, the cutting stock problem is increased in number of equations as a linear programming problem. Thus, an m-ordered width problem with k stock widths, each with a limitation in supply, becomes an $(m + k)$-equation linear programming problem. No essential complications are introduced into the knapsack calculations by the additional equations.

One last illustration will be given of the exploitation that can be made of the fact that costs C_j can be assigned to stock widths W_j by considerations other than just the width W_j. One can imagine that the stock widths W_j are manufactured by machines at different physical locations and that the demand for widths w_i are at different physical locations, so the cost of transporting the material from the manufacturing location to the demand location must be added to the manufacturing cost. Under these circumstances, the cost assigned to an activity cutting from a stock width W_j is the cost of a unit length of stock material W_j at the location where it is manufactured plus the total cost of shipping a unit length of each of the widths cut in the activity to the location where it is demanded. In this case, it turns out that the modification necessary in the knapsack routine is very minor indeed.

INTEGER CUTTING STOCK PROBLEMS

A cutting stock problem is said to be integer when the demands are integer multiples of a given unit of length and when the activities in a solution of the problem must have levels which are also integer multiples. Thus, the problem must be formulated as an integer programming problem. In particular, it will follow that the solution of an m-equation cutting stock problem may have more than m activities. Actually, the integer case can be treated as an enlarged linear programming problem, as described in Gomory (1958), by regarding the integer problem as another linear programming problem resulting from the integer problem by the addition of a number (possibly quite large) of equations which force the solution of the large linear programming problem to be integer. Unfortunately, treating a cutting stock problem in that fashion results in a matrix which is large in two dimensions, large in number of equations and in number of variables, and no methods are known for efficiently computing solutions to such problems. The integer cutting stock problem must therefore be regarded as theoretically unsolved, although there are practical methods of approaching it which have had success.

One direct practical approach to an integer cutting stock problem is to solve it just as a linear programming problem and then to round the answer in some fashion to integers. The resulting integer solution rarely produces the demanded amounts of the ordered widths, but in many practical problems that is not necessary; in each order a certain tolerance is admitted, and the customer will be satisfied with receiving an amount within the tolerance limits of the demanded amount. It is worth noting that if, after rounding, the solution produces amounts within tolerances of the demands, then the solution is an optimal solution to the integer cutting stock problem with the produced amounts as demands. Consider, for example, the noninteger solution illustrated in Figure 1. If 1.8 and 3.6 are rounded up to 2 and 4, while 8.4 is rounded down to 8, a demand of 10 rather than 9 for width 3 has been met, while the demand of 12 for widths 5 and 7 has been met exactly. If 10 is tolerated in place of 9, then the rounded solution is optional for the new demands, since the solution of Figure 1 is optimal for the demands. In some cases, if demands have been underfilled after rounding, the unsatisfied demands can be treated as another small cutting stock problem and solved by hand.

ECONOMY OF SCALE AND CUTTING STOCK PROBLEMS

Cutting stock problems occur with great frequency throughout industry. The principle of economy of scale appears to be the cause of its universality. Just as, in the case of the manufacture of any object, the cost per object generally decreases when the number of objects manufactured is increased, so also, in the manufacture of materials, the cost per unit amount of material generally decreases when the size of the piece of material increases, at least until a certain size is reached. But large pieces of material are rarely wanted, and a cutting stock problem therefore arises in cutting down to usable size the stock manufactured in an unusable size. For example, newsprint is manufactured in widths which are too wide for use in newspapers, trees are allowed to grow to sizes much larger than can be used by any furniture manufacturer, and boxcars are made in sizes much larger than the boxes which may be packed into them.

However, if material is manufactured in large sizes for the sake of economy, then there must be economical methods of cutting the material into useful sizes. For one-dimensional cutting stock problems, this corollary to the principle of economy of scale has no mathematical implications, but for higher-dimensional problems, there is an important consequence.

HIGHER-DIMENSIONAL CUTTING STOCK PROBLEMS

In this section, results that are reported more fully in Gilmore and Gomory (1965) are summarized. The only higher-dimensional problems we shall consider will be ones in which rectangles have to be cut from rectangular stock or in which cubes have to be cut from cube stock. We could again consider integer and noninteger varieties of these problems, but the only methods we have for approaching the integer problem are those discussed in the section on integer cutting stock problems; therefore, we restrict our discussion to the noninteger case.

For a noninteger cutting stock problem in which rectangles are cut from a single rectangular stock, one can picture the rectangular stock being extruded as a continuous rectangular bar from some machine and then being cut into smaller rectangular bars by first cutting the continuous bar into pieces of various lengths and then cutting each piece down the length into smaller rectangular bars. When the problem is formulated as a linear programming problem, an activity of the problem describes how the stock bar can be cut down its length into smaller bars, and the level of the activity determines how much of the stock bar is to be cut in the described fashion. To provide a diagram of an activity, therefore, it is only necessary to picture the end of the stock bar as illustrated in Figure 2, although it should be clearly recognized that we are discussing in this section only noninteger problems and not an integer problem of cutting up rectangular plates. For integer forms of the problems of this section, see the section on integer cutting stock problems.

In the most general two-dimensional cutting stock problem, the demand for the ordered rectangles of given dimensions and amount can be met by using any activity which cuts rectangles from rectangles. The activity in Figure 2 or the one in Figure 3 would be acceptable even though the complication of the pattern might force the use of expensive and slow-cutting equipment. Cutting such a pattern is expensive because we cannot use a guillotine-type cutter, that is, a cutter which, once beginning on a cut on one side of a rectangle, must continue cutting in a straight line until it reaches the other side. A two-dimensional cutting stock problem in which general cutting is permitted can be expressed as a practical linear programming problem, but then no method of solution for the pivot problem is known. Fortunately, however, the corollary to the

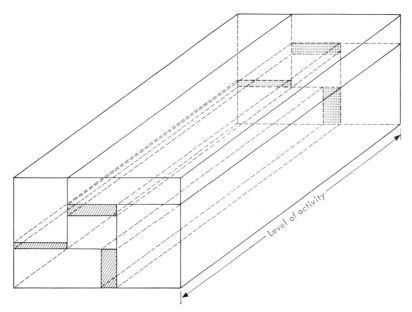

FIGURE 2. Activity for a two-dimensional noninteger cutting stock problem

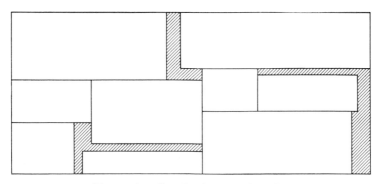

FIGURE 3. Completely general cutting

principle of the economy of scale discussed in the previous section operates in many industries, so these two-dimensional cutting stock problems, for which special cutting only is permitted, are numerous and frequently solvable as well. We shall examine several of these special problems here. For some of these, solutions are known for the pivot problem; for others, solutions are not known.

In Figure 4 a cutting pattern is illustrated which can be cut in two stages of guillotine cutting plus a third stage (which we ignore in our count of stages) of trimming to size. The first stage of guillotine cuts is executed by making three cuts down the entire length of the rectangle, and the second stage of guillotine cuts is executed by taking the strips resulting from the first-stage cutting and chopping them across this width into desired rectangles, or at least rectangles that can be trimmed by one guillotine cut to a desired rectangle. The cross-hatched areas are all the waste pieces resulting from the cutting. The pivot problem for two-stage guillotine cutting can be solved by solving what is the equivalent of two one-dimensional pivot problems, that is, two knapsack problems. In the solution to the first problem, values are assigned to strips which are the length of the stock rectangle and which have widths equal to the widths of ordered rectangles; the solution to the second problem tells in what numbers these strips are to be used to obtain maximum value from a stock rectangle.

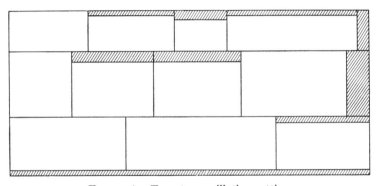

FIGURE 4.   Two-stage guillotine cutting

Variants of the two-stage guillotine problem arise when the second-stage cutting has to be done by groups of strips rather than in single strips. Figure 5 illustrates one such problem when the second-stage cutting has to be done in exactly one group; Figure 6 illustrates a problem in which the cutting has to be done in exactly two groups. Thus, the two-stage guillotine problems can be classified as having a g-group second stage, where g can be 1, 2, 3, $\cdots$, or as having a free second stage when the strips are each chopped individually. The g-group second-stage problems are considerably more difficult to solve than the free second-stage problems, although approximate methods are readily devised.

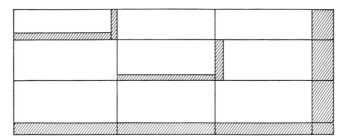

FIGURE 5. Two-stage guillotine cutting, one group of strips

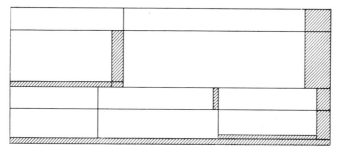

FIGURE 6. Two-stage guillotine cutting, two groups of strips

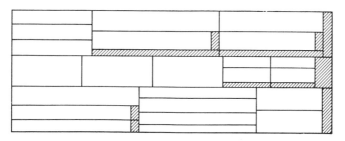

FIGURE 7. Three-stage guillotine cutting

A three-stage guillotine cutting pattern is illustrated in Figure 7. The pivot problem for a three-dimensional cutting stock problem restricted to three-stage guillotine cutting can be solved by solving $2 + m$ knapsack problems.

A number of other two-dimensional problems are discussed in Gilmore and Gomory (1965), the pivot problems for some of which are solvable.

Gilmore and Gomory (1966) discuss both the theory and computation of a number of these problems. Clearly, much research remains to be done in identifying the kinds of problems with solvable pivot problems and in developing new methods of solving the pivot problems.

REFERENCES

BELLMAN, R. 1954. Some applications of the theory of dynamic programming—a review. Operations Res., 2:275–88.
DANTZIG, G. B. 1957. Discrete variable extremum problems. Operations Res., 5:266–76.
EISEMANN, K. 1957. The trim problem. Management Sci., 3:279–84.
GILMORE, P. C., and R. E. GOMORY. 1961. A linear programming approach to the cutting stock problem. Operations Res., 9:849–59.
———. 1963. A linear programming approach to the cutting stock problem—part II. Operations Res., 11:863–88.
———. 1965. Multistage cutting stock problems of two or more dimensions. Operations Res., 13:94–120.
———. 1966. The theory and computation of knapsack functions. Research report. Yorktown Heights, N. Y.: Thomas J. Watson Research Center, IBM Corp.
GOMORY, R. E. 1958. An algorithm for integer solutions to linear programs. Technical report no. 1. Princeton, N. J.: Princeton-IBM Mathematics Research Project.
KANTOROVICH, L. V. 1962. Mathematical methods of organizing and planning production. Management Sci., 6:366-422. (Translation of a report presented to Leningrad State University, May 1939.)
REITH, P. F. n.d. The trim problem. Amsterdam: IBM Applied Science Department.

DISCUSSION

O. A. KRAL: Have you ever investigated the area of going in the opposite direction, where you have estimates of distributions of desired widths, and tried to design the optimal width, let us say, of an extrusion process? This is just the reverse of what you are talking about here.

P. C. GILMORE: Yes, we have done this in the sense that companies have supplied us with what they regarded as typical orders for a one-dimensional cutting stock problem. The problems were solved for a series of stock widths. It is interesting to note the enormous variation in wastage that can occur. The study was intended to decide what width paper machine should be installed in order to fill the orders that were expected. In Gilmore and Gomory (1965), cited in my paper, we studied a range of widths from 160 to 260 inches for one particular problem and found that the percentage waste varied from highs of close to 9 to lows of close to 0. From these studies it is clearly very difficult to predict a good stock width.

R. R. HUGHES: Shouldn't this sort of problem be treated as a two-stage stochastic problem, with probability distributions for the demands rather than mere single-valued estimates?

P. C. GILMORE: Yes, it should be.

C. B. TOMPKINS: I do not intend to attack this approach at all, but there are related problems which are interesting combinatorially and which may not, perhaps, involve optimizing. For example, there is the business of making uniforms for the armed services, where the cloth is furnished by the government and the pieces are shaped in a peculiar fashion. The pieces must have a particular orientation relative to the cloth, and the cost function is wastage. Furthermore, the pieces for one particular uniform have to come from the same region on the bolt, because the dyes are not uniform. Thus, there are many applications in which the validity of an abstraction such as the one you made could be challenged. In these cases, it is an intriguing and completely unsolved problem to devise reasonable operations which stay within your limitations and which still give you perhaps not an optimal solution but a very good chance of bettering a more or less random solution.

The only point I really want to make is that in solving a problem like this, one must always establish in the economic sense the validity of his abstraction.

P. C. GILMORE: I do not wish to infer that our assumption about rectangles is an assumption that rectangular shapes are the only ones to be cut, but this is the way many problems come to us. It is very true that there are more complex problems (fitting problems, cutting problems, etc.) which fall into the category of what I like to call "rainy Sunday afternoon problems." Producing patterns for these problems is a task which is best done quietly on a rainy Sunday afternoon when you have plenty of time. However, you asked for nonoptimal methods which might assist. In any cutting stock problem there are really two problems involved: the problem of generating the patterns and the problem of balancing out the patterns that you use in order to meet the demands that are required. What linear programming does for you is to balance out the demands. We have found that in one-dimensional and in some higher-dimensional problems the generation of the patterns can also be done automatically. However, it is still possible to generate the patterns on a rainy Sunday afternoon and to bring them to work on Monday in order to balance them by linear programming.

14

On Finding Integer Solutions to Linear Programs[1]

M. L. BALINSKI

University of Pennsylvania and *Mathematica*

INTRODUCTION

The primary goal of this paper is to discuss the methods—mathematical and computational—which surround the problem of finding integer solutions to linear programs. Perhaps the most important part of the paper is an up-to-date survey of computational experience with integer programming algorithms. It is argued that this experience should be viewed as strong encouragement for the applied mathematician seeking solutions to particular combinatorial problems to use existing programs, or better yet, to develop new codes. In any case, experience indicates that solutions to large practical problems can be found in "reasonable" time. This is contrary to what the folklore of the field would make one believe. Furthermore, the computational experience seems to point to a number of interesting questions for the combinatorial mathematician.[2]

The paper is divided into five sections. Section 1 contains a short review of some uses and potential applications of integer programming, including historical and general remarks on the methods. Section 2 reviews the known sufficient conditions which assure that a linear program has optimal integer solutions. Section 3 develops the integer programming algorithms of Gomory and relates them to the Euclidean algorithm. Section 4 considers one approach to the "mixed" integer problem (that is, where not all variables are required to be integer-valued). Finally, Section 5 summarizes the known computational experience and argues that more computational success should be realized than heretofore suspected.

---

[1] This work was supported, in part, by Mathematica under contract with the Army Research Office, Contract No. DA-31-124-ARO(D)-31. Reproduction, translation, publication, use, and disposal in whole or in part by or for the United States government is permitted.
[2] Further experience is reported on in Balinski (1965).

BACKGROUND

We take the integer programming problem to be: Find $x_1, \cdots, x_n$ and $y_0, y_1, \cdots, y_m$ with x_j and y_i integer-valued for a set of variables J which maximize

$$y_0 = a_{00} + \sum_i a_{0i}(-x_i)$$

when   (14.1)

$$y_i = a_{i0} + \sum_i a_{ii}(-x_i) \geq 0, \qquad x_j \geq 0,$$

where, for the sake of simplicity, we assume that all a_{ij} are integer.

Many problems of practical and other interest can be formulated as linear programs by the use of one or more additional constraints which state that some variable is required to take on an integer value. It is interesting to note that optimization problems over nonconvex and/or disconnected polyhedral sets of points, the minimization of nonconvex piecewise linear functions, the traveling salesman and salesmen problems (Miller, Tucker, and Zemlin, 1960), the $p - (p = ?)$ coloring map problem, the search for orthogonal Latin squares, and other design problems can be formulated as integer programs (see Dantzig, 1960, for a summary of these and other "uses"). Problems of a perhaps more practical nature which can be so formulated are: scheduling problems of various types (Cord, 1963, Manne, 1960, and Wagner, 1959); fixed-cost problems (Balinski, 1961); more particularly, warehouse location problems (Balinski and Wolfe, 1963, Manne, 1964, and Vietorisz, 1963); even a state districting problem in which the goal is "equalization" of the vote (Weaver and Hess, 1963); the minimization of Boolean functions or the minimum disjunctive normal form problem (Cobham, Fridshal, and North, 1961 and 1962, and Cobham and North, 1963) and its generalization to a delivery problem (Balinski and Quandt, 1964); problems in constructing minimum-redundancy prefix codes (Karp, 1961); and, of course, any economic activity analysis or linear programming problem which concerns indivisible activities or commodities. Many combinatorial problems can be stated as integer programs: the marriage problem, the system of distinct representatives problem, the assignment problem and its generalization to transportation, transhipment and network flow problems, the caterer problem, and others (see Ford and Fulkerson, 1962, and Hoffman, 1960, for a survey of these and other combinatorial applications). However, these problems are cases in which solutions to linear programs are already integer-valued; that is, they provide the solution to the integer program with no additional work. The duality in linear programming can then be used to derive purely combinatorial results (these uses are neatly summarized in Hoffman, 1960). Other combinatorial problems which can be formulated as integer programs are not so well behaved; the hierarchy of covering problems of graph theory (Edmonds, 1962, Fulkerson and Ryser, 1961, and Norman and Rabin, 1959)—of which the delivery problem cited above in Balinski and Quandt (1964) is a generalization—provides an example. Nevertheless, it should be added here that an algorithm is known for the simplest of these covering problems (Norman and Rabin, 1959), and it is precisely the "generalized" covering problems for which integer programming algorithms have been so successful (see the final section of this paper).

The basic approach common to most methods for solving (14.1) is that of successively deducing supplementary linear constraints, which must be satisfied by any feasible integer solution, until a "transformed" linear program is obtained whose solution has the required integer property. In certain problems (see the next section) no extra constraints are necessary: solutions to (14.1) considered as linear programs already are integer-valued. The primitive constraint generation idea appears to have been first advanced by Dantzig, Fulkerson, and Johnson (1954) and, subsequently, by Markowitz and Manne (1957), where it was used in an *ad hoc* manner on specific problems. In 1958, Gomory developed a systematic method—guaranteeing convergence—applicable to general problems (14.1) in which all variables x_j and y_i are required to be integer (see Gomory, 1958, 1960*b*, and 1963*b*). Subsequently, Beale (1958) and Gomory (1960*a*) developed algorithms for the "mixed" problem in which only a subset of the variables are required to be integer-valued. Then, Gomory in 1960 generalized the new constraint generation idea to obtain a method, for the problem in which all variables must be integer, which requires only addition and subtraction in computation ("an all-integer integer" method; Gomory, 1963*a*). In a parallel development, Land and Doig (1960) developed a "search-type" algorithm; however, it has not been tested computationally on any problems save by hand.[3] Recently, papers on "nonlinear" integer problems have appeared. Kunzi and Oettli (1963) describe a method for minimizing a quadratic positive semidefinite function subject to linear and integer constraints which is based on solving a sequence of mixed integer problems (Gomory, 1960*a*). Then, Witzgall (1963) generalized the ideas in Gomory's all-integer integer method to solve a problem in which the objective is linear and the constraints are integer and linear or "parabolic"; that is, they are of a form which may be transformed linearly into constraints of type $t \geq \sum t_i^2$.

Thus, the basic approach has been one of "convexification" or, equivalently, of transformation of constraints via introduction of new non-negative integer-constrained variables. Geometrically, this process isolates a feasible point with the required integer property by making it the

---

[3] Reported by Ailsa Land in a letter dated February 1964.

extreme point of a new polyhedral convex set S at which the linear form y_0 is maximized over S. The remarkable mathematical fact—and unquestionably the major mathematical accomplishment—is that it has been possible to devise new constraints in such a way that a *finite* number of these new constraints guarantees that a linear program is obtained whose solution has the required integer property (if such a solution exists).

The basic "tool" for carrying out these computations and assuring convergence in a finite number of steps is a "lexicographic" dual simplex method. Briefly, it can be described as follows: Let $Y = (y_0, y_1, \cdots, y_m, x_1, \cdots, x_n)^T$, $X = (1, -x_1, \cdots, -x_n)^T$, $A = (\alpha_0, \alpha_1, \cdots, \alpha_n)$, where the α's are columns, $\alpha_0 = (a_{00}, \cdots, a_{m0}; 0, \cdots, 0)^T$, and $\alpha_j = (a_{0j}, \cdots, a_{mj}; 0, \cdots, -1, \cdots, 0)^T$, the one -1 appearing in the jth of the last n entries. Then the linear program is to maximize y_0 when $Y = AX \geq 0$. The "independent" variables of X in this representation of (14.1) are the "nonbasic" variables. By a number of "pivot steps" (or complete eliminations or elementary column transformations), all variables Y are re-expressed in terms of a different set of nonbasic variables from Y, say $\hat{X} = (1, -\hat{x}_1, \cdots, -\hat{x}_n)$, to obtain a new representation of (14.1), say $Y = \hat{A}\hat{X}$. If the original columns $\alpha_1, \cdots, \alpha_n$ are lexicographically positive (first nonzero entry is positive)—and this can always be arranged—then a dual simplex method selects a sequence of pivot steps such that the columns $\hat{\alpha}_1, \cdots, \hat{\alpha}_n$ of each succeeding representation remain lexicographically positive until all entries of $\hat{\alpha}_0$ (except possibly the first) are found to be nonnegative. Then, setting $\hat{x}_1 = \cdots = \hat{x}_n = 0$, an optimal solution can be read off from $Y = \hat{A}\hat{X}$ (≥ 0). If no such representation can be found, then no feasible solution to (14.1) exists.

ON LINEAR PROGRAMS WITH INTEGER SOLUTIONS

Given an integer program (14.1) to solve, the first—perhaps faint—hope is that its solution as a linear program will turn out to have an all-integer solution. This can happen fortuitously and, as discussed in the final section of this paper, might be "expected" to happen fairly often in certain classes of problems. In certain circumstances it is possible to predict that a linear program will have an integer-valued solution. The well-known case of this occurrence is the class of equivalent problems (Ford and Fulkerson, 1962, chap. 3) which includes the assignment, transportation, and network flow problems. Dantzig pointed out in 1949 (Dantzig, 1951) that the transportation problem—and hence this class of problems—always has integer solutions, given integer "supplies" and "demands." In other terms, the "obvious" linear formulation of these "combinatorial" problems leads to convex polyhedral sets whose extreme points have integer components. Experience indicates that (almost) all real or practical problems which have this property can—if properly interpreted—be displayed as a transportation problem.

The known results concerned with this question relate to conditions on the constraints of a linear program (14.1) which assure that all extreme points have all integer components. Write the constraint set of (14.1) as

$$AX \leq \alpha_0, \qquad X \geq 0, \tag{14.2}$$

where, now, $X = (x_1, \cdots, x_n)^T$, $\alpha_0 = (a_{10}, \cdots, a_{m0})^T$, and $A = (\alpha_1, \cdots, \alpha_n)$ with $\alpha_j = (a_{ij}, \cdots, a_{mj})^T$. A is said to have the *unimodular property* if every minor determinant of A has value 0, $+1$, or -1.

Theorem 1. Extreme points of (14.2) have all-integer coordinates X for every choice of all-integer vector α_0 if and only if A has the unimodular property (Hoffman and Kruskal, 1956).

Proof: Any extreme point of (14.2) can be determined by choosing the appropriate set of n inequalities from the $m + n$ inequalities of (14.2) and solving them as equations to obtain the coordinates of the extreme point X (of course, these values for X must satisfy the remaining m inequalities; see Tucker, 1955).

Clearly, if every minor determinant of A is 0, ± 1 and if α_0 is integer, then any solution to such a derived set of equations must be integer by Cramer's rule.

Conversely, suppose that A is not unimodular. Then we show how to choose an all-integer vector α_0 which admits an extreme point X^* of (14.2), at least one of whose coordinates is noninteger. If A contains an entry not 0, ± 1, say $a_{11} \neq 0$, ± 1, choose $a_{10} = \pm 1$ (a_{10} having the same sign as a_{11}). Then X^*, defined by $x_1^* = 1/|a_{11}|, x_2^* = \cdots = x_n^* = 0$ with $a_{20}, \cdots, a_{m0}$ chosen integer and large enough for X^* to satisfy all inequalities, is an extreme point with x_1^* noninteger.

Otherwise, consider any $k \times k$ submatrix $\bar{A}$ of A ($k \geq 2$) with $|\bar{A}| \neq 0$, ± 1 but all of whose minors have value 0, ± 1. For convenience, take

$$\bar{A} = \begin{bmatrix} a_{11} & \cdots & a_{1k} \\ \vdots & & \vdots \\ a_{k1} & \cdots & a_{kk} \end{bmatrix} = (\bar{\alpha}_1, \cdots, \bar{\alpha}_k), \qquad |\bar{A}| = d \neq 0, \pm 1.$$

By assumption, every entry of $\bar{A}$ and adj $\bar{A}$ is 0, ± 1; and (adj $\bar{A}$) $(\bar{A}) = dI$, implying

$$(\text{adj } \bar{A})\left(\sum_1^k \bar{\alpha}_j\right) = d\epsilon,$$

where $\epsilon = (1, 1, \cdots, 1)^T$. Let $\bar{\alpha}_0 = (a_{10}, \cdots, a_{k0})^T$. If $d > 0$, choose $\bar{\alpha}_0$ (if $d < 0$, choose $-\bar{\alpha}_0$) to be equal to $\sum_1^k \bar{\alpha}_j$ except for the first component which is decreased by 1. Thus,

$$(\text{adj } \bar{A})(\bar{\alpha}_0) = |d| \, \epsilon - (\text{the first column of adj } \bar{A}) > 0.$$

Define, now, X^*: let $\bar{X}^* = (x_1^*, \cdots, x_k^*)$ with $\bar{X}^* = (\text{adj } \bar{A})(\bar{\alpha}_0/d) = (\bar{A})^{-1}(\bar{\alpha}_0) \geq 0$, and let $x_{k+1}^* = \cdots = x_n^* = 0$. Choose $a_{k+1,0}, \cdots, a_{m0}$ integer and large enough for X^* to satisfy the inequalities (14.2). The α_0 so chosen is all-integer; the X^* is a vertex of (14.2); but X^* contains at least one noninteger coordinate, since

$$\bar{X}^* = \epsilon - \frac{1}{d} \, (\text{first column of adj } \bar{A}), \quad |d| \geq 2$$

and since all components of adj $\bar{A}$ are 0, ± 1.

Theorem 1 is useful in recognizing whether a linear program (14.1) does not necessarily have all-integer solutions. The solution-seeker looking for positive affirmation is in a considerably more difficult position. Some sufficient—but not necessary—conditions for A to be unimodular are known.

Theorem 2. If A can be partitioned into two disjoint sets of rows, R_1 and R_2, and if

(a) every column contains at most two nonzero entries;
(b) every entry is 0, ± 1;
(c) two nonzero entries in a column with the same sign do not appear in the same set R_i of rows;
(d) two nonzero entries in a column with different signs do appear in the same set R_i of rows;

then A is unimodular (Heller and Tompkins, 1956).

The proof of this deceptively restrictive-sounding theorem is a simple exercise in induction (see Heller and Tompkins, 1956, for a proof by Hoffman). That the theorem is not so restrictive is due to the fact that it almost describes the most general known sufficient conditions for establishing unimodularity. Specifically, given a unimodular matrix A as described in theorem 2, any combinatorially equivalent (Tucker, 1960) matrix $\hat{A}$, that is, any matrix $\hat{A}$ obtained from A through a "block pivot" or sequence of elementary pivots, is also unimodular. Let Ω be the class of matrices A as described in theorem 2 and their combinatorially equivalent matrices. Then Ω is identical with the most general known class of unimodular matrices heretofore specified (Heller and Hoffman, 1962). Other descriptions are given in terms of A, the incidence matrix of nodes versus arcs of a graph containing no loops with an odd number of nodes (Hoffman and Kruskal, 1956), of nodes versus directed paths of an alternating graph (Hoffman and Kruskal, 1956), of edges versus sets of paths of a directed graph with no loops (Heller, 1957); but these classes of unimodular matrices are either properly contained in or identical with Ω (as shown in Heller and Hoffman, 1962). There do exist, however, unimodular matrices which do not belong to Ω (Hoffman, 1960, p. 124).

It is easy to see that given a linear program with constraint matrix A as described in theorem 2, an equivalent network flow problem may be derived: namely, given A, change the signs in rows R_1 (or row constraints) so that any column which contains two nonzero entries contains a $+1$ and a -1. Further, adjoin rows (or "constraints") containing exactly one nonzero entry ± 1 for and in each column of the matrix which contains only one nonzero entry ∓ 1. Every column of the new matrix A^1 contains exactly one $+1$ and one -1. Associate rows with nodes and columns with arcs directed from the nodes whose rows contain $+1$'s to nodes whose rows contain -1's: A^1 is the incidence matrix for a network flow or transhipment problem. For linear programs with such constraint matrices, numerous efficient algorithms can be used to obtain optimal solutions or to show that none exist (Ford and Fulkerson, 1962).

Gale in Heller and Tompkins (1956) goes on to show that if A is unimodular and satisfies condition (a) of theorem 2, then the other conditions of the theorem must necessarily hold. Thus, it is fair to say that every unimodular A satisfying condition (a) is of the network or transportation type. Perhaps this fact is what underlies practical observations that the unimodular matrices found (so far) "in nature" have been of the transportation type.

INTEGER PROGRAMMING: ALGORITHMS

Given an integer program (14.1) to solve (with all variables required to be integer) which defies all attempts at "unimodularization," we turn to the general integer programming algorithms of Gomory. As outlined above, the underlying technique is that of generating new linear inequalities.

Suppose, then, that at some stage of computation a linear program is encountered, all of whose variables are required to be nonnegative and integer, and all of whose variables are expressed as linear combinations of some nonbasic set, say $x_1, \cdots, x_n$. A typical such expression is (omitting row subscripts)

$$y = a_0 + \sum a_i(-x_i). \tag{14.3}$$

From (14.3) we show how to derive a new linear constraint which must be satisfied by feasible integer solutions, or, equivalently, we show how to define a new nonnegative integer variable y^1 implied by (14.3).

Let $[t]$ denote the integer part of t; $[t] \leq t$. Define, for $\lambda > 0$,

$$a_j/\lambda = [a_j/\lambda] + r_j/\lambda, \quad 0 \leq r_j < \lambda \quad (j = 0, 1, \cdots, n). \tag{14.4}$$

Then (14.3) may be rewritten, after dividing through by λ, as

$$y/\lambda + (1/\lambda) \sum r_i x_i = \{[a_0/\lambda] + \sum [a_i/\lambda](-x_i)\} + r_0/\lambda. \quad (14.5)$$

Now, the lefthand side of (14.5) is nonnegative; hence, so is the righthand side; but $r_0/\lambda < 1$, and the term in curly brackets is integer. Therefore, the term in curly brackets must be nonnegative as well as integer; that is,

$$y' = [a_0/\lambda] + \sum [a_i/\lambda](-x_i) \geq 0 \quad (14.6)$$

is a new constraint, or y' is a new nonnegative integer variable implied by (14.3). This is the constraint developed in Gomory (1963a).

Suppose, now, that $\lambda = 1$. Rearrange (14.5) to obtain

$$\sum r_i x_i = \{[a_0] + \sum [a_i](-x_i) - y\} + r_0. \quad (14.7)$$

The lefthand side of (14.7) is nonnegative; hence, so is the righthand side; but $r_0 < 1$, and the term in curly brackets is integer. Therefore, the term in curly brackets must be nonnegative as well as integer; or, what is the same thing,

$$y' = -r_0 + \sum r_i x_i = -r_0 + \sum (-r_i)(-x_i) \geq 0 \quad (14.8)$$

is a new constraint, or y' is a new nonnegative integer variable implied by (14.3). This is the constraint developed in Gomory (1963b).

Using these new constraints, Gomory proposed two "extreme" algorithms.

Algorithm I (Gomory, 1963b). Obtain an optimal solution to the problem (14.1) considered as a linear program (assuming that one exists since otherwise no optimal integer solution exists). Then, if the solution is not in integers, generate from some row (14.3), with a_0 noninteger, a new row (14.8); adjoin it to the existing constraints to form a new linear program which is (lexicographically) dual feasible but not primal feasible; use a dual (lexicographic) simplex method to re-optimize. If y' of (14.8) becomes basic subsequently, drop it and its defining equation or row. Continue to cycle through these steps until either an integer optimal solution is found or a constraint appears, implying that no feasible solution exists.

In geometric terms, this algorithm considers, successively, optimal extreme-point solutions to linear programs; if such an extreme point X of some cycle has a noninteger coordinate, a closed half space, $y' \geq 0$, (14.8) is introduced which "cuts off" X, since at X the value of y' is negative.

The remarkable fact is that this process converges in a finite number of steps. If, for example, instead of (14.8), the new and valid constraint $\sum x_i \geq 1$ or $y' = -1 + \sum (-1)(-x_i) \geq 0$ (Dantzig, 1959) is taken, then convergence is not assured (Gomory and Hoffman, 1963). The proof of convergence may be given as follows, where we assume that y_0 is bounded below and that the choice of row (14.3) from which to generate a new constraint is always the topmost row with noninteger a_0: Let α_0^k be the column of $m + n + 1$ entries corresponding to the "current" values of the variables $Y = (y_0, y_1, \cdots, y_{m+n})^T$ after concluding the kth re-optimization. By the dual simplex method, $\alpha_0^k > \alpha_0^{k+1}$ for all k. Assume that the process does not converge in a finite number of steps, that is, that no all-integer α_0 is found. Since a_{00}^k is bounded below and since $a_{00}^k > a_{00}^{k+1}$, there must be a greatest integer $n_{00} \leq a_{00}^k$ for all k. But, then, for some k, $a_{00}^k = n_{00} + r_{00}^k$, with $r_{00}^k < 1$; and the new constraint would be generated from

$$y_0 = n_{00} + r_{00}^k + \sum a_{0i}^k(-x_i), \quad \text{where} \quad a_{0i}^k \geq 0,$$

and hence would be

$$y^1 = -r_{00}^k + \sum (-r_{0i}^k)(-x_i) \geq 0. \tag{14.9}$$

The next step of the dual simplex method would choose as pivot some entry of row (14.9), say $(-r_{0i}^k)$, which results in a new value for y_0:

$$a_{00} = n_{00} + r_{00}^k - \frac{a_{0i}^k r_{00}^k}{r_{0i}^k} \leq n_{00}, \quad \text{since} \quad a_{0i}^k/r_{0i}^k \geq 1.$$

Thus, y_0 attains the integer value n_{00} and can be no smaller. Repeat the same argument on each successive entry of α_0^k (each $y_1, \cdots, y_{m+n}$ is bounded below by the integer value zero); unless a constraint implying that no solution exists is found, every entry of α_0^k (k large enough) must become integer, thus contradicting the assumption of nontermination.

Algorithm II (Gomory, 1963a). In this algorithm a dual (lexicographic) simplex method is again used, but all computation is carried out through addition and subtraction of columns; that is, the only pivot entries are -1 so that every successive step can be summarized as a unimodular transformation of (14.1). Given $\alpha_1, \cdots, \alpha_n$ in (14.1) lexicographically positive, choose a row with $a_0 < 0$ for (14.3). Then, take λ large enough, but as small as possible, to ensure that the generated row or constraint (14.6) contains an entry -1 which is an eligible pivot entry for a dual simplex method. This is clearly possible unless $a_j \geq 0$ for all $j \neq 0$ in (14.3), in which case no solution exists. Rules for a choice of λ are: (a) the pivot entry $[a_j/\lambda] = -1$ must be in the lexicographically smallest column having $a_j < 0$; (b) for each column k with $a_k < 0$, find the largest integer μ_k for which $(1/\mu_k)\alpha_k \geq \alpha_j$, and let $\lambda_k = -a_k/\mu_k$ (the choice of $\lambda \geq \lambda_k$ would assure that the new column α_k^1 be lexicographically positive); and (c) take $\lambda = \max \{\lambda_k \mid a_k < 0\}$ to assure preservation of dual feasibility (and if $\lambda = 1$, take $y^1 = y$).

The proof of termination for this "all-integer integer" algorithm can be given in very much the same terms as that for algorithm I, but it now depends on the existence of an optimal integer solution. If no optimal integer solution exists, it is possible for the algorithm to continue without cessation.

Recently, an alternate all-integer integer algorithm has been constructed by Glover (1963), and it is remarkably simple to describe. It is uniformly weaker than algorithm II but is of considerable pedagogical and expository interest in that it shows, quite clearly, a connection between Gomory's algorithms and the Euclidean algorithm. This algorithm consists of two basic ideas. Assume in this discussion that, as for algorithm II, the columns $\alpha_1, \cdots, \alpha_n$ are lexicographically positive.

The first basic idea is this: Suppose that a constraint (14.3) can be found with the properties

$$a_0 < 0; \qquad a_j \geq 0 \quad \text{for all} \quad j \neq 0, k; \quad \text{and} \quad a_k < 0. \qquad (14.10)$$

Then, rearranging (14.3) as

$$(-a_k)x_k \geq (-a_0) + \sum_{j \neq k} a_j x_j,$$

it becomes obvious that $x_k \geq [a_0/a_k] + 1$ for any feasible integer solution to (14.1), since $x_j \geq 0$ for all j and since x_k must be integer. Thus,

$$y^1 = -[a_0/a_k] - 1 + x_k = -[a_0/a_k] - 1 + (-1)(-x_k) \geq 0, \qquad (14.11)$$

where y^1 nonnegative integer is implied from a (14.3) satisfying conditions (14.10). Compare this with the constraint (14.6) obtained under conditions (14.10), $\lambda = -a_k$, and (14.6) becomes

$$y^1 = [a_0/a_k] + \sum_{j \neq k} [a_j/-a_k](-x_j) + (-1)(-x_k) \geq 0. \qquad (14.12)$$

But $[a_0/-a_k] = -[a_0/a_k] - 1$, and since $[a_j/-a_k] \geq 0$ $(j \neq k)$, (14.12) implies or is stronger than (14.11).

The second basic idea is concerned with creating constraints (14.3) which have the properties (14.10). This can again be accomplished through elementary column operations. To construct the desired form, choose some row with $a_0 < 0$. If all $a_j > 0$ $(j \neq 0)$, no solution exists; if exactly one a_j is negative, the desired form has been obtained. Otherwise, choose among the entries $a_j < 0$ that entry a_k having the smallest lexicographically positive column α_k. Then, for each $a_j < 0$, subtract α_k from α_j or a positive integer multiple n_j of α_k from α_j, which assures that $\alpha_j^1 = \alpha_j - n_j \alpha_k > 0$. This is the same as introducing the new constraint

$$y^1 = (-n_j)(-x_j) + (-1)(-x_k) = n_j x_j + x_k \geq 0, \qquad (14.13)$$

that is, introducing the new variable y^1 which must clearly be nonnegative and integer since x_j and x_k are so. If one continues in this way, a row (14.3) with desired properties (14.10) is obtained.

The algorithm (see Glover, 1963) is then a sequence of pivot steps or elementary column operations corresponding to (14.13) and (14.11): Given the first $a_0 < 0$ (excluding the y_0 row), pivot on form (14.13) to obtain a row with properties (14.10); then pivot on form (14.11). The proof of termination is essentially the same as that for algorithm II.

The Euclidean algorithm for obtaining the g.c.d. of a set of positive integers $a_1, a_2, \cdots, a_n$ may be described as an integer programming algorithm. The problem of finding the g.c.d. may be stated as

$$\text{minimize} \quad y_0 = a_1 x_1 + \cdots + a_n x_n \quad \text{when} \quad y_0 \geq 1. \quad (14.14)$$

Modifying algorithm I to handle problems in which not all variables are restricted to be nonnegative, Gomory (1963b) noted that the resulting steps could be interpreted as having imitated the steps of the Euclidean algorithm. It is easy to see that the applications of the more primitive transformations of Glover are, properly modified for variables unrestricted in sign, precisely the steps of the Euclidean algorithm. Write the g.c.d. problem in the format (14.1), letting $a = (a_1, \cdots, a_n)$, as

$$\text{minimize } y_0 \text{ when} \quad \begin{bmatrix} -y_0 \\ y_1 \\ X \end{bmatrix} = \begin{bmatrix} 0 & a \\ -1 & -a \\ 0 & -I \end{bmatrix} \begin{bmatrix} 1 \\ -X \end{bmatrix}, \quad y_1 \geq 0.$$

The row $y_1 = -1 + aX \geq 0$ corresponds to the only nonnegative constrained variable but has its constant term negative. So it is used to create the desired type of constraint by the subtraction of positive integer multiples of columns from other columns in such a way that the columns remain lexicographically positive. Continuing, the row of y_1 must attain the properties (14.10); but it can contain no positive coefficients, since this would imply a lexicographically negative column. Thus, in a finite number of steps, all coefficients except one in the row of y_0 are zero. Suppose that this one coefficient lies in column α, corresponding to the nonbasic (unconstrained) variable y^1, and has value $a_0 > 0$. Then $-y_0 = a_0(-y^1)$ with $-y_0$ to be maximized, that is, y^1 to be taken as small as possible, and $y_1 = -1 + a_0 y^1 \geq 0$ or $y^1 \geq 1/a_0$. Thus, $y^1 = 1$ is a solution with $y_0 = a_0$ and $(-y_0, y_1, X)^T = -\alpha^T$. That this process is the Euclidean algorithm is easy to see—every operation produces a list of n numbers in the first row which have the same g.c.d. as in the previous step—and was noted in another context by Blankinship (1963).

The "underlying approach" in integer programming may be viewed in many ways. One such view is as a process of convexification. Another view is as an instance of the general idea embodied in decomposition approaches (Dantzig and Wolfe, 1961, and Gomory, 1963c). This is the attempt to organize computation in large (and structured) linear programs in such a way that data is generated only when it is needed in the course of computation. In this view, one imagines the integer program (14.1) as really being a linear program in which many (implied) linear constraints (or data) have not been specified but are generated when needed.

The above discussion provides another view. Thus, the Euclidean algorithm is a method for operating on lexicographically positive columns which preserves a key property: at any stage of the computation, the positive integers of the top row have the same g.c.d. as at any other stage. The Glover ideas are interpretable as a direct extension of this, in which it is noted that another key property can be preserved: every new variable introduced into the computation of form (14.13) is a positive integer combination of nonnegative integer variables and is hence itself nonnegative integer. Finally, the Gomory ideas (algorithm II) are interpretable as a further extension of the Glover ideas: every new variable (14.6) introduced into the computation can be analyzed as a transformation which includes one or more Glover transformations (14.11) and (14.13).

The unhappy fact concerning these algorithms is that they are "dual methods": no feasible solution to the problem of interest is obtained until the optimal solution is found—and this may require more iterations than can be afforded. The same is true of the "mixed" integer programming algorithms (Beale, 1958, and Gomory, 1960a) for problems (14.1) in which not all variables are constrained to be integer-valued. There are, however, at least two proposals which offer primal methods. One, announced by Gomory in 1962 but never described in writing, has had poor computational success. Another is described by Ben-Israel and Charnes (1962), but it requires, as a substep, the solution of a system of linear inequalities in integers.[4] Finding a good primal method is most certainly an outstanding problem of great practical interest. The situation is remedied, though in a perhaps artificial way, for the class of mixed integer problems through an approach due to Benders (1962).

PARTITIONING IN MIXED PROBLEMS AND A LOCATION PROBLEM

Given an integer program to solve with some variables constrained to be integer-valued and others not, we turn to a partitioning approach of Benders (1962). Suppose that the problem is: Find $X \geq 0$ and Y integer-valued to

$$\text{minimize } y_0 = C_1 X + C_2 Y \text{ when } A_1 X + A_2 Y \geq B, \quad X, Y \geq 0. \quad (14.15)$$

The idea of Benders may be explained as follows (see Balinski and Wolfe, 1963): Denote the permissible values for Y by R. Then (14.15) is the same as the problem

---

[4] A primal method, which has had poor computational success to date, has been devised by Young (1964).

$$\min_{Y \varepsilon R} \{C_2 Y + \min_{X} [C_1 X \mid A_1 X \geq B - A_2 Y, X \geq 0]\}. \qquad (14.16)$$

But, for given Y, the minimum problem "inside" the square brackets is a linear program in X for which, by duality, the following statement holds:

$$\min_{X} \{C_1 X \mid A_1 X \geq B - A_2 Y, X \geq 0\}$$

$$= \max_{U} \{U(B - A_2 Y) \mid U A_1 \leq C_1, U \geq 0\}, \qquad (14.17)$$

where the lefthand (righthand) side has "value" $-\infty$ $(+\infty)$ if unbounded below (above) and value $+\infty$ $(-\infty)$ if undefined. Thus, (14.16) may be written as

$$\min_{Y} \{C_2 Y + \max_{U} [U(B - A_2 Y) \mid U A_1 \leq C_1, U \geq 0]\}. \qquad (14.18)$$

Consider the convex polyhedral set $S = \{U \mid UA \leq C_1, U \geq 0\}$. It is independent of Y. If it is empty, then, by (14.17), no feasible solution to the original problem (14.15) exists (this is the statement of Farkas' theorem). Otherwise, the maximum value of $U(B - A_2 Y)$, no matter what value of Y, attains its optimum at an extreme point of S or grows without bound along an extreme ray of S. But the extreme points of S are finite in number (call them U^l, $l \varepsilon L$), and the extreme rays of S are found by looking at all extreme rays of $U A_1 \leq 0$, $U \geq 0$ which are also finite in number (call them U^k, $k \varepsilon K$). Now if for some Y there exists a U^k, $k \varepsilon K$, with $U^k(B - A_2 Y) > 0$, then the "value" of (14.17) is $+\infty$, showing that the lefthand side of (14.17) has no feasible solution; thus,

$$U^k(B - A_2 Y) \leq 0, \quad \text{all} \quad k \varepsilon K, \qquad (14.19)$$

provide necessary and sufficient conditions on Y to admit a feasible X. Furthermore, this permits us to rewrite (14.18) as

$$\min_{Y \varepsilon R} \{y_0 \mid y_0 \geq C_2 Y + \max_{l \varepsilon L} U^l(B - A_2 Y) \text{ and } U^k(B - A_2 Y) \leq 0, \text{ all } k \varepsilon K\}.$$

$$(14.20)$$

Thus, this partitioning has transformed the original mixed integer programming problem into a pure integer programming problem in variables Y containing potentially vast numbers of linear constraints on y_0, Y. As in decomposition (of which this is a "dual" form), the hope is that not all of these constraints need be enumerated but rather that only some small subset need ever be considered. The computational procedure consists of solving (14.15) by iteration through a sequence of steps, each consisting of the solution of two subproblems.

Partition Algorithm: Step 1. Given a finite subset of U^i, $j \; \varepsilon \; Q \subset K \cup L$, solve the *restricted integer program* (14.20), that is, solve (14.20) over the restricted set of constraints coming from Q. If no feasible solution exists, then (14.15) has no solution; otherwise, let $\bar{y}_0$, $\bar{Y}$ be an optimal solution (or $\bar{y}_0$ small, $\bar{Y}$ feasible if y_0 is unbounded below). Step 2. Given the trial solution $\bar{y}_0$, $\bar{Y}$, determine whether it is optimal by solving the *linear programs* (14.17) with $Y = \bar{Y}$ and call their common value $f(\bar{Y})$. If $f(\bar{Y}) = +\infty$, then the current $\bar{Y}$ does not admit a feasible X, and a new U^k, $k \; \varepsilon \; K$, has been found which is adjoined to Q. If $f(\bar{Y})$ is finite, let $\bar{X}$ and $\bar{U}$ be solutions. $(\bar{X}, \bar{Y})$ is feasible for (14.15); if, in addition, $\bar{y}_0 \geq C_2\bar{Y} + f(\bar{Y})$, then it is also optimal because $\bar{y}_0$, $\bar{Y}$ is feasible for the entire problem (14.20) while $\bar{y}_0$ can be taken no smaller than its minimum value over the restricted problem (14.20). Finally, if $\bar{y}_0 < C_2\bar{Y} + f(\bar{Y})$, then some one or more linear constraints of (14.20) are not satisfied by $\bar{y}_0$, $\bar{Y}$; the "most violated" one corresponds to $\bar{U}$, that is, is $y_0 \geq C_2Y + \bar{U}(B - A_2Y)$, so $\bar{U}$ is adjoined to Q. The finiteness of the procedure—which consists of cycling through steps 1 and 2—is assured because of the finite number of extreme points and rays of S.

Consider, now, some of the properties of this algorithm. First, at every cycle, one is provided with upper and lower bounds on the value of min y_0. Step 1 provides a lower bound $\bar{y}_0$, since minimization of y_0 is accomplished over a restricted set of constraints. Step 2 provides an upper bound, since either $f(\bar{Y})$ is infinite or $f(\bar{Y})$ is finite, implying that $(\bar{X}, \bar{Y})$ is feasible with value $C_1\bar{X} + C_2\bar{Y} = f(\bar{Y}) + C_2\bar{Y}$. Thus, if computation becomes too expensive, it can be stopped and the best feasible solution $(\bar{X}, \bar{Y})$ taken, together with an estimate of how far it is from optimum. Second, if S is bounded, that is, if the set of rays K is void, then every occurrence of step 2 provides an $(\bar{X}, \bar{Y})$ which is feasible—and one can say that the algorithm is "primal," though perhaps in an artificial way. Third, if S is not bounded, then it may be possible to enumerate its extreme rays initially and thus to impose conditions on Y sufficient to assure that every $\bar{Y}$ from step 1 admits a feasible $\bar{X}$ in step 2. Fourth, the fact of "partitioning" rather than applying some direct mixed integer algorithm preserves the structure of the matrix A_1 in each step. Thus, if A_1 is of transportation type, then every step 2 is a problem of transportation type. All of these properties are desirable; nevertheless, the key question regards the number (or percent) of extreme points and rays of S which need enter the computation. If this number is large, the approach is not successful.[5]

To clarify the above, consider a plant location problem (see Balinski and Wolfe, 1963, Manne, 1964, and Vietorisz, 1963) which may be formulated as

[5] For a report on some recent computational experience, see Balinski (1965).

minimize $\quad \sum_{i,j} c_{ij}x_{ij} + \sum_i f_i y_i$

when $\quad \sum_i x_{ij} \geq 1, \quad 0 \leq x_{ij} \leq y_i, \quad y_i = 0 \quad \text{or} \quad 1$ $\qquad$ (14.21)

$$(i = 1, \cdots, m; j = 1, \cdots, n).$$

In a solution, $y_i = 1$ means that plant i is opened (or built), entailing a fixed cost of f_i; $y_i = 0$ means that plant i is closed (or not built); $x_{ij} = p$ means that p percent of the demand at market j is met by plant i at a total cost of $c_{ij}p$. Given fixed $y_i = 0$ or 1, it is clear that the optimal solution to the resultant problem can be chosen with $x_{ij} = 0$ or 1. However, the constraints on X and Y do not form a unimodular matrix. The necessary and sufficient conditions (14.19) on $Y = (y_1, \cdots, y_m)$ to admit a feasible (X, Y) become simply $\sum_i y_i \geq 1$, that is, $Y \neq 0$, or at least one plant i must be open. The linear subproblem of step 2 is: Given $\bar{y}_0$ and $\bar{Y} \neq 0$,

minimize $\quad \sum_{i,j} c_{ij}x_{ij} = f(\bar{Y}) \quad \text{when} \quad \sum_i x_{ij} \geq 1, \quad 0 \leq x_{ij} \leq \bar{y}_i,$

maximize $\quad \sum_j v_j - \sum_{i,j} u_{ij}\bar{y}_i = f(\bar{Y}) \quad \text{when} \quad v_j - u_{ij} \leq c_{ij}, u_{ij}, v_j \geq 0.$

$\qquad$ (14.22)

These problems have explicit solutions: namely, if $\bar{y}_i = 0$, then $\bar{x}_{ij} = 0$; otherwise, let $\bar{x}_{ij} = 1$ for one j if $\bar{y}_i = 1$ and $c_{ij} = \min_k c_{ik}$; that is, for each sink j, supply its demand from the open source having the lowest linear transportation cost. Also, let $\bar{v}_j = \min \{c_{ij} \mid \bar{y}_i = 1\}$; that is, $\bar{v}_j$ is the linear cost of supplying sink j; and let $\bar{u}_{ij} = \max \{0, \bar{v}_j - c_{ij}\}$; that is, $\bar{u}_{ij}$ is the potential linear saving made possible in supplying j if source i is opened.

Then this solution $\{\bar{u}_{ij}, \bar{v}_j\}$ is adjoined to the set Q to obtain a new constraint for step 1:

$$y_0 \geq \sum_j \bar{v}_j - \sum_{i,j} \bar{u}_{ij}y_i + \sum_i f_i y_i.$$ $\qquad$ (14.23)

Let $I = \{i \mid \bar{y}_i = 1\}$. Then (14.23) may be rewritten as

$$y_0 \geq \sum_j \bar{v}_j + \sum_{i \in I} f_i + \sum_{i \in I} f_i(y_i - 1) + \sum_{i \notin I} (f_i - \sum_j \bar{u}_{ij})y_i.$$ $\qquad$ (14.24)

The sum of the first two terms is the total cost of the "current" plan or feasible solution $\bar{X}$, $\bar{Y}$. The fourth term represents a linear estimate of the change in total cost in going from $\bar{Y}$ to Y with all sources previously open remaining open ($\bar{y}_i = 1$ implying that $y_i = 1$). If exactly one new source h were to be opened ($\bar{Y} = Y$ except $\bar{y}_h = 0$ and $y_h = 1$), then the estimate would be exact; if more than one, it would be an overestimate of linear savings or an underestimate of total cost. The third term is associated with the set of currently open sources ($\bar{y}_i = 1$) and represents an estimate of total savings resulting from closing down open sources; but it overestimates these savings or underestimates the righthand side of (14.24), since it ignores possible resultant increases in linear costs. Thus, the constraint (14.24) or (14.23) could have been deduced directly and, in fact, strengthened by including in the third term of (14.24) a stronger underestimate of increase in linear cost resulting from the closing down of some plant i. This has been noticed by Gomory in Vietorisz (1963) and incorporated in an experimental program currently being tested at IBM.

INTEGER PROGRAMMING: COMPUTATION

It is an unfortunate fact that users of integer programming methods have met with only erratic success. Some problems have been solved; others have not, since the number of iterations surpassed limitations of time and/or expense, and so computation had to be halted. Thus, following the early flush of enthusiasm for integer programming formulations after the inception of the first Gomory algorithm in 1958, activities in this direction shrank.

Why has erratic computational experience been encountered with these algorithms? Some problems are simply "ill-conditioned." But, further, algorithms I and II allow a wide range of arbitrary choice which can seriously affect convergence. There is evidence to support this statement. Ouyahia (1962) remarks that in a problem (14.1) with $m = 20$ and $n = 29$ one version of a code for algorithm II found no solution in over 30,000 iterations, while in another version an optimal solution was found in 70 iterations. Gilmore and Gomory (1963) report on computational experience in solving the "cutting stock" problem. This report has bearing on the convergence problem in integer programming. Their algorithm for that problem is a "primal" decomposition approach to solving a linear program with relatively few rows or constraints and potentially vast numbers of columns or variables (for example, millions), just as an integer programming algorithm is in one interpretation (see the fourth section of this paper) a "dual" decomposition approach to solving a linear program with relatively few columns or variables and potentially vast numbers of rows or constraints (the "convexification constraints"). In integer programming, the basic step is the generation of a new row or new constraint. In the cutting stock algorithm, the basic step is the generation of a new column or new cutting pattern which will yield an improvement relative to the "current" feasible solution. This step is accomplished through the solution of a "knapsack problem." In generating a new column, however, it is possible (a) to obtain a column which leads to the greatest per unit improvement or (b) to stop the knapsack computation and accept the first column found which yields some improvement. The effect of these alternate methods of choice of new column on a set of 21 test problems is given in Gilmore and Gomory (1963). It is conclusively shown that (a) is much superior to (b). For example, the total number of pivot steps necessary for solution in a set of five problems with these alternate methods of choice are shown in Table I. The inference to be drawn is that convergence in integer programming will be highly sensitive to the rule of choice of row (14.3) from which to generate a new constraint (14.6) or (14.8).

TABLE I*

Problem	1	2	3	4	5
Column choice (a)	148	233	161	101	90
Column choice (b)	541	1104	586	545	370

* Based on Gilmore and Gomory (1963).

In fact, the choice of row problem can be extended. If at some stage of computation the linear equations in nonnegative integer-constrained variables y_i and x_j are

$$y_i = a_{i0} + \sum a_{ij}(-x_j)(\geq 0), \qquad (14.25)$$

then any new variable $\tilde{y}$ defined as a nonnegative integer combination of variables y_i must itself be nonnegative integer. Thus,

$$\tilde{y} = \sum_i u_i y_i = \sum_i u_i a_{i0} + \sum_j \sum_i u_i a_{ij}(-x_j)(\geq 0) \qquad (14.26)$$

can be used as the expression (14.3) from which to generate a new constraint. In fact, if algorithm II is used, then the u_i in (14.26) need not be restricted to be integer, for the derivation of (14.6) from (14.3) does not use the fact that y is integer but only that y is nonnegative.

Algorithm I. Gomory (1963b) shows that if the "fractional cuts" (14.8) derived from (14.25) are represented by the vectors of their components $(r_{i0}, r_{i1}, \cdots, r_{in})$, then the class of "strongest cuts" resulting from forms (14.26) are $[\sum u_i r_{i0} \ (\text{mod } 1), \cdots, \sum u_i r_{in} \ (\text{mod } 1)]$. In fact, this class of vectors forms an additive group which is, in some instances, cyclic, all vectors being generated as integer multiples of one vector and reduced modulo 1. No computational use of these facts has been made except for forming expressions (14.26) in which all u_i except one are zero. This is the case in which some one row (14.3), or some one row from (14.25), with noninteger first component $a_0 > 0$ is chosen and the cyclic group of cuts which it generates is considered.

The general intent in choosing or producing a row with noninteger first component $a_0 > 0$ and deriving a new constraint (14.8) is to make that new constraint "strong," that is, for which the ratios (r_0/r_i) are large, for this means that the new constraint has intercepts with the x_i-axes which are deep. Clearly, it will, in general, be impossible to find cuts which are uniformly strong for all j, so other criteria are necessary. Some possible rules are:

Rule Ia. Choose a row (14.3) for which r_0 is largest.

Rule Ib. Choose a row (14.3), and, from its cyclic group of constraints, choose that one with largest r_0. This can be done by an application of the Euclidean algorithm (Gomory, 1963b).

Rule Ic. Choose a row (14.3), and, from its cyclic group of constraints, choose that one with largest (r_0/r_k) for some given k. Again, this can be done by an application of the Euclidean algorithm (Gomory, 1963b).

Rule Id. Choose a number of rows (14.3) with $a_0 < 0$, and, from their respective constraints, choose that one with largest $(r_0/\sum_i^n r_i)$. This represents an attempt at "normalization" and is a simplification of an approach used by Levitan in IPM 3.

Rule Ie. Find a new constraint (14.8) by any rule (say, one of the above). Then, derive from it a constraint (14.6) for some choice of $\lambda > 0$. If $([r_0/\lambda]/\sum_1^n [r_i/\lambda])$ is larger than $(r_0/\sum_1^n r_i)$, consider the new constraint and repeat the operation; otherwise, choose to introduce the last generated constraint. This is a simplification of an approach by Levitan in IPM 3.

It is clear that combinations or sequences of these rules can be applied. Their efficacy can be determined only through computational experimentation.

Algorithm II. The choice of row (14.3) with a_0 less than zero and integer is open. However, once a row (14.3) is chosen, then the smallest possible λ and resultant -1 pivot entry in (14.6) are completely specified.

The general intent in choosing or producing a row with a_0 less than zero and integer is to find a pivot column which is lexicographically large, for this means that the next step leads to a large lexicographic decrease in the column of constants. Experiments have shown that concern with pivoting on large columns is more important than concern with pivoting on rows with $a_0 < 0$, $|a_0|$ large. Now, rank the columns α_j $(j \neq 0)$ in decreasing lexicographic order. Then the rows can be ranked by assigning to each row the rank of the column which must be its pivot column. Let the rank of row i be $r(i)$; it is desirable, then, to choose a row i with $r(i)$ small. By the use of this terminology, some possible rules are:

Rule IIa. Choose from among rows (14.3) with $a_0 < 0$ a row with minimum $r(i)$, that is, a row which leads to a choice of pivot column which is lexicographically largest (Gomory, 1963a).

Rule IIb. Choose a row i corresponding to y_i, according to rule IIa, and find its new constraint (14.6), say $\bar{y}_i$ nonnegative integer. Then choose a row i^*, corresponding to y_{i^*}, with smaller rank, and form, if possible, a new row $\tilde{y} = y_{i^*} + u_i\bar{y}_i$, $u_i \geq 0$, with negative constant term ($a_0 < 0$) and nonnegative entry corresponding to the pivot column of $\bar{y}_i$. Notice that y_{i^*} has a positive constant term; otherwise, its rank being smaller, it would have been chosen as the y_i. Repeat, letting $\tilde{y}$ take the place of y_i, until no row with lower rank can be obtained. Choose this last row as the row from which to generate a new constraint (Gomory, 1963a).

Rule IIc. The procedure of rule IIb may be extended: namely, assign the weight $u_i \geq 0$ to row i of (14.25), and form the new row (14.26), $\tilde{y} = \sum_i u_i y_i \geq 0$. Then compute $u_i \geq 0$ by linear programming in order to form a row (14.25) with constant term $\sum u_i a_{i0} < 0$ and with $\sum u_i a_{ij} \geq 0$ for the largest possible set of smallest (or highest) ranked lexicographic columns. This is easily done through a process analogous to obtaining a first feasible solution in linear programming. The $\tilde{y}$ so found is not necessarily integer-valued; nevertheless, as was seen above, this row (14.26) may be chosen as a row (14.3) from which to generate a constraint (14.6). This leads to a choice of the largest possible lexicographic column. This rule was suggested by Gomory and used in an experimental IBM code named IPLP 6.

Again, it is clear that combinations of rules can be applied. In fact, algorithms I and II can be combined. For example, it may be efficient to first solve the integer program as a linear program, then to use the new constraints (14.8) of algorithm I to obtain an all-integer tableau which is dual feasible, and then to use algorithm II. Or one can begin with a linear programming solution to obtain an upper bound on the value of the objective function to be introduced as a constraint in algorithm II.

Codes and Experience[6]

IPM 1 is a Share code of algorithm II which uses the row choice rule IIa interspersed with a row choice rule which picks out that row with most negative a_0. This code appears to have had the least success of the codes reported on here. IPM 2 is a Share code of algorithm II which uses the row choice rule IIb. IPLP 6 is an IBM experimental code, not released for general consumption, which uses the row choice rule IIc. This code has produced convergence in remarkably fewer numbers of pivot steps than has IPM 2; however, the linear programming technique for generating

---

[6] Secrecy prevails in the field of experience. The completeness of this report is tempered by this fact.

a new row has not been perfected and has taken relatively long times.[7] IPM 3 is a Share code of algorithm I which uses a combination of ideas from the row choice rules Id and Ie. In a fairly extended run of experimental computations on a class of covering problems arising from the minimization of Boolean functions, IPM 3 proved to be superior in number of steps and in time to IPM 2. CEIR code (see Martin, 1963) is a code of algorithm I which uses the row choice rules Ia and Ic. In addition, after a linear programming solution is found, this code continues to generate new cuts until an all-integer tableau is found, whether or not infeasibilities enter. This code appears to have had the greatest computational success; this is in part due to the fact that it is not an "all in core" code and can handle considerably larger problems.

The bulk of the available data on computational experience is concerned with "generalized covering problems." These are problems of the form

$$\text{minimize} \quad \sum_1^n c_j x_j \quad \text{when} \quad \sum_1^n A_j x_j = E, \quad x_j = 0 \quad \text{or} \quad 1, \quad (14.27)$$

where E is a column vector of m 1's and where each A_j is a column vector of m 0's and 1's. In Cobham, Fridshal, and North (1961 and 1962) and Cobham and North (1963), experiments on problems of type (14.27) with IPM 2 and IPM 3 are discussed. IPM 3 appears to be better than IPM 2 for this class of problems, as mentioned above. This is especially true as problems become bigger (that is, as m and n become bigger) or "harder to solve" in the sense that convergence is slow. The authors of these reports found that IPM 2 requires about $2/3n$ steps for convergence in problems roughly of size $m \leq 125$, $n \leq 125$. An interesting fact reported in Cobham, Fridshal, and North (1962) is that reordering of rows and columns of (14.27) was found to affect seriously the convergence rate; however, this might be expected since the row choice rule of IPM 2 is dependent on the first row picked. Also, experiments on a few problems (see Cobham and North, 1963) showed IPLP 6 to be much superior to IPM 2 in number of steps, superior to IPM 3 as well, and less "sensitive" to problems, in the sense that it was less erratic in convergence behavior (Giglio and Wagner, 1964, confirm the erratic convergence of IPM 2). Finally, these reports concluded that integer programming is an effective means of dealing with the minimization of Boolean function problems.

The CEIR code has been used on larger problems. In nine problems of form (14.27), arising from delivery problems, the results shown in Table II were reported.

---

[7] Private communication from R. E. Gomory, February 1964.

TABLE II*

Problem (m, n)	(5, 26)	(8, 24)	(8, 68)	(9, 102)	(9, 202)	(11, 145)	(11, 305)	(15, 142)	(15, 270)
No. of steps	9	7	22	142	26	42	36	43	23
No. of new constraints	0	0	2	20	1	5	1	7	1
No. of $x_j = 1$ in solution	2	3	3	5	3	3	3	5	5

* Based on Balinski and Quandt (1964).

In other work, Martin[8] reports having solved about 20 combinatorial problems of a type similar to (14.27), arising from scheduling problems with $70 \leq m \leq 100$ and $1600 \leq n \leq 2200$. All took in the order of 100 steps and one hour of IBM 7090 computation time, the longest having taken 157 pivot steps. The largest single problem had $m \approx 215$, $n \approx 2600$ and was solved in the same order of steps and time. Not one of these problems required the generation of more than ten new constraints, and the largest single problem required only one new constraint. Thus, it is easy to see why these problems were so successfully solved: few new constraints needed to be introduced. This means that the optimal integer solutions to these problems usually lie on a low-dimensional face of the convex polyhedral set S defined by $\sum A_j x_j \geq E$, $x_j \geq 0$. Thus, the optimal linear programming solution to the problems (5, 26) and (8, 24) are extreme points of S; in problems (9, 202), (11, 305), and (15, 270) and in the $m \approx 215$, $n \approx 2600$ problem, the optimal solutions lie on an extreme edge. Furthermore, in all nine problems in Table II, optimal solution is very "degenerate"; that is, there are fewer x_j positive in a solution than there are m. These observations provide interesting fodder for the combinatorialist: To what extent can one predict these properties (and use them in computation) from the structure of the matrix $A = [A_1, \cdots, A_n]$? Can the notion of unimodularity be extended in a meaningful way to predict when a polyhedral convex set S of dimension n has integer points on its k-skeleton, where $0 < k < n$?

In conclusion, the current folklore in integer programming counsels the user: (1) to use algorithm I if in doubt (the linear programming solution might already be integer); (2) to use algorithm II only when the data a_{ij} of (14.1) has $|a_{ij}|$ small, for example, 0, 1; (3) to introduce,

---

[8] Private communication, February 1964.

if algorithm II is used, bounds on the objective function or on any variables if such are known (see Glover, 1963, and Giglio and Wagner, 1964); (4) to devise and test new row choice rules, disregarding the amount of "side" work it entails (it may pay, as in rule IIc). The evidence indicates that appropriate choice of algorithm and of row choice rule as a function of the class of problems being solved should lead to successful solution.[9]

---

[9] For a report on further computational experience, see Balinski (1965).

REFERENCES

BALINSKI, M. L. 1961. Fixed-cost transportation problems. Naval Res. Logist. Quart., 8:41–54.

———. 1965. Integer programming: methods, uses, computation. Management Sci., 12:253–313.

BALINSKI, M. L., and R. E. QUANDT. 1964. On an integer program for a delivery problem. Operations Res., 12:300–4.

BALINSKI, M. L., and P. WOLFE. 1963. On Benders decomposition and a plant location problem. Working paper ARO-27. Princeton, N. J.: Mathematica.

BEALE, E. M. L. 1958. A method of solving linear programming problems when some but not all of the variables must take integral values. Technical report no. 19. Princeton, N. J.: Princeton Univ., Statistical Techniques Research Group.

BENDERS, J. F. 1962. Partitioning procedures for solving mixed-variables programming problems. Numer. Math., 4:238–52.

BEN-ISRAEL, A., and A. CHARNES. 1962. On some problems of diophantine programming. Cahiers Centre Études Rech. Opér., 4:215–80.

BLANKINSHIP, W. A. 1963. A new version of the Euclidean algorithm. Amer. Math. Monthly, 70:742–45.

COBHAM, A., R. FRIDSHAL, and J. H. NORTH. 1961. An application of linear programming to the minimization of Boolean functions. Research report RC-472. Yorktown Heights, N. Y.: Thomas J. Watson Research Center.

———. 1962. A statistical study of the minimization of Boolean functions using integer programming. Research report RC-756. Yorktown Heights, N. Y.: Thomas J. Watson Research Center.

COBHAM, A., and J. H. NORTH. 1963. Extensions of the integer programming approach to the minimization of Boolean functions. Research report RC-915. Yorktown Heights, N. Y.: Thomas J. Watson Research Center.

CORD, J. 1963. A method of balancing assembly lines using linear programming. Privately circulated paper. Milwaukee: A. O. Smith Corp.

DANTZIG, G. B. 1951. Application of the simplex method to a transportation problem *in* Activity analysis of production and allocation (Cowles Commission monograph no. 13), ed. T. C. KOOPMANS. New York: Wiley, 359–73.

———. 1959. Note on solving linear programs in integers. Naval Res. Logist. Quart., 6:75–76.

———. 1960. On the significance of solving linear programming problems with some integer variables. Econometrica, 28:30–44.

DANTZIG, G. B., D. R. FULKERSON, and S. M. JOHNSON. 1954. Solution of a large scale travelling salesman problem. J. Operations Res. Soc. Amer., 2:393–410.

DANTZIG, G. B., and P. WOLFE. 1961. The decomposition algorithm for linear programs. Econometrica, 29:767–78.

EDMONDS, J. 1962. Covers and packings in a family of sets. Bull. Amer. Math. Soc., 68:494–99.

FORD, L. R., JR., and D. R. FULKERSON. 1962. Flows in networks. Princeton, N. J.: Princeton Univ. Press.

FULKERSON, D. R., and H. J. RYSER. 1961. Widths and heights of (0, 1)-matrices. Canad. J. Math., 13:239–55.

GIGLIO, R. J., and H. M. WAGNER. 1964. Approximate solutions to the three machine scheduling problem. Operations Res., 12:305–24.

GILMORE, P. C., and R. E. GOMORY. 1963. A linear programming approach to the cutting stock problem—part II. Operations Res., 11:863–88.

GLOVER, F. 1963. A bound escalation method for the solution of integer linear programs. Pittsburgh: Carnegie Institute of Technology, Graduate School of Industrial Administration.

GOMORY, R. E. 1958. Outline of an algorithm for integer solutions to linear programs. Bull. Amer. Math. Soc., 64:275–78.

———. 1960a. An algorithm for the mixed integer problem. Memorandum RM-2597. Santa Monica, Calif.: The RAND Corp.

———. 1960b. Solving linear programming problems in integers *in* Combinatorial analysis (Proceedings of symposia in applied mathematics, vol. X), ed. R. BELLMAN and M. HALL, JR. Providence, R. I.: Amer. Math. Soc., 211–16.

———. 1963a. All-integer integer programming algorithm *in* Industrial scheduling, ed. J. F. MUTH and G. L. THOMPSON. Englewood Cliffs, N. J.: Prentice-Hall, 193–206. (First issued as research report RC-189. 1960. Yorktown Heights, N. Y.: Thomas J. Watson Research Center.)

———. 1963b. An algorithm for integer solutions to linear programs *in* Recent advances in mathematical programming, ed. R. L. GRAVES and P. WOLFE. New York: McGraw-Hill, 269–302. (First issued as technical report no. 1. 1958. Princeton, N. J.: Princeton-IBM Mathematics Research Project.)

———. 1963c. Large and non-convex problems in linear programming *in* Experimental arithmetic, high-speed computing and mathematics (Proceedings of symposia in applied mathematics, vol. XV), ed. N. C. METROPOLIS *et al.* Providence, R. I.: Amer. Math. Soc., 125–39.

GOMORY, R. E., and A. J. HOFFMAN. 1963. On the convergence of an integer-programming process. Naval Res. Logist. Quart., 10:121–23.

HELLER, I. 1957. On linear systems with integral valued solutions. Pacific J. Math., 7:1351–64.

HELLER, I., and A. J. HOFFMAN. 1962. On unimodular matrices. Pacific J. Math., 12:1321–27.

HELLER, I., and C. B. TOMPKINS. 1956. An extension of a theorem of Dantzig *in* Linear inequalities and related systems (Ann. of Math. study no. 38), ed. H. W. KUHN and A. W. TUCKER. Princeton, N. J.: Princeton Univ. Press, 247–54.

HOFFMAN, A. J. 1960. Some recent applications of the theory of linear inequalities to extremal combinatorial analysis *in* Combinatorial analysis (Proceedings of symposia in applied mathematics, vol. X), ed. R. BELLMAN and M. HALL, JR. Providence, R. I.: Amer. Math. Soc., 113–28.

HOFFMAN, A. J., and J. G. KRUSKAL. 1956. Integral boundary points of convex polyhedra *in* Linear inequalities and related systems (Ann. of Math. study no. 38), ed. H. W. KUHN and A. W. TUCKER. Princeton, N. J.: Princeton Univ. Press, 223–46.

KARP, R. M. 1961. Minimum-redundancy coding for the discrete noiseless channel. IRE Transactions of the Professional Group on Information Theory, vol. IT-7(no. 1):27–38.

KUNZI, H. P., and W. OETTLI. 1963. Integer quadratic programming *in* Recent advances in mathematical programming, ed. R. L. GRAVES and P. WOLFE. New York: McGraw-Hill, 303–8.

LAND, A. H., and A. G. DOIG. 1960. An automatic method of solving discrete programming problems. Econometrica, 28:497–520.

MANNE, A. S. 1960. On the job-shop scheduling problem. Operations Res., 8:219–23.

———. 1964. Plant location under economics of scale-decentralization and computation. Management Sci., 11:213–35.

MARKOWITZ, H. M., and A. S. MANNE. 1957. On the solution of discrete programming problems. Econometrica, 25:84–110.

MARTIN, G. T. 1963. An accelerated Euclidean algorithm for integer linear programming *in* Recent advances in mathematical programming, ed. R. L. GRAVES and P. WOLFE. New York: McGraw-Hill, 311–18.

MILLER, C. E., A. W. TUCKER, and R. A. ZEMLIN. 1960. Integer programming formulation of travelling salesman problems. J. Assoc. Comput. Mach., 7:326–29.

NORMAN, R. Z., and M. O. RABIN. 1959. An algorithm for the minimum cover of a graph. Proc. Amer. Math. Soc., 10:315–19.

OUYAHIA, A. 1962. Programmes lineaires à variables discretes. Rev. Franç. Rech. Opér., 6:55–75.

TUCKER, A. W. 1955. Linear inequalities and convex polyhedral sets *in* Proceedings of the second symposium in linear programming, vol. II. Washington, D. C.: Nat. Bur. Standards, 569–602.

————. 1960. A combinatorial equivalence of matrices *in* Combinatorial analysis (Proceedings of symposia in applied mathematics, vol. X), ed. R. BELLMAN and M. HALL, JR. Providence, R. I.: Amer. Math. Soc., 129–40.

VIETORISZ, T. 1963. Industrial development planning models with economics of scale and indivisibilities. Research report RC-1061. Yorktown Heights, N. Y.: Thomas J. Watson Research Center.

WAGNER, H. M. 1959. An integer linear programming model for machine shop scheduling. Naval Res. Logist. Quart., 6:131–40.

WEAVER, J. B., and S. W. HESS. 1963. A procedure for nonpartisan districting: development of computer techniques. Yale Law J., 73:288–308.

WITZGALL, C. 1963. An all-integer programming algorithm with parabolic constraints. J. SIAM, 11:855–71.

YOUNG, R. D. 1964. A primal (all integer) integer programming algorithm: antecedents, description, proof of finiteness, exemplification. Working paper no. 52. Stanford, Calif.: Stanford Univ., Graduate School of Business.

15

A Generalized Upper-Bounded Technique
for Linear Programming[1]

GEORGE B. DANTZIG and R. M. VAN SLYKE

University of California, Berkeley

INTRODUCTION

We are interested in linear programs with $M + L$ equations such that each variable has at most one nonzero coefficient in the last L equations (Figure 1). Transportation problems, linear programs with upper-bounded variables, assignment problems, and distribution problems all have this structure.

The main feature of the algorithm is that a working basis of order $2M$ is used for pivoting, pricing, and inversion. This basis for large L can be of significantly lower order than the order of the original system. Another method utilizing a working basis of order M in which the updating of the inverse requires elementary row as well as column transformation is described in Dantzig and Van Slyke (1964b).

To simplify the discussion, we assume all the coefficients in the last L equations to be nonnegative. The constant terms are assumed to be positive. In the final section, the necessary modifications to handle negative coefficients in the last L equations will be outlined.

By dividing each of the last L equations by the corresponding righthand side element and by scaling the variables in the problem, we can assume without loss of generality that each equation in the subset is a partial sum of the variables equal to unity (Figure 2).

In the next section, some terminology is introduced and a few theorems given which are the basis for the proposed algorithm. The method to be used is explained in the third section, and in the following section, the algorithm is set forth in detail. In the fifth section, the algorithm is illustrated by an example. In the final section, the slight modifications needed to handle negative coefficients in the last L equations are given.

[1] This paper is part of a paper entitled "Large-Scale Linear Programming," which was presented by George B. Dantzig at the symposium. This research has been partially supported by the Office of Naval Research under contract Nonr-222(83) and the National Science Foundation under contract G 21034 with the University of California. The material in this paper may be reproduced in whole or part for any purpose of the U. S. government.

max x_0 subject to:

$$A_1^0 x_0 + A_1^1 x_1 + \cdots + A_1^{n_0} x_{n_0} + A_1^{n_0+1} x_{n_0+1} + \cdots + A_1^{n_1} x_{n_1} + A_1^{n_1+1} x_{n_1+1} + \cdots + A_1^{n_2} x_{n_2} + \cdots + A_1^{n_3} x_{n_3} + \cdots + A_1^{n_{L-1}+1} x_{n_{L-1}+1} + \cdots + A_1^N x_N = b_1$$

$$A_2^0 x_0 + A_2^1 x_1 + \cdots + A_2^{n_0} x_{n_0} + A_2^{n_0+1} x_{n_0+1} + \cdots + A_2^{n_1} x_{n_1} + A_2^{n_1+1} x_{n_1+1} + \cdots + A_2^{n_2} x_{n_2} + \cdots + A_2^{n_3} x_{n_3} + \cdots + A_2^{n_{L-1}+1} x_{n_{L-1}+1} + \cdots + A_2^N x_N = b_2$$

$$A_M^0 x_0 + A_M^1 x_1 + \cdots + A_M^{n_0} x_{n_0} + A_M^{n_0+1} x_{n_0+1} + \cdots + A_M^{n_1} x_{n_1} + A_M^{n_1+1} x_{n_1+1} + \cdots + A_M^{n_2} x_{n_2} + \cdots + A_M^{n_3} x_{n_3} + \cdots + A_M^{n_{L-1}+1} x_{n_{L-1}+1} + \cdots + A_M^N x_N = b_M$$

$$A_{M+1}^{n_0+1} x_{n_0+1} + \cdots + A_{M+1}^{n_1} x_{n_1} = b_{M+1}$$

$$A_{M+2}^{n_1+1} x_{n_1+1} + \cdots + A_{M+2}^{n_2} x_{n_2} = b_{M+2}$$

$$A_{M+L}^{n_{L-1}+1} x_{n_{L-1}+1} + \cdots + A_{M+L}^N x_N = b_{M+L}$$

$$b_{m+1} > 0$$

FIGURE 1

max x_0 subject to:

$$A_1^0 x_0 + A_1^1 x_1 + \cdots + A_1^{n_0} x_{n_0} + A_1^{n_0+1} x_{n_0+1} + \cdots + A_1^{n_1} x_{n_1} + A_1^{n_1+1} x_{n_1+1} + \cdots + A_1^{n_2} x_{n_2} + \cdots + A_1^{n_3} x_{n_3} + \cdots + A_1^{n_{L-1}+1} x_{n_{L-1}+1} + \cdots + A_1^N x_N = b_1$$

$$A_2^0 x_0 + A_2^1 x_1 + \cdots + A_2^{n_0} x_{n_0} + A_2^{n_0+1} x_{n_0+1} + \cdots + A_2^{n_1} x_{n_1} + A_2^{n_1+1} x_{n_1+1} + \cdots + A_2^{n_2} x_{n_2} + \cdots + A_2^{n_3} x_{n_3} + \cdots + A_2^{n_{L-1}+1} x_{n_{L-1}+1} + \cdots + A_2^N x_N = b_2$$

$$A_M^0 x_0 + A_M^1 x_1 + \cdots + A_M^{n_0} x_{n_0} + A_M^{n_0+1} x_{n_0+1} + \cdots + A_M^{n_1} x_{n_1} + A_M^{n_1+1} x_{n_1+1} + \cdots + A_M^{n_2} x_{n_2} + \cdots + A_M^{n_3} x_{n_3} + \cdots + A_M^{n_{L-1}+1} x_{n_{L-1}+1} + \cdots + A_M^N x_N = b_M$$

$$x_{n_0+1} + \cdots + x_{n_1} = 1$$

$$x_{n_1+1} + \cdots + x_{n_2} = 1$$

$$x_{n_{L-1}+1} + \cdots + x_N = 1$$

FIGURE 2

SOME THEOREMS AND DEFINITIONS

The ith set of variables or columns S_i will refer (depending on context) to those variables or columns corresponding to the columns of coefficients in Figure 2, with 1 as their $(M + i)$th component. S_0, the 0th set, is the set corresponding to columns with zeros for the $(m+1)$st through $(M+L)$th coefficients.

We assume that the system in Figure 2 is of full rank and denote by $[\mathbf{B}^1, \cdots, \mathbf{B}^{M+L}]$ a basis for the system with $\mathbf{B}^1 = \mathbf{A}^0$. The boldface is to differentiate coefficient vectors, with all $M + L$ of their components, from reduced vectors (to be introduced shortly), which are $2M$ vectors. There will be no boldface for individual coefficients A_i^j since the two different types of vectors differ only in the *number* of components.

THEOREM 1: At least one variable from each set S_i $(i = 0, \cdots, L)$ is basic.

PROOF: Since we have assumed that our system is of full rank, any $M + L$ vector can be represented as a linear combination of vectors in the basis. Consider the vector of ones. There are λ_j such that $\sum_j \lambda_j \mathbf{B}^j = [1, \cdots, 1]^T$. In order for $\sum \lambda_j \mathbf{B}^j_{M+i} = 1$, B_{M+i} must be nonzero for some j_i, and this can only happen if $\mathbf{B}^{j_i} \ \varepsilon \ S_i$.

THEOREM 2: The number of sets containing two or more basic variables is at most[2] $M - 1$.

PROOF: By the assumption of full rank, each basis has exactly $M + L$ vectors. By theorem 1, $L + 1$ of them are in separate sets; this leaves at most $M - 1$ to make up sets of more than one basic variable.

According to theorem 2, we can partition all the sets into those containing exactly one basic variable and those containing more than one basic variable. At any given point in the algorithm, we call $M + 1$ of the sets *essential*.[3] Included in these sets are all the sets with more than one basic variable plus the set S_0. The remaining sets are called *inessential*.

REMARK: By theorem 2, at least one of the essential sets (besides S_0) has exactly one basic variable in it.

Columns of coefficients and variables are called *essential* ($\varepsilon\xi$) or *inessential* ($\not\varepsilon\xi$), depending on whether their set is, respectively, essential or inessential. Basic variables and columns of coefficients are called *essential* ($\varepsilon\xi$) or *inessential* ($\not\varepsilon\xi$) in a similar manner.

---

[2] We are indebted to R. N. Kaul for pointing out that the number of sets should be $M - 1$ rather than M as stated in a preliminary version of this paper (Kaul, 1965, and Dantzig and Van Slyke, 1964a).

[3] We make the assumption that $L > M + 1$, and, as a matter of fact, the algorithm will be practical only if $L \gg M + 1$.

We define the *reduced system* to be the system obtained from the system in Figure 2 by deleting the equations corresponding to the rows of "1" coefficients for the inessential sets. The set of essential basic columns restricted to the reduced system is said to be the *working basis*. Inessential basic variables are said to be at their *upper bound* since their value must be 1 for any basic feasible solution. Columns restricted to the reduced system are denoted by A^i to distinguish them from the $\mathbf{A}^i$ which is the whole column of $M + L$ components. Since we had $M + L$ equations initially and removed $L + 1 - (M + 1)$ equations, A^i has $2M$ components.

THEOREM 3: The working basis is a basis for the reduced system.

PROOF: The number of equations in the reduced system equals the number of variables in the working basis, since for each inessential set there are exactly one equation removed to form the reduced system and exactly one inessential basic variable which is not included in the working basis. All that remains is to show that the columns of the working basis are linearly independent. If they are not, then there exists $\lambda_1, \cdots, \lambda_{2M}$, not all zero, such that

$$\sum \lambda_j B^i = 0,$$

where $\{B^i\}$ $(j = 1, \cdots, 2M)$ are the columns of the working basis. But each B^i in the reduced system differs from $\mathbf{B}^i$, the whole column, only by zero components so that

$$\sum \lambda_j \mathbf{B}^i = 0,$$

contradicting the linear independence of the original basis.

The three theorems proved in this section allow us to work with a reduced system of $2M$ equations. If $L \gg M + 1$, this will allow us to do our simplex operations in a system of a much smaller order than that of the original.

THE METHOD

Suppose that we have a basis $\mathbf{B} = \{\mathbf{B}^i : j = 1, \cdots, M + L\}$ for the whole system, where we assume without loss of generality that $\mathbf{B}^1 = \mathbf{A}^0$, the column corresponding to the variable x_0 to be maximized. Let

$$B = \{B^{k_i} : j = 1, \cdots, 2M\}$$

be the working basis, where $\mathbf{B}^{k_i} \ \varepsilon \ \mathbf{B}$ and where B^{k_i} is obtained from $\mathbf{B}^{k_i}$ by deleting the appropriate components. Again we assume $B^{k_1} = B^1 = A^0$. Our first project is to find the value of the basic variables for the basic solution determined by B. That is, we seek x_{j_k} $(k = 1, \cdots, M + L)$ such that $\sum x_{j_k} \mathbf{B}^k = \mathbf{b}$. Let U denote the set of variables at upper bound, that is, inessential basic variables. Then we have

$$\sum_{B^k \notin U} x_{j_k} \mathbf{B}^k + \sum_{B^k \varepsilon U} x_{j_k} \mathbf{B}^k = \sum_{B^k \neq U} x_{j_k} \mathbf{B}^k + \sum_{B^k \varepsilon U} \mathbf{B}^k = b,$$

since we know that $x_{j_k} = 1$ for $B^k \varepsilon U$. All that remains is to find the value for variables in the working basis, that is, x_{j_k} such that $B^{i_k} \notin U$. Consider

$$\sum_{B^k \notin U} x_{j_k} \mathbf{B}^k = b - \sum_{B^k \varepsilon U} \mathbf{B}^k.$$

The columns on the lefthand side of the above equality are nonzero at most in the components corresponding to the reduced system. Similarly, on the righthand side, for S_i which are inessential, $\mathbf{b}_{M+i} = 1$, and there exists exactly one column $B^{k_0} \varepsilon U$ with $B_{M+i}^{k_0} = 1$. Thus, to find W, the values of the variables corresponding to the working basis, it suffices to consider only the reduced system, that is,

$$W = [x_{k_1}, \cdots, x_{k_2 M}] = B^{-1}[b - \sum_{B^k \varepsilon U} B^k]. \tag{15.1}$$

The next item of interest is to find the prices corresponding to the current basis. Let $\pi_1, \cdots, \pi_M$ denote the prices on the first M equations and $\mu_1, \cdots, \mu_L$ the prices on the last L equations. Since we assumed that $B^1 = A^0$, the first row of B^{-1}, denoted $(B^{-1})_1$, will be a set of prices for the reduced system in the sense that $(B^{-1})_1 B = [1, 0, 0, \cdots, 0]$, a $(2M)$-component vector. We now extend these prices to a set of prices for the whole system. Let $\pi_j = (B^{-1})_1^j (j = 1, \cdots, M)$. Now let us see what the μ_i $(i = 1, \cdots, L)$ have to be. If S_i is essential and $\mathbf{B}^i \varepsilon S_i$, then

$$0 = \sum_{l=1}^{M+L} (B^{-1})_1^l B_l^i$$

$$= \sum_{l=1}^{2m} (B^{-1})_1^l B_l^i$$

$$= \sum_{l=1}^{m} (B^{-1})_1^l B_l^i + (B^{-1})_1^{m+i} \cdot 1$$

$$= \sum \pi_l B_l^i + \mu_i.$$

Hence,

$$\mu_i = -\sum_{l=1}^{M} \pi_l B_l^i \quad \text{for} \quad \mathbf{B}^i \varepsilon \xi. \tag{15.2}$$

The μ_i so obtained are simply the appropriate components of $(B^{-1})_1$. However, the same formula, (15.2), can be used to extend our prices to the full system including inessential sets. This is clear because the prices $[\pi, \mu]$ are determined by the requirement that $[\pi, \mu]\mathbf{B}^1 = 1$ and $[\pi, \mu]\mathbf{B}^i = 0$ $(j = 2, \cdots, M + L)$. For $\mathbf{B}^i \varepsilon \xi$, these equations hold because

π was defined in terms of B^{-1}. For $\mathbf{B}^i \notin \xi$, the requirement is (15.2) again. Since every inessential basic variable appears in exactly one equation of the form (15.2), $[\pi, \mu]$ constitutes a set of prices for the original system.

Now we are able to "price out" the columns of the original system to see which one should come into the basis; for example, using the usual simplex criterion, we might choose the incoming column A^s by

$$\Delta_s = (\pi, \mu)\mathbf{A}^s = \min_i (\pi, \mu)\mathbf{A}^i = \min_i \Delta_i,$$

$$\Delta_i = \sum_i \pi_i A_i^j + \mu_l \quad \text{for} \quad A^i \, \varepsilon \, S_l. \tag{15.3}$$

If $\Delta_s \geq 0$, we have an optimal basic feasible solution; if not, we bring A^s into the basis. We note that the μ_i need not be stored in the computer but may be generated as needed by (15.2). Let us suppose that $A^s \, \varepsilon \, S_\sigma$.

If S_σ is essential, we simply pivot *in the reduced system*, using the usual criterion for picking the row; that is, the row r is given by

$$\theta = \min_{i \neq 1; (B^{-1}A^s)_i > 0} \frac{[B^{-1}(b - \sum_{B^i \varepsilon U} B^i)]_i}{(B^{-1}A^s)_i} = \frac{[B^{-1}(b - \sum_{B^i \varepsilon U} B^i)]_r}{(B^{-1}A^s)_r}, \tag{15.4}$$

where, of course, $(B^{-1}A^s)_r > 0$. We consider only rows in the reduced system, except $r = 1$, since the column corresponding to the functional always remains in the basis. We then proceed with another iteration.

If S_σ is inessential, two things can happen:

1. If A^s drives B^t out of the basis, where B^t is the unique basic variable in S_σ, then A^s simply goes to upper bound instead of B^t, and we need not pivot at all. We just modify the sum $b - \sum B^i$ in (15.1) and (15.4).

2. If, on the other hand, A^s drives out some other basic (and necessarily essential) variable, we redefine the essential sets so as to make S_σ essential and then perform a pivot using (15.4).

Now let us go into this in more detail. In particular, to see whether alternative 1 or 2 occurs, we let $x_s = \theta$ be the increase in the variable x_s. Simultaneously, by the sum constraint, x_t (the coefficient of B^t) is decreasing from $x_t = 1$ to $x_t = 1 - \theta$. To satisfy the remaining equations in the reduced system, we must adjust the variables of the working basis. Equation (15.1) now becomes

$$W(\theta) = B^{-1}[b - \sum_{B^k \varepsilon U} B^k - \theta(A^s - B^t)]$$

$$= B^{-1}[b - \sum_{B^k \varepsilon U} B^k] - \theta B^{-1}[A^s - B^t] \tag{15.5}$$

$$= W(0) - \theta B^{-1}[A^s - B^t],$$

which is required to be nonnegative, except possibly in the first component which corresponds to the functional. If we let the ith component of $W(0)$

be W_i, then the maximum θ for feasibility is

$$\hat{\theta} = \min_{i \neq 1;\, [B^{-1}(A^s - B^t)]_i > 0} \frac{W_i}{[B^{-1}(A^s - B^t)]_i} = \frac{W_r}{[B^{-1}(A^s - B^t)]_r}, \quad (15.6)$$

where $[B^{-1}(A^s - B^t)]_r > 0$. Then $\theta = \min [\hat{\theta}, 1]$, where $W(0) = (x_{k_1}, \cdots, x_{k_2 M})$ are the values for the variables in the working basis from the previous iteration. Of course, the minimum makes sense only over the rows in the reduced system. If $\theta = 1$, then x_s goes to upper bound, and the variable corresponding to B^t goes to zero. If we indicate by a superior bar the new values of the various variables, we obtain

$$\bar{W} = W - B^{-1}[A^s - B^t],$$

$$\bar{B} = B, \quad (15.7)$$

$$\bar{\mu}_\sigma = - \sum_{l=1}^{M} \Pi_l A_l^s.$$

If, on the other hand, $\theta < 1$, we first make S_σ essential (which automatically introduces B^t into the working basis) and *then* introduce A^s into the new working basis. To do this, we must make one of the currently essential sets inessential. This essential set cannot be S_0 and clearly must contain exactly one basic variable. But, by the remark made after theorem 2, there must exist such a set. Denote by S_ρ one such set, and let B^{k_r} be the basic variable in S_ρ.

Now we must obtain an inverse $\bar{B}^{-1}$ for the new working basis $\bar{B}$. $\bar{B}^{-1}$ can be defined by $(\bar{B}^{-1})_i \bar{B}^{k_i} = \delta_{ij}$, where $\delta_{ij} = 0$ ($i \neq j$) and $\delta_{ij} = 1$ ($i = j$). For the old inverse B^{-1}, we have $(B^{-1})_i B^{k_i} = \delta_{ij}$. But $\bar{B}$ differs from B only by the fact that column B^t replaces B^{k_r} and that the row $M + \sigma$ replaces $M + \rho$ in the reduced system. But, except for B^t and B^{k_r}, all the columns involved have zeros in both the $(M + \rho)$th and $(M + \sigma)$th components. Hence, if $(B^{-1})'$ denotes the matrix obtained by permuting the columns of B^{-1} corresponding to the changes in the rows of the working basis resulting from replacing the $(M + \rho)$th equation by the $(M + \sigma)$th equation in the reduced system, we have $(B^{-1})_i' \bar{B}^{k_i} = \delta_{ij}$ for all $k_j \neq t$. To get $\bar{B}^{-1}$, all we have to do is pivot on $(B^{-1})' \bar{B}^t$ on the element corresponding to the $(M + \sigma)$th row. This pivot is particularly easy, since the pivot element will always be one which can easily be verified. U, the set of variables "at upper bound," is now changed by including B^{k_r} and deleting B^t; $\bar{W}$, of course, remains unchanged, except possibly for the order of the components. Using the new $\bar{B}^{-1}$, we could obtain new prices which, however, must be the same as the old ones, since the basis for the original system is the same. Again A^s will price out optimally, but now S_σ is essential, so we just do an ordinary pivot on row r determined by (15.6) and go on to the next iteration. This essentially describes the method. In the next section, the algorithm is described in detail.

DESCRIPTION OF ALGORITHM

Referring to Figure 3, we see that the algorithm takes place in the following steps:

Step 1. We assume that we enter the algorithm with the inverse B^{-1} of the working basis B, the value of the variables in the working basis $W = B^{-1}(b - \sum_{B^i \varepsilon U} B^i)$, and the set of variables U at upper bound. To get this initial solution, the usual phase-I procedure can be used in the obvious way.

Step 2. Let $\pi_i = (B^{-1})_1^i$ for $i = 1, \cdots, M$, where we assume for the sake of simplicity that the column corresponding to the objective variable is the first column in the working basis. For each set S_ν ($\nu \neq 0$), let $\mu_\nu = -\sum_{i=1}^{M} \pi_i A_i^{i\nu}$, where $A_0^{i\nu}$ is a basic column in S_ν. Let $\Delta_j = \sum_{i=1}^{M} \pi_i A_i^j + \mu_\nu$ for $A^j \varepsilon S_\nu$. Let $\Delta_s = \min \Delta_j$, and suppose $\mathbf{A}^s \varepsilon S_\sigma$. If $\Delta_s \geq 0$, we go to step 3; if $\Delta_s < 0$, and if S_σ is essential, we go to step 4. Finally, if $\Delta_s < 0$, and if S_σ inessential, we go to step 6.

Step 3. Terminate; we have an optimal solution.

Step 4. We find A^s in terms of the working basis, that is, $B^{-1}A^s$, and find the pivot row r by equation (15.4).

Step 5. We then pivot on row r, column s in the reduced system giving us a new working basis $\bar{B}$ and an inverse $\bar{B}^{-1}$. After updating W by (15.1), we return to step 1 for the next iteration.

Step 6. We find $B^{-1}(A^s - B^t)$ and determine the value of $\hat{\theta}$ and row r by equation (15.6). If $\hat{\theta} \geq 1$, then $x_s = \theta = 1$, and we go to step 7. If $\hat{\theta} < 1$, then $x_s = \theta = \hat{\theta}$, and we go to step 8.

Step 7. $\mathbf{A}^s$ goes to upper bound in set S_σ, and $\mathbf{B}^t$, the unique variable which was at upper bound, goes to zero. The working basis and the reduced system remain the same, but W and the prices are updated by equations (15.7).

Step 8. Suppose that S_ρ ($\rho \neq 0$) is an essential set with exactly one basic variable B^{kr}. Let $\hat{\mathbf{B}}_i^t = \mathbf{B}_i^t$ ($i \neq M + \sigma$), $M + \rho = 0$, $\hat{B}_{M+\sigma}^t = 0$, and $\hat{B}_{M+\rho}^t = 1$. That is, we move the "1" coefficient in $\mathbf{B}^t$ to the same row as the "1" coefficient in $\mathbf{B}^{kr}$. Then we pivot in the reduced system on $B^{-1}\hat{B}^t$ in the $(m + \rho)$th row, regarding $\hat{B}^t$ as belonging to S_ρ. We then permute the columns of the resulting inverse so that we can replace the $(M + \rho)$th equation by the $(M + \sigma)$th equation in the reduced system, obtaining $\bar{B}^{-1}$. B^{kr} replaces B^t in U, and the elements of W are permuted to reflect the column reordering of $\bar{B}^{-1}$.

Step 9. Now we need to find A^s in terms of the working basis obtained in step 8; that is, we want $\bar{B}^{-1}A^s$. If $\bar{B}^{-1}$ is obtained from B^{-1} by T (a

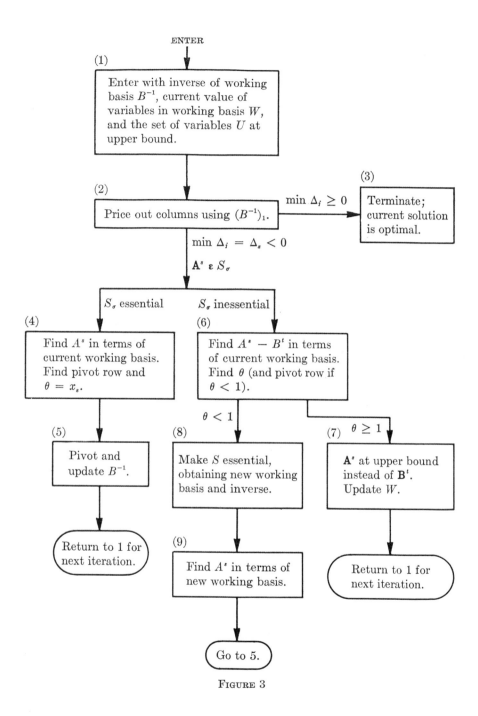

FIGURE 3

pivot transformation matrix) and P (a column permutation matrix), then $\bar{B}^{-1} = PTB^{-1}$. But we have already computed $B^{-1}(A^s - B^t)$ in step 6, and $PTB^{-1}B^t$ equals U, a unit vector with a 1 in the row of the reduced system corresponding to the $(m + \sigma)$th equation of the original system, by the way P and T were chosen. Hence,

$$\bar{B}^{-1}A^s = \bar{B}^{-1}(A^s - B^t) + U$$

$$= PTB^{-1}(A^s - A^t) + U.$$

We then pivot on $\bar{B}^{-1}A^s$ as in step 5, using the row r determined in step 6.

EXAMPLE

Consider the following example for $M = 2$ with the coefficient array given in Figure 4. We are trying to maximize x_0.

S_0	S_1		S_2	S_3	S_4		S_5		
A^0	A^1	A^2	A^3	A^4	A^5	A^6	A^7	A^8	b
1	0	2	3	4	5	1	−1	−12	15
1	1	−1	2	1	4	2	−3	6	7
	1	1							1
			1						1
				1					1
					1	1			1
							1	1	1
$X = 3$	1/2	1/2	1	1	1		1		

FIGURE 4

The initial reduced system contains variables x_0, x_1, x_2, x_3 and the first four equations. $U = \{A^4, A^5, A^7\}$. The inverse of $B = A^0A^1A^2A^3$ is

$$B^{-1} = \begin{bmatrix} 1/2 & 1/2 & -1/2 & -5/2 \\ -1/4 & 1/4 & 3/4 & 1/4 \\ 1/4 & -1/4 & 1/4 & -1/4 \\ 0 & 0 & 0 & 1 \end{bmatrix}.$$

From the first row of B^{-1} we obtain $\Pi = [1/2,\ 1/2]$, and by pricing out basic columns we obtain $\mu = [-1/2,\ -5/2,\ -5/2,\ -9/2,\ 2]$; hence $[\Pi,\ \mu] = [1/2,\ 1/2,\ -1/2,\ -5/2,\ -5/2,\ -9/2,\ 2]$ is the pricing vector. After pricing out, we find that $\Delta_6 = -3$ is the minimum. Since $\mathbf{A}^6$ belongs to S_4, which is inessential, we find

$$B^{-1}(A^6 - A^5) = \begin{bmatrix} -3 \\ 1/2 \\ -1/2 \\ 0 \end{bmatrix},$$

and we use (15.6) to compute $\hat{\theta} = \frac{1}{2}/\frac{1}{2} = 1$, since there is only one positive coefficient in $B^{-1}(A^6 - A^5)$. Since $\hat{\theta} \geq 1$, x_6 goes to upper bound and x_5 goes to zero. The new values for the variables in the working base are given by

$$\begin{aligned} W = [x_0,\ x_1,\ x_2,\ x_3]^T &= W - B^{-1}(A^6 - A^5) \\ &= [3,\ 1/2,\ 1/2,\ 1]^T - [-3,\ 1/2,\ -1/2,\ 0]^T \\ &= [6,\ 0,\ 1,\ 1]^T \end{aligned}$$

and

$$\bar{x} = [6,\ 0,\ 1,\ 1,\ 1,\ 0,\ 1,\ 10]^T$$

$$[\bar{\Pi},\ \bar{\mu}] = [1/2,\ 1/2,\ -1/2,\ -5/2,\ -5/2,\ -3/2,\ 2]$$

since

$$\bar{\mu}_4 = \mu_4 - \Delta_6 = -9/2 + 3 = -3/2.$$

Now we start over with the new prices. This time, $\mathbf{A}^8\ \varepsilon\ S_5$ prices out optimally with $\Delta_8 = -1$. S_5 is also inessential, so we compute

$$B^{-1}(A^8 - A^7) = [-1,\ 5,\ -5,\ 0]^T.$$

Since $[B^{-1}(A^8 - A^7)]_i > 0$ only for $i = 2$, we have $\theta = 0/5 < 1$, which tells us we have to make S_5 essential. To do this, we must make one of the previously essential sets inessential. S_0 is the only essential set with just one basic variable, so we proceed to make S_2 inessential. The new reduced system will include the first, second, third, and seventh equations. We now seek the new inverse $\bar{B}^{-1}$ so that $\bar{B}^{-1}\bar{A}^i$ is a unit vector for $j = 0,\ 1,\ 2,\ 7$. To do this, we consider $\mathbf{A}'^7 = [-1,\ -3,\ 0,\ 1,\ 0,\ 0,\ 0]^T$ where we have changed the "1" from the seventh component to the fourth. We now represent A'^7 in terms of the current basis

$$B^{-1}A'^7 = [-9/2,\ -1/4,\ +1/4,\ 1]$$

and pivot on the fourth component. The matrix which accomplishes the pivot is

$$
T = \begin{bmatrix} 1 & & & 9/2 \\ & 1 & & 1/4 \\ & & 1 & -1/4 \\ & & & 1 \end{bmatrix},
$$

and so

$$
B^{-1\prime} = TB^{-1} = \begin{bmatrix} 1/2 & 1/2 & -1/2 & 2 \\ -1/4 & 1/4 & 3/4 & 1/2 \\ 1/4 & -1/4 & 1/4 & -1/2 \\ 0 & 0 & 0 & 1 \end{bmatrix}.
$$

In order to use the above as the inverse working basis, we obtain A^i from $\mathbf{A}^i$ by taking $A^i = [A_1^i, A_2^i, A_3^i, A_7^i]^T$ and hence $B^{-1\prime} = \bar{B}^{-1}$. Thus the subsystem consists of the equations 1, 2, 3, 5, and 7 of the original system. Now that S_5 is essential we can pivot on $\bar{B}^{-1}A^8 = TB^{-1}(A^8 - A^7) + U_4$:

$$
\bar{B}^{-1}A^8 = T[-1, 5, -5, 0]^T + U_4
$$

$$
= [-1, 5, -5, 1].
$$

The values of X are the same, but the components which are in the working basis change; i.e.,

PREVIOUSLY $W = [x_0, x_1, x_2, x_3] = [6, 0, 1, 1]$

NOW $\bar{W} = [x_0, x_1, x_2, x_7] = [6, 0, 1, 1]$.

If we now pivot on the second component of $\bar{B}^{-1}A^8$ using

$$
T^1 = \begin{bmatrix} 1 & +1/5 & & \\ & 1/5 & & \\ & 1 & 1 & \\ & -1/5 & & 1 \end{bmatrix}
$$

and interchange the second and fourth rows by using a permutation matrix, P, to get the unit vectors $\bar{B}^{-1}A^i$ ($j = 0, 2, 4, 7, 8$) in numerical order on j, we obtain

$$\bar{B}^{-1} = \begin{bmatrix} 9/20 & 11/20 & -7/20 & 42/20 \\ 1/20 & -1/20 & -3/20 & 18/20 \\ 0 & 0 & 1 & 0 \\ -1/20 & 1/20 & 3/20 & 2/20 \end{bmatrix}$$

$$\Pi = [9/20, \quad 11/20]$$

and

$$\mu = [-7/20, \ -47/20, \ -47/20, \ -31/20, \ 42/20].$$

The full pricing vector is then

$$[\Pi, \mu] = [9/20, \ 11/20, \ -7/20, \ -47/20, \ -47/20, \ -31/20, \ 42/20].$$

Upon pricing out, we find $\Delta_j \geq 0$ for all j, and hence we have an optimal solution, the value of which is

$$\bar{W} = [x_0, \ x_2, \ x_7, \ x_8]$$
$$= P^1 T^1 \bar{W}$$
$$= [6, 1, 1, 0]$$

with $x_3 = x_4 = x_6 = 1$ at upper bound. So the full optimal solution is

$$X = [6, 0, 1, 1, 1, 0, 1, 1, 0].$$

NEGATIVE COEFFICIENTS

When negative coefficients appear in the last $M + L$ equations, the algorithm is changed in a quite obvious way. We can assume without loss of generality that the coefficients are $+1$ or -1 and that the last L righthand side components are $+1$. Theorems 1, 2, and 3 still hold. For each inessential set, the basic column must obviously have a $+1$ coefficient in the last L components for any basic feasible solution. In the pricing process, if the column A^i to be priced has a negative coefficient in the last L components, the appropriate μ is subtracted from rather than added to ΠA^i. Also, if an inessential variable with a "-1" is to be introduced, the set must first be made essential. Apart from these modifications, the algorithm proceeds exactly as before.

REFERENCES

DANTZIG, G. B., and R. M. VAN SLYKE. 1964a. Generalized upper bounded techniques for linear programming—I. ORC 64–17. Berkeley: Univ. of California, Operations Research Center.
———. 1964b. Generalized upper bounded techniques for linear programming—II. ORC 64–18. Berkeley: Univ. of California, Operations Research Center.
KAUL, R. N. 1965. Comment on generalized upper bounded techniques in linear programming. ORC 65–21. Berkeley: Univ. of California, Operations Research Center.